# Hypnotic Scripts That Work

## The Breakthrough Book - Version 7.0

### A Hypnosis Script Encyclopedia for Professional Hypnotists

by John Cerbone, BCH, CI

Clinical Hypnosis Instructor

© 2007 Cerbone Hypnosis Institute

# HYPNOTIC SCRIPTS THAT WORK

## The Breakthrough Book Version 7.0

A Hypnosis Script Encyclopedia for Professional Hypnotists

- ☐ Featuring 100 + All Original Effective Hypnotic Suggestion
- ☐ Breakthrough Technique Scripts
- ☐ New! Easy to Use Table of Contents and Topical Index!
- ☐ This Book is Now in Use on 5 Continents

This is the book that Ormond McGill, the Dean of American Hypnotists called: "A Wonderful, Wonderful Work! Something every modern Hypnotherapist must have (for use) in their practice!"

## Your Inside Secret to Session Success

Conceived and Written By

## John Cerbone, BCH, CI

**Clinical Hypnotist Instructor**

**Cerbone Hypnosis Institute**
**718-227-4868**
**HypnotistPro.com**

Published by Profits Publishing of Sarasota, Florida
http://profitspublishing.com

# Foreword

Thank you for purchasing this updated edition of my book: Hypnotic Scripts That Work, The Breakthrough Book - Version 7.0.

This work represents years of my work in the field of clinical hypnosis. As a trained Hypnotic Professional, you will notice, I have come to utilize deepening techniques, the use of truisms and confusion method techniques within these suggestion scripts to further deepen the hypnotic state while the client (patient) is hypnotized to increase impact and long-term effectiveness. These scripts and techniques are written in the style and language of this profession. All of these original suggestions, techniques and methods contained herein have proven effective and beneficial for the majority of clients (patients) utilizing them, quite often achieving beneficial results in one or just a few sessions. For many Hypnotists utilizing this work, you may very likely find your clients (patients) achieving breakthroughs quite rapidly. In this edition, I've included a section at the end of the book called *Extras*, a grouping of various suggestions I've written targeted to a range of client's weak spots to insure greater lasting, high-impact success. This book is ergonomically designed, the words are intentionally spread out across the pages to make it lighter to carry and thereby easier to use and transport.

**Important Notes:** As with any professional tool, it is assumed and understood that you will be pre-reading each of the scripts before using them and will make the appropriate adjustments based upon the needs of your client. This book is solely and strictly intended for use *only* by professionals in the field of hypnosis, including but not necessarily limited to professionally trained: Hypnotists, Clinical Hypnotists, Psychologists, Psychotherapists, Psychoanalysts, Psychiatrists and other skilled Mental Health Professionals, all of whom have been properly trained and certified in the use of professional hypnosis/clinical hypnosis. This information is being shared so that people will be helped, lives will be improved and so other professionals as listed above can and will build further benefit and improvement from their work into the world.

I wish to sincerely thank my clients (patients), my family, loved ones, friends and colleagues for their tireless support and inspiration, which has helped to make this work possible. I wish to thank all of those individuals with whom I have trained over the years and all of those practitioners who have gone before me, as well as those who represent the future of these noble professions. And as a purchaser of this work, I want to sincerely and personally thank you for your interest and support. I truly wish you and those whose lives you help to improve through your service and dedication, limitless creative inspiration and unstoppable success in each and every area of your lives.

Sincerely,

John Cerbone

John Cerbone,
Certified Clinical Hypnosis Instructor and Master Hypnotist

© 2007 Cerbone Hypnosis Institute

HypnotistPro.com

# Table of Contents

# ANXIETY, FEAR, PANIC

Also see LEARNING ENHANCEMENTS:
Learning Enhancement - Overcoming School Fears

# Anti-Anxiety Suggestions and Managing Panic Attacks

**Note:** You must be a qualified and certified Clinical Hypnosis professional and have a written note of authorization to perform this or any other complementary hypnosis session from the attending physician, psychiatrist, psychologist, etc., no exceptions.

Each and every day and night you do better and better for yourself by relaxing into your life and in each and every moment, you begin to feel more and more comfortable, because you can just allow yourself, just as you once did in your past, to begin to feel happier, more confident and more successful, because you are and have in fact, begun a brand new chapter of your life. Beginning right now and for the rest of your life, you are more successfully rising above any and all fears and worries, because you can and because its best for you and all of those you love, but most especially it's best for you. You begin to think in new and profoundly better ways, feeling better and better each and every day and night. You truly begin right now to relax and trust in your life, in all that you do, all that you think and all that you create for yourself. What once happened in your past is inconsequential and unimportant, your point of power is right now and for right now, in this moment and only getting stronger and stronger each and every day and night, you let go of the unpleasantness from your past and you begin to relax and trust in your life right now. You begin right now instead to know that you are finding new and better ways to live your life, feeling more and more fulfilled by just being yourself, which is really just fine with you. For in each and every moment, you are forgiving and healing and rising above your past challenges in new and magnificent and truly profound ways, amazing and impressing and amazing everyone, most especially yourself. Each and every day and night, while you are awake, while you are asleep and even while you dream, your relationship with yourself and all that is your life and your thoughts and your world is improving, and all of it improves in the most beneficial ways and becomes more worthwhile, more alive, more vital, growing stronger and stronger, more respectful, more lovingly powerful to you and for you, allowing you to thrive and rise above any and all past limits and to heal and become whole in ways that are most successful, most perfect and beneficial to you. You are and you remain at ease even while alone or even with other people and even while alone with your thoughts and feelings. You begin to know all that is your world and your life is wishing you success and abundance and harmony in all that you do, for your life truly supports you in the most beneficial ways, today, tomorrow and forever! You really truly remember and you have always known from deep, deep down inside, that you are always supported by life and as you have begun this brand new more empowered chapter of your life, you begin to relax, succeed and thrive, relaxing through any and all stress and tension and any and all emotional uneasiness from your past. You are and you truly do in fact begin to enjoy life and living. Each and every day and night, you feel and you truly are more supported, more protected and cared for by life, by the Universe and by Divinity, letting anything and everything that's overwhelming to be handled by Higher power. As you learn to relax, better and better, you allow yourself to open your dynamic and powerful mind to, like a sponge, absorb all that you perceive, to retrieve and instantly access all that you need to easily, powerfully and profoundly with clearness, direction and purpose.

Worry (fear) is an empty vessel, it holds nothing, it does nothing and is useless. Instead, each and every day and night, you rather, trust in yourself and all of you now begins to actually flow with your life. Any and all adversity that you may encounter, actually polishes you, like water rushing past a boulder in a fast running stream, you are actually polished by any and all challenges and adversities in your life. You are free from being concerned with the word problem, for a problem is by its very nature something that's difficult to change. So even better and instead, you become challenge oriented, which means accepting any and all challenges, rising up to meet any and all challenges, because you can, you will and you do, overcome all challenges with poise, power, elegance, grace, ease and amazing success. You learn each and everyday and night to let go of struggle as a concept in your life and truly, your correct response to a challenge is to relax right out of struggling in any and in every way, physically, emotionally, mentally and even spiritually. You also begin to trust in yourself and your life, because that's the very best choice to make and you are always making the best of all possible choices. All of your decisions are correct ones, for at anytime in your past, present or future, you have either learned or succeeded. All of you beneficially gains from any and all choices and decisions that you make, either learning or succeeding, so in every way and the most vital and important ways, you always win, you are a winner, you succeed unstoppably, congratulations!

In each and every situation and circumstance, you are always guided and following your own inner wisdom, which is something you come to trust and something you come to follow. You always allow your best to come through and you are always being yourself, you are enough, just what you are supposed to be, for what else could you be? You relax and you enjoy your life and everything for you just always flows, just like a mighty river or ocean, flowing past, over, around and through any and all obstacles, always going where it needs to be and you get to know more and more each and every day and each and every night, that the flow of your life is eternal. Whenever you feel stress or tension of any kind, you correctly choose, always making the best and correct choice, to breathe deep and steady relaxation breath, you relax all over, relaxing all that you are and all of your tension and stress after just a few short breaths, just melts away, you can actually feel it leaving you, just lifting up off and far, far away from you and you have limitless confidence in yourself and your ability to relax and release away any and all stress. Any and all thoughts and ideas are valid, but as you learn to better relax yourself, you begin to focus on relaxing and releasing the thoughts, feelings and ideas that do not serve you in wonderful ways. So you would rather focus upon, the thoughts, sensations, images and feelings that truly support you in the most beneficial ways. You relax and release all that is stressful, so you feel confident, powerful, strong and relaxed. And from all of this you begin to view you life in a more loving and supportive way, giving yourself a break, letting go of damaging self-criticism and self-judgment. You are beginning right now to see, to feel, to notice, to appreciate and to support yourself the ways an ideal unconditionally loving and nurturing parent would a wonderful and beautiful child. You correctly, deeply and truly realize, that feelings are just feelings, there are times when you can be hot or cold, tired or energetic, hungry or filled up, because feelings are just feelings and they can never really hurt you in any way, but right now, you have really chosen to rise above any and all feelings, any hurts, any pain, both real or imagined, because you deserve to, you are able to, you can, you will, because you have decided to do so and you can and you will, just because you are unstoppable in your achieving this, or in achieving anything you've set your powerful, dynamic, creative and unstoppable successful mind to; you feel like you can take on the world, talk to the world, rise above, and succeed in all that you can and will accomplish. You feel like you can smile on the inside and even on the outside, because you can and will begin to do all that it takes to succeed, because you really want to, you are able to overcome any and all hurdles, including, relax, (name items) studying, relax, school, relax, having a conversation (etc.). All of your life supports you and really you deeply know this to be the truth, a new and most powerful ever building truth in all that you are physically, emotionally and mentally and even spiritually is yours. The whole world in its own perfect way is supporting you and you are never really alone. Just visualize a beautiful spring day, birds and bugs moving about, children playing, people nearby, all of these sounds, sights and sensations, support you in all of the most perfect and bountiful beneficial ways. The whole world in its own perfection supports you and is there for you.

You will always remember to breathe deep and steady powerful soothing, breath, calming, centering, stilling, harmonizing and balancing breath, easily and completely overcoming and all fear, doubt, worry and panic. That which once overwhelmed you is now both easily and forever powerfully overwhelmed by you and the power of your breath, as you leave all fear, panic and discomfort, far, far behind you forever.

All fear, doubt and panic are now and forever forgiven, released and vanquished and you feel forever and only getting stronger, better and more effectively balanced, harmonized and healed.

# Enhanced Stress and Anxiety Management -1

Relax, deeper and further, further and deeper, right now and in this moment, you are experiencing something new, your body and your emotions and your mind and even your spirit and in fact, all that You are memorizing this feeling of deep, deep, relaxation, as a way to be, as a way to thrive, as a way to health, wholeness and healing, as a way of balance, as the real way to live, a place to return to whenever you need it, your refuge, you oasis, your shelter. And whether you realize it yet or not, you will be able to successfully bring yourself back to this place of deep, calming, comfortable, wonderful relaxation, completely stress-free, anxiety-free, easily, peacefully and powerfully, succeeding powerfully and completely, allowing yourself to thrive, relax, to freely flow, to gain and win by relaxing, to begin anew, having a new stress-free, anxiety-free relationship with yourself and your life, easily able to overcome any and all stress and any and all anxiety peacefully, powerfully, always and forever. You truly realize, recognize, feel and know right now that you are easily able to remain successfully detached from any and all current or future stressful circumstances, instantly, after just a few deep soothing balancing breaths. And just like a big boulder in a fast-running stream of water and you are and have always been in fact, really been polished by what's going on around you, while You are become and absolutely remain, comfortably and successfully, emotionally and mentally detached from any and all stress. Truly, you feel like a sea of calm and tranquility, in each and every moment of your life. And just after just a few short deep and powerful, soothing breaths, your whole body will peacefully and calmly truly relaxed, you'll feel stress-free, for in reality and in fact, you'll be stress-free, calm, tranquil and comfortable. And just after just a few short deep and powerful, soothing breaths, your whole body will peacefully and calmly truly relaxed, you'll feel anxiety-free, for in reality and in fact, you'll be anxiety-free. You'll feel calm and relaxed, calm and peaceful, calm and able, calm and serene, calm and completely stress- free, anxiety-free. For in fact, truly, you'll be calm and relaxed, calm and peaceful, calm and able, calm and serene, calm and completely stress-free, anxiety-free, feeling great in amazingly wonderful ways. Your heart rate will calm down, it is slow, strong and steady, your breathing is steady and relaxed, peaceful powerful and relaxed and strong, calming you an soothing you. Your muscles will unwind, uncoiling, yielding, feeling good and you're feeling able, peaceful, powerful and great on the inside and feeling great on the outside. And you'll be easily able to be emotionally detached from what's going on around you, relaxing, becoming and remaining peaceful, just moving on to a higher and more balanced perspective. You'll be clear, sharp, relaxed, focused, mentally precise, emotionally detached from the circumstances around you, easily gaining perspective to rise above, to transcend any and all limits, feeling so very deeply relaxed and calm and yet in command of your world and your life, free of ever being swept up again by stress or anxiety, allowing each and every circumstance around you, to support and fine tune you and your body and your emotions and your life, in amazing ways. You begin to realize from powerful, supportive places from deep, deep within you, that right now, you are truly beginning a brand new, more powerful, chapter of your life. In fact, you know from deep, deep inside, a new chapter of your life unstoppably begins right now, only getting stronger and better, more powerful and easier, one in which you relate to stress differently and better, releasing any and all anxiety in more healthy ways, only the very best of ways, better, peacefully, powerfully, completely relaxing all that you are through any and all stress, you're stress-free, anxiety-free and doesn't it feel great! Yes, in fact you are truly succeeding in amazing ways, truly the unstoppable power of your creative successful dynamic subconscious mind, for right now in this moment and in each and every moment, succeeding in amazing ways. For right now in this moment, and in each and every moment, you are feeling inspired, beginning anew, feeling polished, relaxed, safe, powerful stress-free, strong, relaxed, absolutely thriving, throughout everything and anything, throughout anything and everything that once ever caused you stress or anxiety. And in this moment of deep relaxation and healing, the energy of every past victory, triumph, breakthrough and success you've ever had is upon you now, allowing you to move to a new level, a new chapter and new and better you emerges right now and it feels great. You are a winner, fortified by an unstoppable, unshakable force, confident, clear, capable, strong, completely and absolutely stress-free, regardless of event or circumstance, always performing at your very best. You're sense of inner peacefulness, calmness, wholeness, balance, wellness, gentleness, ease, harmony and comfort is supporting you amazingly, a calm yet almost tickling gentle internal giggling sense of laughter forever guides your way into the rest of your life.

Relax even deeper, even better memorize the sensation of this feeling right now, relax and just like riding a bicycle, walking or driving a car, you can feel this calming moment, its soothing rhythm and balance, it's powerfully balancing and relaxing harmony, it true centeredness. You allow yourself to relax through any and all stress, relaxing into the moment, you just go with the flow of your life, the life you create, its freely flowing, and in fact, you're really are beginning to feel great on the inside and even on the outside, your smiling on the inside, freely flowing, you win. And in fact, you are so relaxed, so peaceful, you are really feeling better than you have in years. You are completely calm on the inside and on the outside as well. Smiling, even feeling good about any challenge of future stress, you're easily able to overcome, because right now in this moment you have absolutely begun a brand new better chapter of your life, stress-free, anger-free, calm, comfortable, so peaceful, so powerful, so relaxed, unshakable and steady. In fact, if at any future moment, you may or might feel, any stress, anger, or unsteady in any way, you just take a few deep, relaxing, slow, steady and soothing deep, deep, breaths, you feel all instability and uneasiness, any and all stress, fear, anger, panic, rage and any and all unsteady feelings, just draining out, just draining out of you, further, and further, draining away from you, far, far away, from you as you relax, deeper and further, easier, better and faster than ever before. Your ability to release stress is both now and forever enhanced and activated.

As I count from 3 to 1, you relax deeper and further, further and deeper, absolutely allowing any and all disharmony, to completely drain, dynamically releasing and any and all anger, any and all stress, all upset to release, all stress both powerfully and truly to release, as you peacefully relax, deeper and further, you feel tranquil, in fact, you are tranquil, comfortable, calm, peaceful, so right, so centered, relaxed. (count) Your heart rate and breathing are now powerfully relaxed, you are optimistic, you are doing great and getting better in ever growing, more powerful ways. And you actually feel thankful for whatever life lessons stress has taught you and has been there to teach you about, because you've gained from it. But even better right now in this and every future moment, you are in fact truly living in a new chapter, a healthier stress-free chapter of your life. You have chosen from deep within, to learn whatever lessons stress had once taught you, but now, in a more, peaceful, more powerful, more gentle way, you are correctly choosing to relax your way out of, through and around, any and all stress, flowing like a mighty river or ocean. And you become clear, sharp, confident, strong, focused, having learned all or those lessons, having learned, forgiven, completely, moving on. You feel like you are actually beginning, to thrive, to win, to gain, to succeed, to begin anew, a new chapter, and new and improved, stress-free you. In fact you almost feel, like you've begun again, stress-free, calm, relaxed, almost like being reborn into a stress-free world, completely noticeably unaffected by stress in amazing ways, only getting better each and every day, each and every night, each and every moment. You live, you thrive, you succeed now, stress-free, determined to be happy, relaxed, stress-free. In fact, you are an unstoppable stress-free force. Stress-free, calm, peaceful, relaxed, you win, in absolutely amazing ways. For you have truly learned that the proper and correct response to any and all stress is to relax your way through it, just relaxing your way through it and as you relax, you become clear, everything becomes calm, you focus. It's almost like you've relaxed your way through an invisible barrier of some kind, or like you've relaxed your way through a force field of resistance, moving on with your life, happy, peaceful, tranquil, serene, stress-free.

You begin to rethink and re-identify yourself and your life, as you forever re-pace your life, in a way that allows you to be and then remain, absolutely and completely, impervious to old forms of stress, in reality, and truly, you are and you remain, stress-free, calm, peaceful, focused, relaxed, and balanced. So take a deep breath, and embrace the feeling of a calm, stress-free body, calm, stress-free balanced emotions, calm, optimistic, clear, relaxed, yet focused thoughts, that support and allow you to relax, you feel good throughout all that You are stress-free, peaceful and in harmony with the world and with your life, and all of those whom you love and with all that needs doing and will get done, having set a wonderful stress-free pace and tone to your life and your world, you function smoothly, relaxed, calm, determined, creative, unstoppably successful, you succeed in amazing ways and it's very easy for you and it only gets better and better in any and all future moments. So feel all that You are body, emotions, mind, relaxing, thriving and succeeding, for that's who You are you made a breakthrough, you are victorious, successful, limitless, completely re-adapted, re-paced, re-identified, harmonized, stress-free and you win! You relax and go forward into every moment of your life, stress-free and peaceful, a winner in every way, trusting in your life, trusting each and every circumstance, each and every event, each and even moment, and you win, forever and always, stress-free.

## Enhanced Stress and Anxiety Management -2

You are finding newer and better ways, newer, more effective, clever, life supporting, healthy and better responses for dealing with stressful times. You are truly relaxing into your life and into your world so very comfortably. You are effectively and powerfully adapting by creating better ways of relaxing your way out of and beyond any and all stressful times. Your absolute and best, most correct response to any and all stress is to take slow and steady deep, deep breaths and to feel a new and better calming tranquility enveloping you, as you relax deeply, surely and serenely on each and every breath; all of this only getting better, faster, deeper and more profound each and every time you perform this newer and better way of responding. You are breathing deeply, releasing and forgiving all uncomfortable moments from your past, healing and releasing, relaxing while profoundly restoring yourself. While releasing stress and feeling profoundly calm, you are balanced, centered and relaxed, truly trusting in your life and feeling all the support that life readily and easily gives you, most especially when in a rush, knowing you'll get all that needs doing done. You are breathing deeply, while releasing stress and feeling profoundly calm, balanced, centered and relaxed, truly trusting in your life and feeling all the support that life readily and easily gives you, most especially when around any type of commotion. You are breathing deeply, while releasing stress and feeling profoundly calm, balanced, centered and relaxed, truly trusting in your life and feeling all the support that life readily and easily gives you, most especially when you have, might have, or even think, feel or imagine that you have, a lot of responsibilities, or maybe even if you are on a tight schedule. You are breathing deeply, while releasing stress and feeling profoundly calm, balanced, centered and relaxed, truly trusting in your life and feeling all the support that life readily and easily gives you, most especially when around anyone that is fussy, including any time when your spouse is or may be fussy. You are breathing deeply, while releasing stress and feeling profoundly calm, balanced, centered and relaxed, truly trusting in your life and feeling all the support that life readily and easily gives you, most especially when tired, or even feeling energetic. Your life now is supporting you better; you are truly and deeply trusting in all of this endless and highly effective support. You are truly learning to trust in the fact that you are truly creating the kind of comfortable, well healed, balanced, happy and determined-to-be-happy life you truly deserve and now effectively and imaginatively create. You have forever and effectively relaxed your way into a brand new, more supportive and better chapter of your life.

## Free Flowing Speech - Free of Stuttering

You are truly moving into a brand new and more unstoppable, more improved and better chapter of your life, as you've now and forever made a powerful decision to improve your life in well-deserved and wonderful ways. You are beginning to feel more and more comfortable about who you are, what you are doing and whomever you are connected with, are expressing yourself to, in any and all circumstances. You are alive, you are living, finding new and better ways to respect yourself and to enjoy your life; you are here right now in this present moment, you are meant to be here, you are meant to be a part of life, to share, to explore, to adapt, to connect, to share, to clearly express yourself and to be a part of it all in each and every aspect of your life. You are dynamically and unstoppably becoming more and more secure about who you are, what you must, can and will more easily and adaptively express, and what you have to say, as everything amazingly just seems to flow easily and naturally. It's almost like everything you are saying is being converted into some sort of singing, all of it just flowing so every easily and naturally from your brain; your breathing is perfect for the moment, air and energy just flowing through your vocal chords and throat and out of your mouth, all things working in powerfully correct and precise ways to insure your ever growing success. Your powerful and unstoppable mind is now creating better harmony, depth, comfort and ease to allow all that is in your mind to just so very easily flow out of your mouth in clear, precise and unobstructed ways, all imbalances, disharmonies and blockages now and forever being dissolved away, released, relaxed through, more powerfully forgiven and melted away and moving on from, in each and every past circumstance than ever before, and moved on from on each and every breath that you take and with each and every beat of your heart, while you are awake, while you are fast asleep, even while you are dreaming, new and supportive and healing, corrective thoughts and supportive feelings. You are powerfully free of listening to or analyzing whatever it is you have to say, as you say it from now on and only getting better and better and more eminently successful, you know it from your brain, you know it from your thoughts, you know it from your feelings, you know it from your powerful and fully functioning mind, so all of it just balances, flows and comes out beautifully, as you thrive and succeed, precisely and unstoppably. Your thoughts, feelings and desires to express, now being powerfully, dynamically and forever corrected, almost like from deep, deep inside of you someone has reset a switch, a dial, a computer, a thermostat of some kind, easily allowing you to express and share all that you want to, need to and must, clearly, fluidly, and adeptly, in amazing ways, amazing and impressing everyone, most especially you. Your powerful mind is now unstoppably working in your favor, as you relax deeper and further into this, to heal, recondition and rejuvenate you. Your powerful and unstoppable mind is now willing so much, even more, to work in your favor, by forgiving, releasing and healing any and all past discomfort, beginning a brand new, happier, brighter, better and more useful chapter of your life right now. All of this is only getting more powerful, more effective and more precise every time you repeat this enjoyable exercise. You relax, as you allow your words to powerfully and simply flow, expressing effectively what's on your mind. You are unstoppably committed to treating yourself free of harshness; instead, you are taking better care of yourself and forgiving the past and moving on into the very brightest of futures, freely flowing speech and speaking patterns are now emerging, whether you realize it yet or not, and you are relaxing into this and succeeding unstoppably, not because I say so but because it is the nature of your own unstoppable mind to do so on each and every breath and heartbeat. You relax into a brighter and better day and better way, you speak slowly, calmly, precisely, clearly, calmly, naturally, easily, with just the right amount of emphasis, yet, all of this just comes to you, as you are free of over-thinking this, just letting this happen for you, to you and flowingly for those around you.

Each and every time you go to speak, it's almost like a switch has been thrown, allowing brilliant and flowing and powerful communication to take place. You are free of listening to or gauging what you are saying; your mind, your thoughts and your mouth work as a cascade of flowing brilliance and you are so much more easily able to get your thoughts out and your points across. You are easily getting your feelings of calm and balanced and precise focus across, in an articulate, precise, powerfully potent and effectively flowing way. You are unstoppably getting your point across and as you relax deeper and further, further and deeper, it's almost like every time you hear a phone ring, it's like someone from deep, deep inside of you has thrown a switch, a dial, activated a computer or a thermostat of some kind, allowing your very best thoughts, words, ideas and concepts to articulately and glibly flow. You are powerfully free of over-thinking this, as it just flows ever onward, like a mighty river flowing down the side of a beautiful mountain, flowing on and beyond any and all obstacles, unencumbered, ever onward; your ability to express and communicate, active, adaptive, effective, flowing, glowing and doing all that needs to be done. In this newer and ever emerging chapter of your life, you are now forgiving and releasing any and all blockages, doubts, panic and fears, including any and all harsh judgments, whether your own or from someone else, almost like you've been washed clean and are powerfully and unstoppably beginning anew and fresh. You are clean, forgiven, released and healed. You are fearless, calm, balanced and relaxed. Your correct and now only response to anything and everything, that in the old chapter of your life once created any sort of discomfort in this area, is now to relax your way though it, flow beyond it and move on, whether you're alone or with someone else; in fact, you might be feeling empowered, inspired, Divinely guided, powerfully and truly unstoppable. Your breathing is calm, balanced and relaxed; your heart rate, calm, slow and serene; your throat loose, calm and comfortable. You become relaxed and tranquil, feeling so very calm and cool. Your correct response to any and all old patterns of fear, stress or old discomforts, is to be worry-free, calm, balanced, struggle-free and relaxing your way into a new and better, more supportive way of life; better ways of responding and reacting, as your mind now relaxed, open, accessible, flowing, glowing, responsive, inventive, creative, determined, passionately succeeding, adaptive, powerfully, precisely and effectively recalling, remembering, answering, responding and performing optimally, easily able to say "Hello" and relax into your very best thoughts, ideas, feelings and guidance to get any and all jobs effectively done. So each and every day, and each and every night, you are becoming more and more sure of yourself, powerfully confident, finding inner peace and serenity. You are becoming more and more self-forgiving, giving yourself a break, easily and effectively responding. You are now reconditioned to excel, in precise, wonderful and highly effective, even surprising ways, in any event or circumstance you may or might find yourself in. Even if you do mispronounce or get caught-up on a word, a wave of self-forgiveness energy will seemingly sweep over you, you'll blow it off and move on, just as you exhale your next breath, giving yourself the kind of care and loving that an ideal parent would a wonderful and loving child, regardless of what you always did in the past or might do. You even find yourself becoming struggle-free, free of struggling, problem-free, free of problems, now re-identified, as a person who is now flowing with life, CHALLENGE-oriented, easily rising up to meet any and all challenges in surprisingly adaptive, clever and convenient ways. You now find yourself taking the opportunity to effectively answer the phone, looking forward to it, as you are now determined to master your challenges in your life. You are so very and completely confident and sure of yourself, and so very deeply and truthfully sure of your newer and better emerging self; you are feeling completely unstoppable and looking forward to this, in any area, whether it's business or personal areas of your life, forgiving and releasing any and all past blockages, and those old blockages just dissolve away, and you flow ever onward with ease, self-acceptance and self-appreciation. In fact, you are now activating what you now know you always had and it's increasing, increasing, increasing, more fluid speech even when you are excited or stressed, or even while you are not excited or stressed. You are feeling fine and wonderful, sure, confident, safe and serene, embraced by the energy of all of your past moments of victory, triumph, breakthrough and success. You are creating new and more surprisingly better opportunities for yourself, feeling so super-motivated to share the very best gift you have to offer the world, YOURSELF. You seize the day, feeling more secure than ever before and creating more unlimited opportunities for yourself, magnetizing from your heart, mind, thoughts, actions and vital life force energies, only the very best for yourself. You will only receive powerful and precise, highly effective beneficial improvement in the correct and most powerful ways from this, going into this wonderful relaxation state faster, deeper, stronger and better, with more limitless results in many unlimited ways every time you repeat this extremely enjoyable, wonderful, dynamic, highly effective and precise exercise.

## Free Flowing Speech on the Phone – Healing Doubt, Panic and Fear

Your powerful mind is now unstoppably working in your favor, as your relax deeper and further into this, to heal, recondition and rejuvenate you. Your powerful and unstoppable mind is now willing so much every more, to work in your favor, by forgiving, releasing and healing any and all past discomfort, beginning a brand new, happier, brighter, better and more useful chapter of your life right now. All of this is only getting more powerful, more effective and more precise every time your repeat this enjoyable exercise. You relax, easily allowing your words to powerfully and simply flow, expressing effectively what's on your mind, most especially whenever you start a new job. All of your words are now effectively flowing, just like when you've been at a new job for over a month or so, because in this new place of relaxed and ever building empowerment, you are relaxing into this and just letting it happen. Each and every time you hear a telephone ring, it's almost like a switch has been thrown, allowing brilliant and flowing and powerful communication to take place. You are free of listening to or gauging what you are saying, your mind, your thoughts and your mouth work as a cascade of flowing brilliance and you are so much more easily able to get your thoughts out and your points across. You area easily getting your feelings of calm and balanced and precise focus across, in an articulate, precise, powerfully potent and effectively flowing way. You are unstoppably getting your point across and as you relax deeper and further, further and deeper, it's almost like every time you hear a phone ring, it's like someone from deep, deep inside of you has thrown a switch, a dial, activated a computer or a thermostat of some kind, allowing your very best thoughts, words, ideas and concepts of articulately and glibly flow. You are powerfully free of over-thinking this, as it just flows ever onward, like a mighty river flowing down the side of beautiful mountain, flowing on and beyond any and all obstacles, unencumbered, ever onward, your ability to express and communicate, active, adaptive, effective, flowing, glowing and doing all that needs to be done. In this newer and ever emerging chapter of your life, you are now forgiving and releasing any and all blockages, doubts, panic and fears, including any and all harsh judgments, whether your own or from someone else, almost like you've been washed clean and are powerfully and unstoppably beginning anew and fresh. You are forgiven, released and healed. You are fearless, calm, balanced and relaxed. Your correct and now only response to anything and everything that in the old chapter of your life, that once created any sort of discomfort in this area, is now to relax your way though it, flow beyond it and move on, whether your alone or with someone else, in fact, you might be feeling empowered, inspired, Divinely guided, powerfully and truly unstoppable. Your breathing is calm, balanced and relaxed; your heart rate, calm, slow and serene; your throat loose calm and comfortable. You become relaxed and tranquil, feeling so very calm and cool. Your correct response to any and all old patterns of fear, stress or old discomforts, is to be worry free, calm, balanced, struggle free and relaxing your way into a new and better more supportive way of life, better ways of responding and reacting, as your mind now relaxed, open, accessible, flowing, glowing, responsive, inventive, creative, determined, passionately succeeding, adaptive, powerfully, precisely and effectively recalling, remembering, answering, responding and performing optimally, easily able to say "Hello" and relax into your very best thoughts, ideas, feelings and guidance to get any all jobs effectively done. So each and every day and each and every night, you are becoming more and more sure of your self, powerfully confident, finding inner peace and serenity. You are becoming more and more self-forgiving, giving yourself a break, easily and effectively responding. You are now truly reconditioned to excel, in precise, wonderful and highly effective, even surprising ways, in any event or circumstance you may or might find yourself in. Even if your do mispronounce or get caught-up on a word, a wave of self-forgiveness energy will seemingly sweep over you, you'll blow it off and move on, just as you exhale your next breath, giving yourself the kind of care and loving that an ideal parent would a wonderful and loving child, regardless of what you always did in the past or might do. You even find yourself becoming struggle free, free of struggling, problem free, free of problems, now re-identified, as a person who is now flowing with life, CHALLENGE-oriented, easily rising up to meet any and all challenges in surprisingly adaptive, clever and conveniently. You now find yourself taking the opportunity to effectively answer the phone, looking forward to it, as you are now determined to master your challenges in your life. You are so very and completely confident and sure of your self and so very and deeply and truthfully sure of your newer and better emerging self, you are feeling completely unstoppable and looking forward to this, in any area, whether it's business or person areas of your life, forgiving and releasing any and all past blockages, and those old blockages just dissolve away, and you flow ever onward with ease, self-acceptance and self-appreciation. In fact, you are now activating what you now know you always had and it's increasing, increasing, increasing, more fluid speech even when you are excited or stressed, or even while you are not excited or stressed. You are feeling fine and wonderful, sure, confident, safe and serene, embraced by the energy of all of your past moments of victory, triumph, breakthrough and success. You are creating new and more surprisingly better opportunities for yourself, feeling so super-motivated to share the very best gift you have to offer the world, YOURSELF. You seize the day, feeling more secure before and creating more unlimited opportunities for yourself, magnetizing from our heart, mind, thoughts, actions and vital life force energies, only the very best for yourself. You will only receive powerful and precise, highly effective beneficial improvement in the correct and most powerful ways from this, going into this wonderful relaxation state faster, deeper, stronger and better, with more limitless results in my unlimited ways every time you repeat this extremely enjoyable, wonderful, dynamic, highly effective and precise exercise. You are feeling fine, so calm, so peaceful, so relaxed. You are feeling inspired now, capable, comfortable, able to take on any challenge, completely inspired and ready to thrive. It's almost as if, the energy of every past victory, triumph, breakthrough and success you've ever had is flowing down like a blessing upon you. It's almost as if in fact, truly, someone from deep, deep inside of you has thrown a switch, reset a dial, activated a computer or a thermostat of some kind, easily allowing you to become and remain calm, cool and collected in your thoughts, within your ability to express yourself and to convey your knowledge in creative, bold, gripping and powerfully effective ways. Your thoughts are calm, you are feeling, glib, persuasive, determined, free-flowing, smooth and convincing. For truly now you empowered and deeply and passionately inspired to convey all and any points with comfortable ease. Your heart rate, body and skin are all calm, soothing, rhythmic and balanced. You now and forever release and forgive any and all past blockages, uncomfortable memories and any and all pain. In fact, you are moving on into a brighter and more brilliant future, easily able to express yourself in any situation articulately, with grace, poise, skill, ease while easily magnetizing and generating interest from all who hear your words and gain from your knowledge (most especially when you have to enjoyably give a speech or when sitting in senior level meetings, even while in social settings when dealing with managers or executives you feel calm, relaxed, and balanced, just flowing and melting into new waves of comfortability and also at times you relax, you take it easy, you are so very calm, so in your zone). Your correct response to any and all old modes or stress or tension, is to rise up, to become bigger than the challenge at hand and to rise above it powerfully and dynamically, stress free, balanced, focused, relaxed, calm, clear and precise ways. All emotions, thoughts, ideas, action and feelings are working unstoppably in your favor to support you and to allow you to succeed, and it feels great. You are in fact now re-identified as a person who has moved on and is able to speak at anytime and in any place and you deeply and truly certain and sure of this. The only opinion of you that matters is your own, and you know you can do it. You respect yourself and know you have limitless reserves of talent, tapping into those reserves whenever you need to.

You only allow your very best to come through in the most self-assured of ways. All that you have to say gets easier and better as you feel so in our zone, so comfortable, so calm, so relaxed, so peaceful and so very richly inspired. Each person there to hear you, is truly a fan and a supporter. You are so sure of your self, you know it now and forever. Your words just seem to flow, breathing so very calm, so very balanced and so very relaxed, throat open and words just so easily flowing. You are highly efficient and effective, so worthy and deserving of praise, so self-starting, so self-supported, so ready, willing and able, so ready, skin so comfortable, so ready, so peaceful, so having moved on, so ready each and every day, each and every moment before and even during the week before. You are so ready, you are sure of yourself and your abilities in a newer and brighter and happier chapter of your life, just like you've begun anew. You are the focused, yet from now on and only getting better and easier and more powerful, you have newer and better thoughts and feelings that support you in profoundly better ways. You are allowing yourself to either thrive and succeed or just to communicate freely and clearly, breaking through the past and becoming victorious in all future speech giving opportunities. Your concentration and your focus are laser-beam like precise.

You see yourself as a superior as a teacher, a leader, as one who leads another to knowledge. All who are listening to you are deeply interested in what you have to say, as you lead them to the knowledge and the wisdom your words have to impart to them to enlighten and enliven, to streamline, make more efficient, to create and to make better. Like a model family and wonderful friends, those who listen to your words are supporting you. You know from deep down inside they want you to succeed. They are rooting for you, they are on your side and they want you to succeed. So you do, in newer and more creative and brilliantly powerful ways. And everything just seems to flow, for your ability to communicate, clearly and confidently, successfully, succinctly, directly, with cool and calm emotions, harmonized and balanced thoughts, each and every self-supporting action, just works. All of you is just freely flowing, you are supported, by your very own thoughts, words and emerging talents as your thriving confidence just seems to build and build. You feel like you've got the whole world in your back pocket, like you are ready to communicate to the world or at least to some of the people who have come to hear your important brilliance flow out from your words and thoughts. You are and you remain so relaxed, so determined and so very cool and calm in the most brilliant and powerful of ways, communicating, clearly, you are balanced, you are a self assured and unstoppable force, appreciated, calm and forever succeeding.

---

# Free of Fear of Bugs

You will always remember to breathe deep and steady powerful soothing, breath; a calming, centering, stilling, harmonizing and balancing breath, easily overcoming any and all fear, doubt, worry and panic. That which once overwhelmed you is now both easily and forever powerfully overwhelmed by you and the power of your stilling and calming breath, as you leave all fear, panic and discomfort, far, far behind you forever. All fear, all doubt and all panic are now and forever forgiven, released and vanquished.

You always knew, truly from deep down inside, the time would come when you'd be forever free of these old fears, so it's like we are now powerfully accelerating all of that into the right here and the right now. Bugs are meaning less and less to you, as you are feeling mightier and mightier, bugs meaning less and less to you as you keep a new and budding sense of power within yourself as you powerfully rise to the top and succeed at this, while releasing all old patterns of discomfort. You are learning to forgive, adapt and release those patterns from your life right now, almost as if someone from deep, deep inside of you is resetting a switch, a dial or a computer or thermostat of some kind allowing you to now and forever be fearless around any bug at any time (nod your head 'yes' for me because you know it's now and forever true). Each and every time you see a bug, it will be like you are vaguely seeing one miles away, because you'll remain so completely detached, so completely calm, so very comfortable and so completely at ease. It's almost like you've accelerated yourself into a place 5 years down the road and you have even gotten better and powerfully even more comfortable around bugs, completely reconditioned both now and forever to your greatest benefit. Even if you do see a bug of any kind, you will absolutely and powerfully remain very, very, calm and balanced, peaceful and at ease, and your only prevailing thought and emotional sense around the bug will be, "I am unstoppably calm and balanced; the bug is nothing, nothing, nothing. am a human and I am mighty." I am amazingly powerful; I've moved on." Bugs are just silly; you might even just laugh at them.

You now are finding newer, more powerful and effective ways to be comfortable around or near bugs (just like you once were, your Mom was, etc.) as you master all past challenges, now releasing any and all past challenges right now, just rising to the top and moving on into a better and brighter place in your life, on each and every breath as you unstoppably go ever onward, moving into a brighter and better more healthy place. For it really doesn't matter what you once felt or feared in the past, because yes, you have in fact truly moved on, into a brighter and better more powerful future, more calm, more balanced, more relaxed, more comfortable around any and all bugs. You are calm, comfortable and powerfully and truly getting only better and better, anxiety-free and balanced, almost as if someone from deep, deep inside of you has thrown a switch of some kind, resetting the past and making your life a more profoundly comfortable and trusting place, a masterpiece that you create, releasing anxiety, remaining calm, balanced and relaxed, most especially in relation to your relationship with bugs. You are now more powerfully, unafraid and anxietyfree, like you are now imagining and living from your very best possible outcome, just like a valve holding fear and anxiety energy has been completely and forever drained, any and all anxiety and fear are draining, draining and powerfully released, on each and every breath that you take, even if a bug is there. Because you know from deep, down inside, that you are mightier and more powerful than any and all bugs. Bugs are less and less meaningful to you, in even surprising ways, and you are finding newer, better and more clever ways to accomplish this, amazing even yourself. It's even very pleasantly surprising at how easy this has become for you. I wonder if you yet even realize, for already it's almost like how you can forget a dream upon awaking in the morning, because you are beginning to forget the old reaction patterns you once had in place of the new ones that now and forever support you in the most amazing of ways, calm, balanced, still and peaceful, happy, calm and steady, rising to the top, you are unstoppable, forgiven, released, cleansed and healed.

Your awareness grows, your life expands, and you are both now and forever free. Your whole body, each and every emotional feeling and response and from all that is your mind, in fact, truly each and every thought and feeling are being now powerfully realigned in profoundly better and more powerful ways to allow you to unstoppably be trusting and more readily able to go to a friend's house and be forever free of ever worrying about bugs, as you are now liberated and able more than ever before. You are easily able to be calm and balanced whether a bug is there or not, free of thinking anything that can or might stand in your way, because you now see the order of life more clearly, you are a higher being than a bug, you are above it in the order of things, as you master your past and your life, past, present and future. You powerfully forgive and release your past, moving into a newer and brighter and better way of life and living, easily able to accomplish all of this. You are easily able to know, feel and experience that bugs are nothing; you are fine, life is fine and things are magnificently okay with you, so you enjoy life now, forever freed, and you thrive.

## Free of Fear of Dogs

Each and every time you see a dog, it will be like you are seeing one on TV, because you'll remain so detached, so calm, so very comfortable and so completely at ease. You always knew truly from deep, down inside, the time would come when you'd be forever free of these old fears, so it's like we are now powerfully accelerating all of that into the right here and the right now. It's also most like you've accelerated yourself into a place 5 years down the road and you have even gotten better and powerfully even more comfortable around dogs, completely reconditioned to your greatest benefit around your new best friends, and your loveable, loyal companions. Dogs have been called man's best friend, you now are finding newer, more powerful and effective ways to like dogs, and to let them like you, as you master all past challenges, now releasing them on each and every breath as you unstoppably go ever onward, moving into a brighter and better more healthy place. For it really doesn't matter what you once felt or feared in the past, because you have truly moved on, into a brighter and better more powerful future, more calm, more balanced, more relaxed, more comfortable around man's best friend, the dog. You are calm, comfortable and powerfully and truly getting only better and better, anxiety-free and balanced, almost as if someone from deep, deep inside of you has thrown a switch of some kind, resetting the past and making your life a more profoundly comfortable and trusting place, a masterpiece that you create, releasing anxiety, remaining calm, balanced and relaxed, most especially in relation to your relationship with dogs. You are now more powerfully, unafraid and anxiety-free, like you are now imagining and living from your very best possible outcome, just like a valve holding fear and anxiety-energy has been completely and forever drained, any and all anxiety and fear are draining, draining and powerfully released, on each and every breath that you take, even if a dog barks. Because you know from deep, down inside, that the dog is actually being friendly. Your awareness grows, your life expands; you are both now and forever free. Your whole body, each and every emotional feeling and response and from all that is your mind in fact, truly each and every thought and feeling are being now powerfully realigned, in profoundly better and more powerful ways, to allow you to unstoppably be trusting and more readily able to go to a friend's house and be forever free of ever worrying about their dog, as you are now liberated and able more than ever before. You are easily able to pet a dog without thinking that it will bite you, because you now see the order of life more clearly: you are a higher being than a dog, you are above it in the order of things. As you master your past, you powerfully forgive and release your past moving into a newer and brighter and better way of life and living, easily able to accomplish all of this. You are easily able to know, feel and experience that petting a dog that has teeth, is fine and okay for you, so you do it, you enjoy it, and you thrive.

## Free of Fear of Lizards

With each and every breath that you are taking, and with each and every beat of your heart; lizards or iguanas are of little or no value to you, except for your victory right now over them. They are of little or no value to you, except for your victory right now over them, as you are rising above, becoming assuredly happy and free of any and all doubts, panics and fears, happily and surely, free, free at long last and it feels fantastic. You are empowered, you are dynamic, you are mighty, you are and have released and undeniably forgiven any and all old thoughts, patterns, feelings and fears that once might have or in fact had created this, in each and any way, in the most unstoppable of ways. You are big, they are little; you are big, they are tiny; you are big, they are nothing; you are moving on. You rise to the top; they are unimportant; your power is up and on inside of you; you are empowered as never before; they are almost meaningless to you, except for the fact that you've risen above past barriers having to do with them. It's almost like someone from deep, deep inside of you has tapped off and drained any and all doubt, fear, upset, panic or fear out of and off, far, far away from you. In fact, it's almost like someone has reset a dial a switch, a computer or a thermostat of some kind from deep, deep inside of you, easily allowing you to be and forever remain, calm, comfortable, balanced, at ease and relaxed, fearless, unafraid, brave, courageous, bold, mighty, self-assured, rising above any and all old patterns or doubts skillfully, and in remarkable ways. Your newer and more correct response to any and all old and former patterns of fear regarding lizards or iguanas, is to now deep-breathe slow and steady, powerful, soothing breath; feeling calm, balanced, comfortable and relaxed all over and in every way, just like waves of calming, soothing relaxation energy are flowing down and over you, balancing you and keeping you calm and relaxed, deeply and truly, from powerful and fortified places from deep within. You are and you remain powerfully and completely calm, fearless, balanced, and relaxed, trusting in life and feeling very comfortable, in spite of any and all challenges, most especially when or if you see a lizard or iguana. You are and you remain powerfully and completely calm, fearless, balanced, and relaxed, trusting in life and feeling very comfortable, in spite of any and all challenges, most especially if any get near you. You are and you remain powerfully and completely calm, fearless, balanced, and relaxed, trusting in life and feeling very comfortable, in spite of any and all challenges, most especially if you think you will or might see a lizard, as they are just so unimportant to you. You rise above any and all old fears or patterns or thoughts that once might have brought you fear, so that you can truly and actually in fact, enjoy your vacation. Rising above the past, you find the courageousness of your inner hero, tapping into your very best moments, powerfully and most especially moving beyond the childish fears you once had as kid. Now that you are an adult, the light of your knowledge, the wisdom from your years of experience, embraces you, strengthens you, and allows you to live your life, enjoy your life and any vacations you need to take. Moving on clearly, confidently, and unstoppably into a brand-new and reconditioned chapter of your life, you are free, free at least. And this only gets easier, better, stronger and more powerful, each and every time you repeat this enjoyable exercise; and you do better and better each and every time you encounter any challenges.

# Free of Skin Picking

You are free of picking on yourself or at yourself. You are fine. You are enough. You look fine. You are enough. You are treating yourself better and getting only better at taking care of yourself, day by day, night by night, moment by moment, whether with other people or even and most especially if you are alone. You are in fact becoming free of all repetitive and self-destructive behaviors.

Now relax, deeper and further, further and deeper and in this place of deep, true and profound relaxation, you are now forgiving, both known and unknown events, harsh or negative judgments, criticisms, circumstances and opinions, whether those opinions were yours or someone else's, regardless of where they came from, in order to move into a brighter, healthier, better and more whole chapter of your life. You are finding newer and better more healthy ways of loving yourself better, releasing past uncomfortable moments, truly doing better than picking on your skin or face. Free of picking on yourself, feeling fine, upbeat, calm, enough, balanced, loved and wonderful in powerful and effective ways. You are

# Free Flowing Speech on the Phone – Healing Doubt, Panic and Fear

Your powerful mind is now unstoppably working in your favor, as your relax deeper and further into this, to heal, recondition and rejuvenate you. Your powerful and unstoppable mind is now willing so much every more, to work in your favor, by forgiving, releasing and healing any and all past discomfort, beginning a brand new, happier, brighter, better and more useful chapter of your life right now. All of this is only getting more powerful, more effective and more precise every time your repeat this enjoyable exercise. You relax, easily allowing your words to powerfully and simply flow, expressing effectively what's on your mind, most especially whenever you start a new job. All of your words are now effectively flowing, just like when you've been at a new job for over a month or so, because in this new place of relaxed and ever building empowerment, you are relaxing into this and just letting it happen. Each and every time you hear a telephone ring, it's almost like a switch has been thrown, allowing brilliant and flowing and powerful communication to take place. You are free of listening to or gauging what you are saying, your mind, your thoughts and your mouth work as a cascade of flowing brilliance and you are so much more easily able to get your thoughts out and your points across. You area easily getting your feelings of calm and balanced and precise focus across, in an articulate, precise, powerfully potent and effectively flowing way. You are unstoppably getting your point across and as you relax deeper and further, further and deeper, it's almost like every time you hear a phone ring, it's like someone from deep, deep inside of you has thrown a switch, a dial, activated a computer or a thermostat of some kind, allowing your very best thoughts, words, ideas and concepts of articulately and glibly flow. You are powerfully free of over-thinking this, as it just flows ever onward, like a mighty river flowing down the side of beautiful mountain, flowing on and beyond any and all obstacles, unencumbered, ever onward, your ability to express and communicate, active, adaptive, effective, flowing, glowing and doing all that needs to be done. In this newer and ever emerging chapter of your life, you are now forgiving and releasing any and all blockages, doubts, panic and fears, including any and all harsh judgments, whether your own or from someone else, almost like you've been washed clean and are powerfully and unstoppably beginning anew and fresh. You are forgiven, released and healed. You are fearless, calm, balanced and relaxed. Your correct and now only response to anything and everything that in the old chapter of your life, that once created any sort of discomfort in this area, is now to relax your way though it, flow beyond it and move on, whether your alone or with someone else, in fact, you might be feeling empowered, inspired, Divinely guided, powerfully and truly unstoppable. Your breathing is calm, balanced and relaxed; your heart rate, calm, slow and serene; your throat loose calm and comfortable. You become relaxed and tranquil, feeling so very calm and cool. Your correct response to any and all old patterns of fear, stress or old discomforts, is to be worry free, calm, balanced, struggle free and relaxing your way into a new and better more supportive way of life, better ways of responding and reacting, as your mind now relaxed, open, accessible, flowing, glowing, responsive, inventive, creative, determined, passionately succeeding, adaptive, powerfully, precisely and effectively recalling, remembering, answering, responding and performing optimally, easily able to say "Hello" and relax into your very best thoughts, ideas, feelings and guidance to get any all jobs effectively done. So each and every day and each and every night, you are becoming more and more sure of your self, powerfully confident, finding inner peace and serenity. You are becoming more and more self-forgiving, giving yourself a break, easily and effectively responding. You are now truly reconditioned to excel, in precise, wonderful and highly effective, even surprising ways, in any event or circumstance you may or might find yourself in. Even if your do mispronounce or get caught-up on a word, a wave of self-forgiveness energy will seemingly sweep over you, you'll blow it off and move on, just as you exhale your next breath, giving yourself the kind of care and loving that an ideal parent would a wonderful and loving child, regardless of what you always did in the past or might do. You even find yourself becoming struggle free, free of struggling, problem free, free of problems, now re-identified, as a person who is now flowing with life, CHALLENGE-oriented, easily rising up to meet any and all challenges in surprisingly adaptive, clever and conveniently. You now find yourself taking the opportunity to effectively answer the phone, looking forward to it, as you are now determined to master your challenges in your life. You are so very and completely confident and sure of your self and so very and deeply and truthfully sure of your newer and better emerging self, you are feeling completely unstoppable and looking forward to this, in any area, whether it's business or person areas of your life, forgiving and releasing any and all past blockages, and those old blockages just dissolve away, and you flow ever onward with ease, self-acceptance and selfappreciation. In fact, you are now activating what you now know you always had and it's increasing, increasing, increasing, more fluid speech even when you are excited or stressed, or even while you are not excited or stressed. You are feeling fine and wonderful, sure, confident, safe and serene, embraced by the energy of all of your past moments of victory, triumph, breakthrough and success. You are creating new and more surprisingly better opportunities for yourself, feeling so super-motivated to share the very best gift you have to offer the world, YOURSELF. You seize the day, feeling more secure before and creating more unlimited opportunities for yourself, magnetizing from our heart, mind, thoughts, actions and vital life force energies, only the very best for yourself. You will only receive powerful and precise, highly effective beneficial improvement in the correct and most powerful ways from this, going into this wonderful relaxation state faster, deeper, stronger and better, with more limitless results in my unlimited ways every time you repeat this extremely enjoyable, wonderful, dynamic, highly effective and precise exercise. You are feeling fine, so calm, so peaceful, so relaxed. You are feeling inspired now, capable, comfortable, able to take on any challenge, completely inspired and ready to thrive. It's almost as if, the energy of every past victory, triumph, breakthrough and success you've ever had is flowing down like a blessing upon you. It's almost as if in fact, truly, someone from deep, deep inside of you has thrown a switch, reset a dial, activated a computer or a thermostat of some kind, easily allowing you to become and remain calm, cool and collected in your thoughts, within your ability to express yourself and to convey your knowledge in creative, bold, gripping and powerfully effective ways. Your thoughts are calm, you are feeling, glib, persuasive, determined, free-flowing, smooth and convincing. For truly now you empowered and deeply and passionately inspired to convey all and any points with comfortable ease. Your heart rate, body and skin are all calm, soothing, rhythmic and balanced. You now and forever release and forgive any and all past blockages, uncomfortable memories and any and all pain. In fact, you are moving on into a brighter and more brilliant future, easily able to express yourself in any situation articulately, with grace, poise, skill, ease while easily magnetizing and generating interest from all who hear your words and gain from your knowledge (most especially when you have to enjoyably give a speech or when sitting in senior level meetings, even while in social settings when dealing with managers or executives you feel calm, relaxed, and balanced, just flowing and melting into new waves of comfortability and also at times you relax, you take it easy, you are so very calm, so in your zone). Your correct response to any and all old modes or stress or tension, is to rise up, to become bigger than the challenge at hand and to rise above it powerfully and dynamically, stress free, balanced, focused, relaxed, calm, clear and precise ways. All emotions, thoughts, ideas, action and feelings are working unstoppably in your favor to support you and to allow you to succeed, and it feels great. You are in fact now re-identified as a person who has moved on and is able to speak at anytime and in any place and you deeply and truly certain and sure of this. The only opinion of you that matters is your own, and you know you can do it. You respect yourself and know you have limitless reserves of talent, tapping into those reserves whenever you need to.

You only allow your very best to come through in the most self-assured of ways. All that you have to say gets easier and better as you feel so in our zone, so comfortable, so calm, so relaxed, so peaceful and so very richly inspired. Each person there to hear you, is truly a fan and a supporter. You are so sure of your self, you know it now and forever. Your words just seem to flow, breathing so very calm, so very balanced and so very relaxed, throat open and words just so easily flowing. You are highly efficient and effective, so worthy and deserving of praise, so selfstarting, so self-supported, so ready, willing and able, so ready, skin so comfortable, so ready, so peaceful, so having moved on, so ready each and every day, each and every moment before and even during the week before. You are so ready, you are sure of yourself and your abilities in a newer and brighter and happier chapter of your life, just like you've begun anew. You are the focused, yet from now on and only getting better and easier and more powerful, you have newer and better thoughts and feelings that support you in profoundly better ways. You are allowing yourself to either thrive and succeed or just to communicate freely and clearly, breaking through the past and becoming victorious in all future speech giving opportunities. Your concentration and your focus are laser-beam like precise.

You see yourself as a superior as a teacher, a leader, as one who leads another to knowledge. All who are listening to you are deeply interested in what you have to say, as you lead them to the knowledge and the wisdom your words have to impart to them to enlighten and enliven, to streamline, make more efficient, to create and to make better. Like a model family and wonderful friends, those who listen to your words are supporting you. You know from deep down inside they want you to succeed. They are rooting for you, they are on your side and they want you to succeed. So you do, in newer and more creative and brilliantly powerful ways. And everything just seems to flow, for your ability to communicate, clearly and confidently, successfully, succinctly, directly, with cool and calm emotions, harmonized and balanced thoughts, each and every self-supporting action, just works. All of you is just freely flowing, you are supported, by your very own thoughts, words and emerging talents as your thriving confidence just seems to build and build. You feel like you've got the whole world in your back pocket, like you are ready to communicate to the world or at least to some of the people who have come to hear your important brilliance flow out from your words and thoughts. You are and you remain so relaxed, so determined and so very cool and calm in the most brilliant and powerful of ways, communicating, clearly, you are balanced, you are a self assured and unstoppable force, appreciated, calm and forever succeeding.

## Overcoming a Fear of Falling Down

You relax even deeper, you are tapping into the vital energy and power of your mind, with calm and ever supportive and balanced emotions, tapping into the power of your very best moments, like times when you rose up to protect, defend or care for a loved one. Times when you were amazingly able to rise to the top and overcome just about anything. Times when you were unstoppable, times when you almost felt like you could move mountains, times when all things were possible, times when your only option was and now is boundless and unstoppable success. This is that time, sense a spark of enlightenment, a newer and more unstoppable feeling of power, empowerment and blessings from on high coming down upon you, moving you forward, as your heart is now beaming with a new sense of exhilaration, pride, clarity, optimism, and a budding and ever building sense of can-do spirit. You are beginning to imagine that you are bigger, greater and mightier than any challenge you are being presented with, easily moving on and now and forever forgiving those past challenges and now learning from them more gently, at any and all moments in your life. Little steps mean a lot. You are powerfully now feeling able, driven, powerful and even courageous, rising to the top, embraced by every past victory, triumph, breakthrough and success you've ever had. You are becoming problem-free, and challenge- oriented. You now know and realize what a famous past American President once said, "The only thing we have to fear is fear itself." But that doesn't even matter, because in this and all future moments, whether inside or outside, with each and every beat of your heart and with each and every breath that you take, you are becoming mightier than any and old patterns, ways of thinking, doubts, fears and challenges into a brighter better day, a brighter better night, a brighter and better life, more easily able to get back on your feet, moving, going where you need to, in ways that are safe, serene, secure, in balanced, wholesome and healthy ways, feeling even fluid, trusting in life and all the many times you've gone where you've needed to go, fearless and determined, letting go of old and painful past judgments, only focusing on the main prize, the prize of moving on and getting your life back.

As you relax deeper and further, you imagine the following: all the times you've gone and done what needed to be done, all the times that you got things done, all the times you got where you were going safely, were the majority of the times of your life, the very, very large vast majority of your life, the highest percentage of your life, and those are the times you are now and forever focusing upon to allow you to thrive and succeed at you becoming fearless, doubtless, driven to rise up and succeed at this, taking on any and all challenges, filled with new vitality, optimism, determination, powerfully reconditioned and trusting in the powerful support of your life, doing all that it takes to succeed at trusting in your life, your balance, your support, tapping into the energy of the courage and courageousness of all of those in your family whom have gone before you, almost like they are now blessing you to move on and move and trust in life, and get back to surely moving again, whether you can make it on your own or with assistance, just as if it were years ago, things are great, and you are moving on again with your life, unhindered, unimpeded, unrestricted, letting yourself and your very best to come back out again, unopposed, taking your first few steps, like learning to walk as a child, having learned to avoid the falling, moving on, re-excited about your life and all of the wonderful treasures that it holds for you and waits to share with you, boldly moving on, not because I say so, but because you have unstoppably relaxed your way into a newer, brighter and better chapter of your life and you are now and forever bound and determined to make the most of any and all opportunities, finding new balance and support, learning to take the very best care of yourself, embraced, loved, guided and supported by all the love that you've ever had in your life, the love of your loved ones, your husband, and everyone who has ever loved you, and even better right now, a new and better more abiding sense of "I can, of course I can" and true and lasting love for yourself. Like the children's story The Little Engine That Could, every old "I can't both now and forever easily becomes, "I think I can, I think I can . . . I can" and now it becomes for you, "I do, for I am forever easily unstoppable." Each and every thought, feeling and action you take are focused only upon supporting you in this, even in surprising ways. So you move, you thrive, you succeed, taking the best care of yourself and moving around, getting and taking back the precious gift that is your life and learning that you are the mighty one in your life, and that you are succeeding, in the most adaptive, flexible, correct, precisely effective and powerfully correct of ways.

## Overcoming a Fear of Heights

You always knew that one day you would become more mighty and courageous than any challenge life has ever presented you, just as you have always done, one step at a time in any and all moments in your past, which have brought you this far. Just like when you were a child and grew up past certain other issues, once substantial and now silly, like a fear of the dark, a fear of being alone, you evolved and moved forward with your life and all that you are; in fact, being polished by the process, you have truly become stronger and mightier. As you relax and float and flow deeper and further, further and deeper, as I count backwards from three to one: 3. . . 2. . . 1, you will now and forever undeniably and unstoppably bring forward your mighty inner hero, the part of you that is fearless and doubtless, courageous and mighty, skillfully adaptable and unbeatable, the part of you that is capable of unlimited heroic feats of courage and light, like saving children from great danger like a fire, which now you're certain truly allows you to transcend any and all old limitations from your past, perhaps from previous chapters of your life, just as you have always done, whenever and wherever challenged in your life, while you are now trusting in a better and more supportive set of life-changing thoughts, life-improving emotions, life-improving actions and life-improving reactions, while you are becoming, realizing and truly coming to undeniably know that you are and you remain forever unstoppably inspired to become and remain mightier than any challenge in your life, as you are now problem-free, and challenge-oriented – failure-free, choosing only to learn or succeed, breaking through here unbeatably, inspired by the energy of every past victory, breakthrough, triumph, and success you'd ever had; all of that energy right now is enlightening you and driving you forward like a legendary hero of old, reorienting you, foundationally recalibrating you unbeatably and in the most unlimited of ways, toward transcending all moments of blockage and imbalance from previous past chapters of your life now have gone forever, by allowing you to flow beyond those moments into a brighter better life and a brighter better you, filled with limitless possibilities, rising to the top, and taking charge, just as you have always done. This mighty inner hero, this unbeatable, adaptably rising up and unstoppable inner you, has decided to relax beyond all old barriers from previous moments in your life, rise up, practically without thinking, feeling supported, wonderful and fine, into a more comfortable and self-supporting existence that allows you to flow ever-onward into a healthier and better, more self-supporting and free, brand new chapter of your life, where your very best and most unlimited of dreams are realized; all blockages and fears are cleverly, adaptively, dynamically, most assuredly and forever dynamically vanquished, almost as if you are being Divinely-guided from on high, to break through in the most unbeatable of ways, feeling truly, from powerful places, deep, deep inside of you, even knowing for a fact in this brand new chapter of your life, that you truly are indeed safe and taking the very best care of yourself. You are fine, you are balanced and safe and secure. Knowingly, glowingly, for a fact, surely this is the case.

In your mind, for a moment, imagine seeing even feeling as if, a valve of some type has been opened, as all of the murky and liquidly fear energy from past moments of your life is now being vanquished away, drained all away, like some liquid is flowing from this valve and a pipe onto the earth and flowing powerfully away in a stream from you, as the reservoir of any and all unneeded and unhealthy, unwanted fear from past moments, all of the energies of discomfort, imbalance, and distrust, are now being drained away, far away, from your life, and from your mind, and from your feelings, and from your experiences, and from your sense of past memories, while you're imagining the limitless support, of golden-white sunshine on a bright day, evaporating all of that easily vanquished, now forgiven, released and let go of fear, is right here and right now, once and for all, released, removed and gone, all of this getting only easier and better each and every time you repeat this wonderfully enjoyable technique of relaxation on your own and ahh, it feels so good, to be so free. Now imagine that reservoir from which this now gone fear was drained from, completely clear and clean, as the first valve is closed while a second valve is now open.

From the second valve you notice or imagine, sense it, or even feel a new energy of inspiration and light, an energy of dynamic and limitless, creatively adaptive courageousness, and your ability to transcend any and all old limits, from previous chapters of your life, now and forever and done, this new improved and life supporting energy is filling this area with a golden-white light liquid of mighty inspiration and courage and fearlessness, as you feel a warm glow spreading through your heart and mind, and a perfect balance, a harmony creating a new and better wisdom and trust in your life, sensing, feeling and knowing that this new reality is yours, a truly inspired balance of heart and mind, that you are generating the very best and just-right-for-you internal and external harmony, all pervasive, within your life. You now and forever just know, that you are mightier and more courageous than any past moments in your life. You are inspired and it is just bubbling up on its own, in impressive and amazing ways, even surprising you how easy this is and truthfully you now recognize and embrace the idea and very true fact that you have always gotten it done, whenever anything was ever needed, you got it done as you know truly come to know, and recognize, that all old blockages and fears that have repressed or slowed you down in any way, are now laughable to you, now as you are and remain, cleverly adaptive, hindrance-free, unblocked and free, with a budding, building sense of optimism, as you are now heroically willing to become unbeatable, seizing this and all moments with an inspired can do-spirit, dynamically breaking through here

unbeatably, right here and right now, but trusting in your life, truly feeling fearless and mighty in all moments in your life, comfortably and so in your zone.
You begin to find that you are more easily able to breathe, deep and steady breath, while finding your body relaxing, as you are trusting in life, and you know from the places in your heart and mind that you are supported, and each and every moment of your life in your past has supported you; most assuredly as the sun comes up in the morning each day, it will come up tomorrow as well, and therefore you are more readily, steadily, safely and dynamically supported by new thoughts, feelings, inspirations and emotions as never before.

It has been truthfully said, that a thought is just a thought; a feeling is just a feeling; and so far as anyone knows, most especially you, right now in this your true moment of power, a thought or a feeling can never destroy you, but even better right now, your thoughts and your feelings are being powerfully reoriented, re-re-calibrated and re-organized dynamically and unbeatably all within your favor, in a more self-supportive way by your mighty inner hero from deep inside your heart and your mind to vanquish any and all shadows that once ever stood in your way, wherever they came from known or unknown to you.

There are times you can be hungry or full; there are times when you can be awake or sleepy; there times when you can be hot or cold, but a feeling is just a feeling; a thought is just a thought and in these moments your thoughts and your feelings are reorienting themselves to support you and to vanquish any and all useless and now forgiven and released blockages and imbalances to create a mightier, more trusting, more self-supporting you who takes the very best care of themselves, vanquishing dynamically all past imbalances, with skill, grace, and profound ease.

Your correct response to all the issues that once created anxiety, fear, or imbalance of any type is to reflexively begin deep breathing slow and steadying, life-affirming and supportive, centering, balancing restorative breath, as your thoughts and feelings become ever more calm and focused, centered and ultimately self-supporting, as you are now telling yourself a better truth while instilling within yourself a budding and building sense of self support, knowing and truly experiencing the feeling of your mighty inner hero emerging from places deep inside of your heart and your mind, allowing you to profoundly break through, and in the most inspired of ways, allowing those imbalances to forever be shed and stripped away from your life, imbalances now correctly forever channeled into your now done past, as you have grown into a brand new aspect of your life, almost as if truly right now in this moment someone, from deep, deep inside of you, has reset a switch, a dial, a thermostat, or having effectively activated a computer of some kind, which is fully allowing you to move beyond, and to effectively rise up in the most mighty of ways, into a brand new chapter of your life, where you trust in your life and all of your experiences, sensing and honoring the strength and balance of your body and its inner and outer wisdom, and in the way you have carefully laid out circumstances around you, taking the very best safety precautions, yet taking care of yourself completely, free of over-thinking, well, truly feeling mighty, heroic, courageous, positively re-identified, deep breathing your way to ultimate success, safe, sure, serene, balanced, centered, mighty, and even courageous, while always taking the very best care of yourself.

## Overcoming Claustrophobia – 1

Right now, you have truly decided that the time has come, to really just let go of old ways of living, physically, emotionally and mentally, even feelings and sensations that stand in your way, no longer serving you, in order to balance your life, because you have come to the decision that you are going to live a more trusting, more empowered and relaxed, beneficial way of life. So right now, you are relaxed, you are calm and you are at peace and from deep, deep inside of you, each and every day and night, you are remembering, perhaps even memorizing what this sort of deep, deep relaxation feels like and how to easily and completely bring yourself back to this relaxed state of consciousness and way of being and feeling. And you truly begin to realize that this relaxation you are now experiencing, which only gets better and better, stronger and stronger and easier to return to, each and every time you practice it or experience it, is what is healthy and absolutely correct for you in each and every moment of your life. You have made an important decision and truly correct choice, you have chosen correctly to respond to any and all stress, any and all fear, any and all doubt, any and all disharmony of any kind, by allowing yourself, to both deeply and powerfully, relax through any and all adversity, actually recognizing from truly powerful deep places within yourself, this is the only correct response for you and the best choice to make and a relaxation reaction you can easily achieve, supporting yourself as never before. You have really recognized that rather than struggling through a given situation you can and you will relax through any and all adversity and every moment of resistance. That's right, relaxing and relaxation are the correct responses for you, because it's much more healthy, much more beneficial and the really best way to succeed for you. So right now, you've unstoppably decided that you can relax through any and all struggle because relaxation is the best way for you to succeed. And while you relax, you allow yourself, calmness, clearness and the empowering ability, to allow for transcending and empowered thoughts and feelings to flow and to come through supporting you in new and wonderful ways, for you to express to yourself. You are expressing greater and grander truth, a truth where you feel relaxed, problem-free yet challenge oriented and mightier than any challenge, meeting any and all challenges presented to you in any way by rising above them or simply by relaxing through them. You are becoming more and more calm while living your life and more and more calm when any and all stressful situations come up and you deeply realize, that all of this world, your home, is here for you to explore, wide open spaces, and even the not so wide open spaces, any and all spaces and places for you to feel at home, powerfully and truly safe and really comfortable, in all that you do. And you have all the time in the world to relax and to enjoy these places, free from all time constraints, you have limitless amounts of time, so no matter how long anything takes, you relax, breathe and enjoy, you relax, you breathe, you trust and feel so very calm. Truly, life always takes care of you, as it always has in each and every moment of your life, most especially, you always recognize and embrace this truth powerfully, right now and into the future.

Now think about seeing yourself in a vision of the future. Imagine seeing yourself boarding an elevator (name location). And as you do this time and every time, you allow yourself to very deeply, very powerfully, very truly relax all over, just like when you are in a warm bathtub of water, so comfortable, so warm, so very truly relaxing and unwinding and you are breathing slow steady comfortable relaxation breath, with each and every breath that you take calmly, powerfully and peacefully, you relax on each and every breath that you take, going into your relaxation, doubly deep, doubly deep, doubly deep, with each and every breath that you take and with every slow, steady, and comfortable life giving beat of your heart. You are always and forever as free as you need to be and you correctly choose this as a powerful calm, determined new truth, in a brand new happier and healthier chapter of your life, beginning right now, always and forever. It really doesn't matter what happened in your past, because right now all of those memories of past experiences are just that, past experiences that fill you with joy, ease, peace and contentment, moments you are moving beyond. They are all simply past experiences, free from all effect upon you right now and even forever. And with each and every breath that you take, slowly, deeply calmly and comfortably, they are just drifting away, drifting away, drifting away, far, far away from you. What takes their place is a calm yet strong and powerful peacefulness, a trust in your life your world, in your life and in all that you are. You trust in life, you were meant to be here and deserve to be here, because you are always supported, you are always calm and you are always rising up in the most relaxed and peaceful and profound ways. And almost even before you realize it, your trip is safely over. You arrive at your destination quickly and efficiently. You learn to relax, to breathe relaxation and to remain calm (3x).

You are and you remain relaxed, truly and powerfully relaxed, safe, powerfully and calmly and truly determined to remain balanced, safe, both mentally and emotionally ready to conquer the world, most especially times when you are in: (name locations) relax, elevators; relax, public bathrooms; relax, rooms without windows; relax, on a plane; relax, when traveling in any way; relax, traveling through tunnels; relax, while on a boat; relax, while on a bus; relax, when meeting new people; relax, when meeting new and interesting situations to explore; relax, whenever there is a change in your routine, you correctly choose to grow and to flow with it, because you create your life, and you are relaxed and you are in control and you are always succeeding and powerfully thriving, relax, whenever you travel or visit; something each and every day and night you learn more and more to enjoy, you relax and enjoy successfully, more and more each and every time, relax, throughout each and every new opportunity; that you joyously and happily participate within, succeeding in all that you do, learning more and more each and every day and night to really truly enjoy yourself, realizing that you are the very best thing in your life, your most valued and valuable asset, enriching the experience of all of those whose lives you share, you even relax where there are rooms with doors; because the doors will always function to allow you access. You are always and every time succeeding and thriving in this new and liberated and lightener chapter of your life. Powerfully and successfully relaxing into the joy, happiness and peacefulness, your life becomes right now and more and more each and every day and night, absolutely thriving and flourishing in all that you do, are and your life becomes, each and every day and night, easily and only better and better, while you are awake, while you are asleep and even while you dream.

## Overcoming Claustrophobia – 2

You are calm and deeply breathing now and so with each and every breath you take and each and every beat of your calming and steady heart, you are finding newer and better ways of relaxing your way through any and all stress, any time, anywhere, in closed or even open spaces, most especially elevators, not because I say so, because you have actually, unstoppably and undeniably moved into a new and more supportive chapter of your life, relaxing your way through any and all former blockages, flowing past any and all resistance, forgiving and forever releasing, any and all former blockages, flowing past, through, over and around any and all resistance. In fact, truly and in reality, you are calm, balanced and anxiety-free whenever you have to go someplace and an elevator is involved, trusting in your life and in your world and finding newer and better ways to trust in your life and circumstances, that have always truly supported you, do actually support you, and as you now know and truly recognize forever support you. Even if old, uncomfortable or unpleasant thoughts or feelings of any type or level should or might even emerge, your most correct, most natural, easiest, best, normal and most vitally correct response, is to rise above and relax your way out of and away from any and all old thoughts that ever once stood in your way, activating the truly supportive energy, thoughts and feelings of every past triumph, victory, breakthrough and success you've ever had, as you correctly breathe deep and steady breath, calming yourself all over, relaxing yourself and steadying yourself on each and every calming breath that you take. You are feeling fine, balanced, calm and relaxed, you are the master of your thoughts, now almost as if from deep, deep inside of you, a switch, dial, computer or a thermostat of some kind has been forever reset, allowing for calmer and calmer thoughts and feelings of trust and support to emerge from deep, deep within you, flowing ever onward and outward, calming you completely in body, emotions, mind, through each and every thought, truly and powerfully and unstoppably allowing you to relax, balance and make supportive each and every thought, truly allowing you to take back and make supportive, your thoughts in regard to where you have to go and what has to be done. The best way to control, might be to not control, but to trust, to flow, to relax, to follow your best instincts, follow and trust in the advice you might give a trusted and beloved friend, take long-lasting and beneficial action, feeling tranquil, calm, peaceful and serene, bringing up any and all past moments of these feelings and reliving them.

You focus and function calmly and decisively in any and all stressful situations, by activating clearer, better and newer reactions, thoughts, feelings and patterns. In this newer, better and truly more supportive chapter of your life, you are taking charge of your life, forgiving the negative past judgments from both others and yourself that once hurt or adversely affected you, feeling a newer and forever more lasting sense of taking back control of your life, a personal sense of victory is now and forever building, building, building and now becomes strengthened and forever foundational and a permanent part of your life, whether at home, or even at work, in fact, any place in your life. You are effectively building a new chapter of your life, truly refocused and powerfully motivated, absolutely sure of this in surprisingly potent and powerful ways. You are truly as free as you've ever desired to be.

With each and every breath you take, you are powerfully liberating the feelings, energy and sensations associated with these following thoughts, ideas and concepts into a vital and profoundly true reconditioning and redefinition of who you are, where you live from, how you respond and whom you grow forever to be into your life: you are feeling loose, relaxed, comfortable and free, trusting in the fact, that in your past vulnerability lies your greatest strengths. You're feeling safe, secure, strong, comfortable, adaptable, reliable and trusting, both of your arms and both of your legs loose, relaxed, comfortable, you are slowly and deeply breathing your way into calmness and relaxation, truly and definitely creating newer and better sensations of life trust and support, in big or little spaces, both inside or outside, free, safe and sound, liberated, loose and comfortable, moving on, able and assured, adaptable, safe, and strong, rising up to the top, flowing over any obstacles and perhaps even feeling great, mighty, relaxed, potent, vital, your trust in life just growing and growing, adapting in ways that truly, impressively and with high and precise effectiveness, move you forward, forever free, regardless of event or circumstance, location or place, big or small, forever forgiving and releasing the past, liberated and free, stress-free, feeling happy, content, maybe even peaceful, un-trapped, safe, secure, trusting and free, easily adaptable and moving ever onward, feeling dramatically and powerfully liberated, safe, and free.

# Overcoming Dizziness, Fear, Panic and Anxiety

**Note:** You must be a qualified and certified Clinical Hypnosis professional and have a written note of authorization to perform this or any other complementary hypnosis session from the attending physician, psychiatrist, psychologist, etc., no exceptions.

You find yourself feeling calmer, more peaceful, more supported by life. Your life and your thinking become and only getting better and better, becoming more focused, more calm, more peaceful, more grounded and rooted in the world. You are willing to see things as they are, willing to deal with whatever needs dealing with, free of being overwhelmed, you are powerfully and unstoppably determined to get beyond all past limits, so . . . you rise up, sure of yourself, feeling truly and powerfully, steady, safe and strong, willing to live in balance and harmony, finding a new stability in all that you do, all that you are and in every way that you live. You've made up your powerful and determined mind to improve and heal, so you forever do. Each step, brings you to your destination, your body, emotions and mind are forever re-tuned, balanced, reorganized, harmonized, healing and actually healed! You find your peace, you find your center, you are willing to live, to love, to enjoy, to move on, transcending any and all limits. You relax deeper and further, you are willing to trust in your life process, only creating more stability, peace, kindness, safety and gentleness for yourself and those you love, most especially for yourself. You create your life, you create your world and magnetize your experiences or now and forever repel any and all negative or upsetting experiences from your life, truly having re-identified yourself, as liberated from the past, polished from all experiences you've ever had, shining on, in an ever peaceful world. You find any and all new situations to be challenges and opportunities, forever succeeding and learning, growing in your life. You find your breathing is calm and peaceful; you're using your deep and slow, steady breathing, as a way of stabilizing yourself, your body, your emotions, your mind and all that you are is feeling calm and peaceful, able to truly relax yourself through anything and everything you once found challenging, including: (add symptoms) . . .

Your mood forever lightens, you are willing to experience joy in your life, laughing at life's absurdities, finding joy in all you do. Your ability to release anxiety is ever growing, you are easily able to breathe into deep and profound relaxation, easily able to breathe your way through all past, present and future challenges including: (add symptoms) . . . .; forever better able to relax whenever you need to, but most especially with: (add symptoms) . . . , you embrace your most special of gifts, your life, and all of its power, all of its Divine support and guidance. For right now you feel deeply guided to thrive and succeed, easily able to move on, in ease, peace and comfort, soothed, gentle, playful, almost and practically restarted, like before any and all of these past unpleasant moments ever started, almost like you've reconnected to your earlier self, having bridged the gap, having once and for all and forever leapt . . . over a past painful chapter of your life, relaxing into a body, emotions, thoughts of ease, peace, calmness, steadiness, comfort, enhanced happiness, trust and living, life, joy and ever-growing love in each and every moment, while you're awake, while you're asleep, even while you dream, every moment of your being is now growing more unstoppably determined to find balance, calmness and health, and you know the truth, you are getting better and better by leaps and bounds, making unstoppable strides in all that you do and are forever.

## Overcoming Driving Fears and Anti-Anxiety Suggestions

Relax, relax, relax, into deeper and deeper levels of ever deepening relaxation, relaxing beyond any and all old barriers, both real or imagined, relaxing ever deeper and deeper, drifting, floating and dreaming, into a brand new and better chapter of your life. Relax and recall, that in each and every past moment of your life, each and every anything you once called a problem was really in fact a challenge, and a challenge is something you rise up to meet and to face and to overcome, vanquish and move beyond, glorying in your ability to become mightier than. You now truly know yourself this way, this is you!

In this moment, you are only getting stronger; more and more powerful is your ability to forgive, heal, release, and flowingly move beyond any and all things that can ever stand in your way; almost as if from deep, deep inside of you, someone has thrown a switch, a dial, a computer or a thermostat into activation to allow you to melt away any and all fears, shining light and heat onto the icy energy of those fears, wherever they came from and just ever melting them away, just like some release valve has been opened and all of those energies are forever now draining away, alleviating you, releasing you, unstoppably forgiving, liberating and completely and truly freeing you from any and all things that stood in your way of driving and maintaining your safe and alert transportation while operating a car.

You always knew one day, one night, you'd be free of the thoughts, feelings, actions and reactions, thoughts, memories, moods and feelings, that once stood in your way. Now is that moment, you step up, you seize that moment; you are forgiving and healing any and all thoughts, feelings, actions and reactions that ever once stood in your way, regardless of where they came from, whether you are aware of where or why they came from, powerfully, sweepingly, right across the board, finally free and forever beyond restrictions, because it's time to do that and you are ready, rising up, mighty and powerful, problem-free, powerfully challenge-oriented, ready to face down any and all challenges, you – the mighty one. You, the empowered and unbeatable one; you, unstoppable at any and all of this; not because I say so, but because it's the nature of your own powerful and dynamic mind to do so. Imagine the thoughts, feelings, actions and reactions of a professional driver; what they know, you know. What they see, you see. What they hear, you hear. What they sense, you sense. Their maintained correct safety zone; your powerful and forever true, carefully-maintained-with- ease safety zone. Free of confinement, just open, sharp, focused and relaxed, flowing onward and safely, serenely with calm and soothing breath, onward to your destination.

How they respond, you respond. How they act and react, you act and react. Where they look, you look. How they maintain safety, you maintain safety. How they check their mirrors, you check your mirrors, every 5 – 8 seconds. You maintain a comfortable safety zone, free forever of old hurts, for yourself or others. How they signal, you signal. How they see the traffic lights and road signs, so do you. How they apply more or less gas or more or less brakes, so you do! How they proceed or back off, so you proceed or back off. How they are comfortable and in their zone, so you are! How they trust, so you trust. Whether on a local road, or a highway, they are at home. Like a child enjoying a coloring book, staying safely inside the lines, you stay inside the lines, relaxed, calm and alert and focused, safe and serene, at home and comfortable. Truly and substantially, your life is taking care of you, safely and serenely, just as it always has. Just as the Sun comes up in the morning, each and every morning, eternally, you trust in the fact you are safe and protected, practically Divinely-guided, powerfully protected and precisely safe in your driving. You are handling any and all things the car would be dealing with; your car and driving experience, an extension of your focus and thoughts, precise and focused, free and adaptive, handling anything and everything with the comfort and skilled ease of a master driver. For you are powerfully in control, taking it all in stride, just having broken through here, unstoppable, in knowing, glowing confidence and ease.

For you are mighty now, activated, freed and forgiven, whole and healed, rising up to meet new and sensible challenges, while maintaining safety and powerful selfassurance, comfort, skill, adeptness and ease. It feels great to be liberated into the very best chapter of your life. Truly from deep down inside and in each and every way, you now know, it feels great to be so free.

## Overcoming Fear of Flying

Relax, relax, relax. And as you relax, you allow a new, healthier and better choice in your life to take place, a potent and powerful choice to successfully and unstoppably take place. A brand new day has dawned in your life, almost like first being born, a truly brand new beginning, a day where you can take a plane anywhere at any time and still feel relaxed, peaceful and calm and this only gets better and easier each and every day and night. In this moment of deep and powerful relaxation, you have come to truly recognize and embrace a new truth, that you are safe and protected and that you are realizing and living from the idea that flying is absolutely and truly the safest form of transportation available in the world today. Today, planes are better maintained, flight crews are better trained and more efficient and all of the ground support structures like radar and air traffic control are state of the art, utilizing all of the most modern and safest equipment. In fact, flying is safer than riding in a car or walking down the street in many cases. So right now, whether or not you realize it yet or not, your mind is making powerful and permanent choices from deep, deep inside of you to upgrade your thinking and even upgrading your ways of feeling. Your powerful, dynamic and always successful subconscious mind is working away as you relax deeper and further, making and creating new, happier, healthier, better choices and you have chosen to correctly respond to any stress, any disturbing thoughts or feelings in your new correct manner, by choosing to relax through any and all stress, just letting it all go. And you've even come up with a new way to beat any and all stress and any and all tension, by correctly choosing to relax by always remembering to deep breathe your way into relaxation, in fact, you are always aware, that your easiest, most potent and powerful way to relax, is to deep breathe, slow and steady deep, deep relaxation breath, which will always allow you to relax all of your body, all of your emotions, all of your mind, and even all of your spirit, relaxing you all over. You have chosen correctly to let go of and relax far, far away from any and all old worries from the past, choosing instead to be happy, calm and powerful. All of those old useless, unwanted, unneeded, irrational, even silly worries and all of their negative energy are going, going, gone, just because that's what you've chosen powerfully and correctly to do. And it's so easy for you. Even now, you are just letting all of these past experiences just go, almost like how you can forget your dreams after just a few moments after you awaken, you are just willing to forget and let go of your unwarranted and unnecessary fears, and all of their past influence upon you, they are getting harder to remember, harder to think about. In fact they are just becoming and remaining more comfortable and you are just moving on, having lost all of their past influence upon you, just drifting and floating away, forgetfully away, far from you. You can actually feel those useless and negative energies just lifting up, off and far, far away from you. A powerful new feeling is emerging in place of your old feelings, a part of you that has always gotten through, the part of you that has always succeeded, the part of you that has thrived, been victorious, the part of you that knows no doubt, no fear or disharmony. And all of the energy of all of your past moments of this kind of success powerfully embrace you and is upon you now, as you now feel completely reconditioned and fortified. And you just know, very powerfully, from deep, deep inside, that all of you has been upgraded, changed, improved and you can feel your inner wisdom and courage surfacing as you relax, deeper and deeper. You truly know, you are empowered in these new future moments of your life! I even wonder if you can truly recognize, how powerful you really are and that by deep breathing slow and steady powerful life changing relaxation breath, you are giving yourself a very potent and most powerful gift, the gift of being able to relax your way through anything and everything in your life, but most especially taking a trip on a plane, something you now look forward to with a powerful happy anticipation. This happy positive anticipation stays with you, in all moments before, during and after your trip, because you've just let the past go triumphantly and you've actually begun a brand new happier chapter of your life, which just gets better and better, beginning right now and for the rest of your life. As you relax deeply and profoundly, you realize, you even notice and powerfully recognize, that you are almost feeling happier and happier, almost as if a happy, even silly, rhythmic song is going through your head, just the kind of a song that would make anyone who heard it, smile, laugh and feel warmed by this song, your song's happy embrace. This gentle song allows you to smile, and release any and all tension, in the most amazing and beneficial of ways, because you are now truly empowered, mightier than any and all challenges. Congratulations, you relax and you win, amazing and impressing everyone, most especially you. Each and every day and night, your courage, strength, unstoppable determination and new ability to relax your way through anything and everything are a powerful and motivating inspiration to both men, women and children, alike, you win, as never before!

## Overcoming Fear of Travel and Agoraphobia

Relax and in this moment of deep, deep relaxation, you've unstoppably decided to create a new and better chapter of your life, right now you powerfully relax into this allowing a new chapter of your life to begin, a new, improved better chapter, focused on clearing out everything and anything uncomfortable from your past that once stood in your way, stood in the way of letting you live and enjoy your life, living and enjoying outdoors or traveling, even letting go of the limiting opinions of "so called experts" that once stood in your way, because you are now fully in charge of your life and in charge of your calming, soothing thoughts, you are calming and balancing your emotions and with just a few deep and steady powerful soothing relaxation breaths, you calm down, you focus, you can actually feel all disharmonious and unbalanced emotionally charged energy, thoughts and feelings, drifting out of you, off you, and far, far away from you. Yes, you really have and you are living in a new and better way. I wonder if you even yet realize how easy this is going to be for you, because it will be, actually in fact, it is. And this powerful choice, your powerful choice, your limitless opportunity, is yours right now, only getting stronger, stronger and more apparently obvious, each and every passing day, each and every passing night and most obviously, every passing moment.

So now, take a deep soothing relaxation breath and relax, just let it go. Take another deep soothing relaxation breath and as you let it go, you begin more and more, even better and better, to forgive your past, any and all of its pain, all uncomfortable moments, just letting all of it go, having passed from that point, having graduated from that place, having moved on. Yes, you've begun a brand new healthier, happier chapter of your life, having let yourself out of your past restrictions, having moved on, beginning to re-identify yourself, in new improved, better and more amazing ways. You are a survivor, who has choices, you now choose to live, seeing your past as something that you have not only survived, but also have moved on from. You begin to re-identify yourself as a person who has been truly polished by your past and just as you've always done, you choose right now to rise up, easily able to overcome any and all challenges, any and all circumstances, any and all events, easily able to overcome any and all thoughts, any and all feelings, any and all challenging anything, because you truly know and you truly feel you are the powerful one in charge of your life, in fact, you are the mighty one in your world. You always have and always will overcome. You are undeniably and unstoppably determined to succeed in amazing, creative and inspired ways. You are a powerful winner, you are an unstoppable force, you can, you will, you are you shall succeed in moving on, thriving on the challenge and you can actually feel the embrace of all of the energy of your past victories, breakthroughs, successes and most inspired moments, coming upon you and into each and every moment of your life, coming upon you right now, only getting better, stronger, more unstoppable, each and every time you repeat this most enjoyable exercise. You feel like you can take on the world, or at the very least, because its easy for you, take on absolutely while (list fears): traveling via bus, train, plane, boat, far from home with people other than your spouse and children, and driving far alone, traveling again comfortably via all means of transportation, free of all and any old anticipatory anxieties, just breathing it any and all away, powerfully and deeply relaxing into this, thriving and succeeding into this unstoppably, because you can, you will, you do, you are unstoppably and absolutely determined, undeniably able with limitlessly inspired success energy, succeeding easily, naturally, boundlessly, fearlessly, strongly, passionately, creatively, drawing upon and tapping into the inspiration of the creative and most powerful deep recesses of your subconscious mind, both easily and very powerfully, just a breath away, in the very most beneficial and truly amazing ways!

## Overcoming Fear

It's almost like any and all unneeded fear, any and all unwanted fear, truly, any and all un-necessary fear is being activated from a valve of some sort from deep, deep inside of you. As the valve is opened and fear-energy is rapidly flowing, any and all fear is just flooding up and out as it is bubbling up, bubbling up and coming up to the surface in a flood right now, like water or energy just flooding out and up to the top and now it's fully out, ready to be swept away.

Now imagine the ever rising and forever unstoppable light of the golden-white sun just warming the fear up and just evaporating it away, drying it up, drying it away, as the golden-white sun heats up and dries it away from you now and forever from your life. You are now, always and forever free, gaining strength, courage and power. And now yet another valve from deep, deep inside of you is now opening and now fully opened. You are being flooded with new and better, more supportive thoughts and energies, the limitless energy of true inspiration, an unstoppable can-do spirit, the ability to easily, powerfully and forever rise above anything and everything that once stood in your way because you can, because you must and so you now and forever do. You instead choose correctly to generate better and more supportive feelings of empowerment, liberation, triumph, victory and success, almost like you are shining a mighty light of golden-white sunlight from all around you and your golden-white sunlight is being turned up, tuned up, turned on, and is forever and always vanquishing any and all doubt and fear, with the light of knowledge, with the light of healing, with the light of enlightenment, the light of truth, with the light of love, with an unstoppable blinding light that vanquishes the old fear as you are unstoppably flowing into any and all situations that once used to cause fear, removing and forever vanquishing those fears from yourself, from your life and from your world, both now, forever and always. Blockage-free, you flow joyously ever onward in remarkable and wonderful ways, even surprising yourself at how easy this is becoming.

You begin to realize that fear in and of itself is nothing and you are truly the mighty one. Right now, you are self-empowered, always and forever; you are ever more empowered to rise to the top and to completely relinquish and vanquish unhappy and unpleasant fear in whatever form it used to take by becoming empowered, mighty, bold, dynamic, fearless in new and more powerful fluidly adaptive ways and by unstoppably rising to the top in the most magnificent and brilliant of ways. Blockage-free, you flow ever onward in remarkable and wonderful ways, even surprising yourself at how easy this is becoming.

Those unneeded and unwanted old fears are like an empty vessel with a hole in it, they do nothing, they hold nothing; in fact, very truly, your old fears are nothing, as you are now empowered, inspired and mighty, doing all that it takes, easier and better because fantastically, you've unstoppably moved on and are free, free at long last, not because I say so but because it is the nature of your own empowered mind and spirit to do so, unstoppably and relentlessly. You've decided to rise up and become mighty in all that you do, in all that you need to do, and just get it done, forever free of excuse or blockage, and you knowingly win, thrive and succeed. You have made up your powerful, effective, clever, adaptive and dynamic mind to thrive and succeed here as you are more determined to win at this more now than ever before, so you do.

Your greatest and most overwhelming passionate desire right now, is to become and forever remain healthy, happy, free and safe, extending your life in healthy ways that work for you best.

# Overcoming Fear, Anxiety and Stress (Job Related)

You are willing and most able to activate from deep, deep within yourself, your very best ability to feel most potently and powerfully brave, courageous, bold, valiant, even unafraid, heroic, whenever you think about the future, as you are now better mapping out your life in better ways, boldly creating and magnetizing from you heart, soul and mind, only the very best for yourself, as you deserve to in the most creative and brilliant of ways. You are always finding newer and better ways to flow and remain calm, balanced, relaxed and focused, flowing ever onward into the kind of a life that you deserve, you create, you thrive within and relax into, easily, dynamically and successfully. You trust in your life, finding better moments to be and remain worry-free, confident and dynamic about finding the right job, that you easily create, truly and deliberately, creating the sort of work and job opportunities that will be and are truly and profoundly fulfilling, both personally and financially. You relax into your life, and find, each and every day newer and better ways to trust in the way you are now taking charge of and creating your life, aging comfortably with grace and ease, you create a life filled with better moments. You improve your view of money, a reflection of the energy you are deliberately putting out into the world feeling certain, calm, balanced and re-identified, trusting powerfully in life, easily finding newer and better ways of creating abundance from all that life has to offer. And your life and your dreams follow your excitement. You easily become and remain mightier than any and all situations that might present themselves, easily deciding to rise above, become mighty, relaxed, calm and composed whenever you think about your past, not only have you survived, but you have triumphed, and you are absolutely moving on, struggle free, problem-free, challenge oriented, easily able to rise up and move beyond any and all apparent and superficial limits, boldly stepping out into a bolder and brighter day and night. You find newer and better inspirational energy from deep, deep, within, almost as if someone from deep, deep inside of you has thrown a switch of re-excitement about your world and your life. You create opportunities, you create new methods of independence, including financial independence, creating all that you need, sure of yourself, you win, calm, balanced and relaxed. You re-identify yourself, giving yourself a chance, a break, a new avenue of thought and feeling of support and guidance, where you are a winner and you are forgiven and you are moving on, fearless and courageous, an accomplisher, finding potent and powerful ways to thrive and succeed, a success you are and you are ever building. Most especially when you are or might be (name fears): going a distance or far from home, you are calm, you are balanced, you are in your safe mental place, safe free, breathing deep and slow steady breath, balanced, calm, relaxed, peaceful and at ease. You are calm, safe, balanced, peaceful and healthy, breathing deep and slow, calming, stilling, soothing steady breath, while waiting on line in a store, bank, in fact anywhere, even if in big or wide open spaces, relaxing into a brand new healthier and better chapter of your life, calm, comfortable and complete, breathing deep and slow, calming stilling soothing steady breath. Even if you are in a crowded place, you are absolutely calm and still, absolutely and unstoppably, free of anxiety or panic, feeling reassured, calm, balanced, and full of self-control, even if you are or might be stressed, especially while in a stressful situation, even while at work hurrying to get a job done or even if someone is bring critical toward you. Your life improves, you are relaxed and determined, you thrive and you succeed. Your life improves, you are relaxed and determined, you thrive and succeed, all that is your life, your health, your thoughts, your calm and balanced supportive feelings and emotions, all are now working in ever increasing harmony to support and balance you as never before in newer and surprisingly pleasant and powerful ways to perfectly take care of you, in this forever lasting, only growing stronger chapter of your life.

## Overcoming Fears: Claustrophobia, Agoraphobia and Travel

You are deep breathing, feeling and remaining calm, balanced, safe and secure, completely relaxed, anyplace you are or might be; breathing deep and slow steady breaths and feeling calm, centered, peaceful and relaxed, most especially whenever you are in the city, almost as if there is some sort of warming and soothing embrace from all of the people there just calming you and making you feel wanted and whole, protected and safe and even cared for. For the whole world is your home, the Universe unconditionally supports you and you now are inspired and know this profound truth, you and your existence are profoundly taken care of and supported, almost as if you are being braced up and completely reconditioned by all that is the world and all that is your life.

For there is no need to escape, you are safe, secure and supported in all that you are and in all that you do, just deep breathing and feeling fine, most especially whenever you are on a bus and subway, calm and balanced, forgiven and completely released. Completely forgiving and releasing anything and everything that ever set up bad moments in your past, for you are forever moving on into a brighter and better future, a brighter and better you and a brighter and better life, forgiving completely, so healed, so restored and unstoppably into a newer and brighter and better chapter of your life.

You just deep breathe, relax through and beyond any and all barriers into newer and more lovingly supportive ways of thinking, truly knowing and then unstoppably feeling: I and calm, I am centered, I am whole, I am serene, (3X) becoming more and more so on each and every slow, calming soothing breath that you are taking and on each and every heartbeat.

You are even feeling mighty, easily able to overcome everything and anything that once ever stood in your way, most especially on long drives or even in airplanes, anywhere is a place for you to feel completely at home, relaxing through any and all barriers and having unstoppably moved ever onward into a new chapter of your life, feeling fine.

It's almost as if you have completely and totally healed say - the past 5 or 6 years of your life, feeling powerful, unlimited and mighty, even better than when you were around 17,18 or even 19. You now know a powerful new life-improving secret, you can easily do anything you've set your inspired and dynamic mind to, relaxing beyond any and all old barriers, you now just so easily do.

## Overcoming Fears: Falling in Snow, Wind, Open Spaces, Bugs & Swimming

Even if walking in the snow and ice, you are becoming, you are and you remain, mighty, powerful and unstoppably determined, because you are now thinking you are powerful and are powerfully keeping your balance, staying and remaining safe, mighty and balanced, whether the snow is heavy or light, even medium, whether there are cars around or not; you are in your zone, safe, protected, even Divinely guided, as the whole world now readily supports you in all that you do and all that is your life. You are becoming, you are and you remain, mighty, powerful and unstoppably determined, because you are now thinking you are powerful and are powerfully keeping your balance, staying and remaining safe, mighty and balanced, even and most especially courageous, valiant, bold, even fearless and mighty, most especially when outside in strong wind because you are forever free of being blown away, staying and remaining steady, safe and strong. You are in your zone, safe, protected, even Divinely guided, as the whole world now readily supports you in all that you do and all that is your life. You are becoming, you are and you remain mighty, powerful and unstoppably determined, because you are now thinking you are powerful and are powerfully keeping your balance, staying and remaining safe, mighty and balanced, even and most especially courageous, valiant, bold, even fearless and mighty, most especially when outside in open spaces, finding better balance and inner strength, because you are in harmony with life, feeling it and knowing you were meant to be here, staying and remaining steady, safe and strong; you are in your zone, safe, protected, even Divinely guided, as the whole world now readily supports you in all that you do and all that is your life. You are becoming, you are and you remain mighty, powerful and unstoppably determined, because you are now thinking and knowing that you are powerful and are powerfully keeping your sense of balance, staying and remaining safe, mighty and balanced, even and most especially courageous, valiant, bold, even fearless and mighty, most especially whenever near bugs of any kind. You are mighty and big; they are nothing, nothing, nothing. Finding true and real, better balance and inner strength, because you are in harmony with life, feeling it and knowing you were meant to be here, staying and remaining steady, safe and strong, you are in your zone, safe, protected, even Divinely guided, as the whole world now readily supports you in all that you do and all that is your life, whether with others or when you are alone. You are determined to overcome anything and everything that once overwhelmed you, willing to try and to understand and to fully enjoy things like being outside, traveling, swimming. You want to learn how to swim, finding the proper instructor, trusting in your life and finding better balance and self-reliance. It's almost like you are jumping over the years back to a time when you were 13 or 14 years old, and only this time, you are making a powerful and forever commitment to yourself, so that even when you were 15 or 16, you were, remained and forever were centered, trusting in life, balanced, restored and relaxed, beyond and through anything and everything that ever once stood in your way.

# Overcoming Fears: Public Speaking Stage Fright and Gaining Self-Acceptance

Relax deeper and deeper and as you do, you allow yourself a new thought, a powerful thought, a thought that will create relaxation and profound improvement in your life, all things that you really and truly deserve. The only opinion of yourself that counts is your opinion of yourself. So each and every day and night, that opinion is improving, and getting better and better. So beginning right now and for the rest of your life, you relax, you love, you trust and you support yourself calmly, easily, brilliantly and very powerfully, with confidence, greater and greater self-love and self-acceptance. Any and all old limiting opinions and stresses and fears from your past, regardless of where they might have come from, whether they came from you or whether they came from yourself or from the words or actions of someone else, any and all old useless and needed limiting concepts that had once held you back, are just drifting away, drifting away, drifting away, far away, very far away from you. And all of them are becoming less and less important to you, with each and every breath that you take and with every beat of your heart and in each and every moment of your life, both now, always and forever, because this is something you have correctly and most powerfully and truly decided. In fact, truly, you are always making only the best of all possible choices for yourself. You are and you remain, calm, relaxed all over, in each and every circumstance, succeeding and powerfully and calmly, you're feeling absolutely determined, determined to excel and succeed. All and every old useless emotional sensations, memories and/or thoughts, are powerfully leaving you, all of them are going, going, gone, and gone forever and always. You'll hardly ever think about them or consider them but even if you do, it will be in relation to how much better off you are without them. What is replacing those old useless feelings and what is becoming more and more important, more and more your own, more and more an actual and real part of you, is your new greater self-confidence, your new stronger and more powerful self, your improved more harmonized you. You believe in you, you trust you, you forgive your past, you feel better and better each and every day and night, embracing your life. You are becoming more and more powerful, more and more dynamic, in each and every respect and in each and every day. Clear, confident, strong; clear, confident; strong, clear, confident; communicative and expressive, relaxed, poised for success; confident, clear and strong.

Relax deeper and deeper now, and allow yourself to see, to picture, to feel, to imagine and/or to even know, yes, that's right. You just know a new more empowered and truly active part of you is unstoppably emerging. You remember or think about a time when you saw a speaker or presentation that was truly wonderful. Focusing front. The audience, both internal as well as external, is truly supportive, because in a supportive, nurturing way, they truly support their teacher and want them to truly succeed.

Now breathe again and exhale, and allow a newer and even stronger image to come into your mind. A truly wonderful and supportive time when you once spoke to just a small group of people, or just even one person, one in this group, whoever they are who truly and powerfully needs to gain understanding from you, a person you can focus on and speak to, just like speaking to a person one on one in a crowded street; they truly are interested in what you have to say, they support you, they care, they are on your team, its almost like in reality, they are waving your flag, they appreciate you and they wish you positive, supportive, successful and loving feelings. You relax, your deep breathe and you allow this new empowered you to educate, to relate, to bring learning and understanding from deep inside of you, from places deep within your greatest understanding, you with relaxed excitement, are fully and truly liberating your inner wisdom. Now as you exhale again, you allow this image to merge with you, feel this energy, one with you, this comfortableness, this poise, ease, relaxed strength and grace, becoming one with all that You are body, emotions, mind and consciousness and you even feel the limitless and everlasting strength of your spirit. You are in powerful inner and outer harmony, you feel like you are smiling in the inside and even on the outside. You are peaceful, strong, and you are always succeeding, becoming in each and every moment, an inspiration to the world, amazing and impressing everyone, most especially and permanently you, forever and always.

Now relax even deeper, and experience the very strong, wonderful, supportive feelings of success, ease, confidence, clear communication and relaxed grace, you are absolutely stress-free, liberated, focused, calm and strong. This is you, eternal, empowered, strong, in an everlasting powerful real harmony. You are now merged with the feelings of each and every new success in all that you do, you are supported by people and by life, because you are vital and valuable and easily able to clearly, calmly and with high effectiveness, express yourself, clearly and confidently, because you can and you will light up the world, with your truly powerful and dynamic gifted mind, as thoughts, words and inspiration, just seem to impressively flow. This is only getting better and better, each and every day and each and every night, while you are awake, while you are asleep, even while you dream. And it feels so good.

# Overcoming Feelings of Panic and Loss

You are in fact truly finding newer and better ways of rising to the top and to succeed at feeling better and doing better in each and every phase of your life. Regardless of event or circumstance, you are learning to take life in more of a flow, changing and improving things you can change and accepting things as they are that are unchangeable. You are finding newer and better ways of dealing with things that are or might be inevitable, deeply and truly learning to trust in your life and to move into better places for yourself, resolving issues and releasing the emotional impact of events and circumstances, while deep breathing, relaxing, remaining centered, calm, balanced and relaxed, just doing better and better, tapping into your own personal well-spring of inner strength and the very best moments of inspiration to succeed at this in the very best of ways that you've ever had. You are beginning to change and improve in your favor, in each and every area of your life, finding inner balance and strength, even surprisingly, creating a newer and better foundation in your life. Your new and correct response to any and all stress, is to breathe, deeply, slowly and calmly, creating serenity around yourself and into all areas of your life and yourself, finding deep and true inner balance in your body, your emotions, your mind and even from the serenity and better knowing aspects of your spirit. You are developing a new and improved, better regard for yourself and your life; truly coming to know that your life is improving, you are trusting in your life, and you now know the world is filled with people some of whom you've yet to meet, who are there for you, as you create a place of peace and ease for yourself. You are fulfilling your greatest dreams, even able to thrive, becoming and truly remaining more and more better able to rise up and to transcend any and all challenges, in each and every moment of your life, problem-free, releasing the idea of problems from your life now, forever and ever, becoming and remaining challenge-oriented, boldly and courageously facing any and all challenges in spite of and because of the intensity of their challenge, because you can, you will and you must, and so you do, amazingly strengthened by the experience.

You develop and enjoy all that you are, easily forgiving all past blockages, releasing and relinquishing both any and all blockages from your past and their effect on you, at any and all moments. You begin to take on your life in a more natural way, enjoying your vim, vigor and vitality and natural drives and urges as a man, truly enjoying all of your natural urges and instincts, just as both nature and God intended you to live. You relax even deeper, you enjoy your life, doing what's right for yourself and your world, finding and creating better ways of building your manhood, being a man, building into being a great man/woman, that you already are in the eyes of so many, developing a newer and more powerful sense of what all of that means, both instinctually, and naturally, relaxing into this, a brand new, happier, healthier and more peaceful, harmonized, healed chapter of your life, as your unstoppable new and ever-building, reliable self-confidence just flows and builds. You relax even deeper now, heart rate calm and balanced, breathing slow and steady, skin cool and calm, memorizing this as a way to be and a way to live; you recognize and realize that relaxing into your life and allowing yourself and being all that you are is enough, is just fine with you, you are so much less self-critical, so much less self-conscious and self-judgmental, yet, even better, you are always finding amazing new and better ways to live your life to the fullest and enjoy your life, each and every day you are relaxed, released and confident, each and every day and night you are so much more self-supportive, so much more self-reliant, so much more self confident, so much more comfortable and at ease with you just being you, nowhere to run, you're relaxing into just being there, so much more less concerned of what others think of you, finding newer and more balanced ways of relaxing your way into being there, forever giving up any and all blockages, by forgiving them, easily moving and flowing beyond them, to a happy life and fulfillment, so much more able, so much more fearless, so much more bold, so much more secure, so much more proud, confident, rewarded, so much more pleased within yourself, so much more relaxing into the Divine ebb and flow of the Universe, so happy to live your life and to feel alive in great and wonderful ways. And whether or not you realize it yet, or even if you just one day notice it, you are powerfully re-identifying yourself and liberating your life into the place of joy, happiness and peace that you deserve it to be; you are unstoppably determined to create this. Each and every day and night you are powerfully and creatively determined to become and forever remain, you are so much more comfortable, relaxing your way into, through and around any and all situations, at ease, peaceful, contented, happy, calm, flowing with your life, after just a few deep, slow and steady breaths, most especially very calm and comfortable in a (Name locations) BUS, in a CLASSROOM, in a MEETING, on an INTERVIEW, at

a GATHERING...in fact, everywhere and ANYWHERE, you are relaxing into your life
and feeling fine, comfortable, fine, anxiety free, peaceful, calm and relaxed, you even
say to yourself, while deep breathing slow and steady breaths, truly liberating the full
energy of the meaning from the words, "I am feeling fine, comfortable, fine, feeling
free, anxiety-free, peaceful, calm, relaxed and feeling fine and free." (3x) If at any
time you start to feel any energies reminiscent of any past blockages, you begin to
breathe deep, slow, steady breath, and you begin to feel a shift of energy, causing you
to unblock, relax and release in potent, powerful and potentially limitless ways, and
you'll easily and only getting better and easier each and every time that you do this,
more powerful, more transformative, more amazingly healing, calming you, relaxing
you, restoring you, balancing you, harmonizing you, not because I say so, but
because it's the nature of your own mind and spirit to do so and because you deserve
to thrive and succeed in this brand new, happier and more balanced, relaxed-into
chapter of your life. You become so much more focused upon and live with your
focus upon, all of the things you create and magnetize into your life to create the
masterpiece of a happy and balanced life you deserve.

# Overcoming Panic and Learning to Trust Again in Life

**Note:** You must be a qualified and certified Clinical Hypnosis professional and
have a written note of authorization to perform this or any other complementary
hypnosis session from the attending physician, psychiatrist, psychologist, etc., no
exceptions.

You relax, deeper and further, deeper and further and you now powerfully and
truly realize that this place of peace, rest and relaxation is a place you can easily
come to visit again and again, whenever you need to. It is a sure and very powerful
safe haven, a rest stop on the road of life, for you to recharge, to get inspired, to
become powerfully and completely clear, harmonized and rebalanced. And in this
place of deep rest and profound peace, you are deeply relaxed enough to truly allow a
new thought for a new day to dawn upon you, a very true and powerful unstoppable
thought begins right now, for you are far from helpless, so you decide to help you.
And you are now relaxing into a new chapter of your life, one in which you are truly
empowered, with a calm and powerful heart rate, deep and powerful steady breath,
truly relaxed. Your complete and absolute trust in your life is building and you
recognize that your life is beginning to support you in new, deeply profound and
better ways. Feelings are just feelings and feelings can never hurt you. Thoughts

thoughts are just thoughts, for there are times when you can be hot or cold, tired or energetic, hungry or filled up. Because feelings are just feelings and thoughts are just thoughts, they can and will never really hurt you in any way. But right now, you have really chosen to rise above any and all feelings, any hurts, any pain, both real or imagined, because you deserve to, you are able to, you can, you will, because you have powerfully decided to do so and you can and you will just because you are unstoppable in achieving this or anything you set your powerful and dynamic and successful and limitless mind to; you feel like you can take on the world, talk to the world, rise above and succeed in all that you can and will and in fact do accomplish. In fact, you feel more and more each and every day and night, each and every moment, that you are becoming more and more supported by your life, in amazing, creative and unstoppable ways. Each and every time you repeat this enjoyable deep relaxation exercise, you feel better and better about your life and yourself. And after just a few brief moments of deep relaxation, easily yet powerfully, that calmness powerfully corrects and balances all of you. In fact, truly, your life is under your control, it is your creation and you know this and feel very good about it. And this only gets even better and better day-by-day, night-by -night, in amazingly unstoppable ways. You have now found, truly deeply know and find even better, each and every day and night, a new rhythm within your life, and a new harmony, in fact, you can imagine and even now feel, life just flows through you like a mighty river, supporting you and embracing you in profound and amazing ways. This new harmony, your new harmony, this unstoppable harmonious you, is like a brilliant shining light from your heart out into the world and this light, your light, balances and makes ready the world, so right just for you. In fact you feel completely reborn in many respects, just like years ago when you felt balanced, calm and strong.

Think of who you once were, see it, feel it, think about an image of who you once were, once you have it clearly in your mind, feel this old you, merging with the current you, re-fortifying you, re-establishing your base, with each and every breath and with each and every heart beat, you make this more and more unstoppably so. In fact, you begin to feel comfortable, and peaceful, trusting in your life and in all of your existence.

Imagine yourself now standing near a magical, mystical mountain waterfall stream. In your mind, see all the beauty that there is to see here. Trees and meadows and birds and rocks and the earth and the sky and the clouds, all of nature's gentle sounds and you feel profound and gentle ease and peace, completely calming you from deep, deep within. In this place, there is no want no need, no fear just you and the balance of nature.

Imagine yourself now stepping under this soothing and relaxing magical, mystical mountain waterfall stream. Feel the energy of this waterfall stream washing away, both inside and out, all of your old doubts, old fears and any and all old panic, any and all old disharmony, completely and truly, absolutely restoring and balancing you, you feel encouraged, powerfully supported and your courage is coming up. In fact, yes, you may begin to feel mighty, mighty, yes you are mighty, you are a survivor and you begin to live, that's right, live and enjoy your life. And right now, something amazing is happening, all of the very real, powerful, life changing, old inspirational feelings of your past victories, triumphs and breakthroughs are now coming upon you, right now, fortifying you, whether you realize it or not, harmonizing you, re-initializing you, restoring you and your faith in your life, blessing you and reactivating all of your life harmonies, balances, structures and support is coming back, powerfully and truly. And you are calm, peaceful, relaxed and very sure of yourself, you feel good, better than you have in years. Each step forward is a major stride, even little steps forward, mean a lot. Each and every day, all of your painful past falls away, falls away, absolutely and undeniably making it easier and easier for you to live in the supportive present, each present moment, paves the way for a brighter future of ease, peace, gentleness, calmness, support, strength, wholeness, wellness, the future just gets brighter and brighter, better and better. If at any time you need to feel this, all you need to do is to stop, to breathe and you will just easily relax, relaxing into your life, and reactivating any and all of this unstoppable support, in the truest and most amazing of ways. You succeed forever, amazingly.

# Overcoming Panic and Learning to Trust Again in Life

**Note:** You must be a qualified and certified Clinical Hypnosis professional and have a written note of authorization to perform this or any other complementary hypnosis session from the attending physician, psychiatrist, psychologist, etc., no exceptions.

You relax, deeper and further, deeper and further and you now powerfully and truly realize that this place of peace, rest and relaxation is a place you can easily come to visit again and again, whenever you need to. It is a sure and very powerful safe haven, a rest stop on the road of life, for you to recharge, to get inspired, to

And you are now relaxing into a new chapter of your life, one in which you are truly empowered, with a calm and powerful heart rate, deep and powerful steady breath, truly relaxed. Your complete and absolute trust in your life is building and you recognize that your life is beginning to support you in new, deeply profound and better ways. Feelings are just feelings and feelings can never hurt you. Thoughts are just thoughts and through your powerful now unleashed ability to forgive all within your past right now, as you are doing right now, your thoughts can never hurt you. You correctly, deeply and truly realize, that feelings are just feelings, thoughts are just thoughts, for there are times when you can be hot or cold, tired or energetic, hungry or filled up. Because feelings are just feelings and thoughts are just thoughts, they can and will never really hurt you in any way. But right now, you have really chosen to rise above any and all feelings, any hurts, any pain, both real or imagined, because you deserve to, you are able to, you can, you will, because you have powerfully decided to do so and you can and you will just because you are unstoppable in achieving this or anything you set your powerful and dynamic and successful and limitless mind to; you feel like you can take on the world, talk to the world, rise above and succeed in all that you can and will and in fact do accomplish. In fact, you feel more and more each and every day and night, each and every moment, that you are becoming more and more supported by your life, in amazing, creative and unstoppable ways. Each and every time you repeat this enjoyable deep relaxation exercise, you feel better and better about your life and yourself. And after just a few brief moments of deep relaxation, easily yet powerfully, that calmness powerfully corrects and balances all of you. In fact, truly, your life is under your control, it is your creation and you know this and feel very good about it. And this only gets even better and better day-by-day, night-by -night, in amazingly unstoppable ways. You have now found, truly deeply know and find even better, each and every day and night, a new rhythm within your life, and a new harmony, in fact, you can imagine and even now feel, life just flows through you like a mighty river, supporting you and embracing you in profound and amazing ways. This new harmony, your new harmony, this unstoppable harmonious you, is like a brilliant shining light from your heart out into the world and this light, your light, balances and makes ready the world, so right just for you. In fact you feel completely reborn in many respects, just like years ago when you felt balanced, calm and strong.

Think of who you once were, see it, feel it, think about an image of who you once were, once you have it clearly in your mind, feel this old you, merging with the current you, re-fortifying you, re-establishing your base, with each and every breath

and with each and every heart beat, you make this more and  
In fact, you begin to feel comfortable, and peaceful, trusting  
your existence.

Imagine yourself now standing near a magical, mystical mou  
stream. In your mind, see all the beauty that there is to see here. T  
meadows and birds and rocks and the earth and the sky and the clou  
nature's gentle sounds and you feel profound and gentle ease and pea  
calming you from deep, deep within. In this place there is no want to n  
just you and the balance of nature.

Imagine yourself now stepping under this soothing and relaxing magical,  
mystical mountain waterfall stream. Feel the energy of this waterfall stream washing  
away, both inside and out, all of your old doubts, old fears and any and all old panic,  
any and all old disharmony, completely and truly, absolutely restoring and balancing  
you, you feel encouraged, powerfully supported and your courage is coming up.  
In fact, yes, you may begin to feel mighty, mighty, yes you are mighty, you are a  
survivor and you begin to live, that's right, live and enjoy your life. And right now,  
something amazing is happening, all of the very real, powerful, life changing, old  
inspirational feelings of your past victories, triumphs and breakthroughs are now  
coming upon you, right now, fortifying you, whether you realize it or not, harmonizing  
you, re-initializing you, restoring you and your faith in your life, blessing you and  
reactivating all of your life harmonies, balances, structures and support is coming  
back, powerfully and truly. And you are calm, peaceful, relaxed and very sure of  
yourself, you feel good, better than you have in years. Each step forward is a major  
stride, even little steps forward, mean a lot. Each and every day, all of your painful  
past falls away, falls away, absolutely and undeniably making it easier and easier  
for you to live in the supportive present, each present moment, paves the way for a  
brighter future of ease, peace, gentleness, calmness, support, strength, wholeness,  
wellness, the future just gets brighter and brighter, better and better. If at any time  
you need to feel this, all you need to do is to stop, to breathe and you will just easily  
relax, relaxing into your life, and reactivating any and all of this unstoppable support,  
in the truest and most amazing of ways. You succeed forever, amazingly.

# Overcoming Panic

You always knew the fear and panic you once used to feel in your life wasn't forever, and so right now, in this very moment, only getting stronger and better, more and more powerful, more and more high impact and profound, more and more real, more and more here and now, more and more powerful and strong, adaptive and fluid, working only in powerful and decisively in your favor, those old and childish fears now and forever drained off and away, far, far away from you and gone. You can actually just feel it going, going and gone; you are free, free, free of any and all of the old ways, thoughts, feelings, memories and ideas, actions and reactions that ever caused you to surrender your power to any feelings of fear. You know, it's almost like in reality and truly in fact, someone from deep, deep inside of you has reset a switch, a dial, a computer or a thermostat of some kind, easily allowing you to move on, not because I say so, but because it's the nature of your own powerful and dynamic mind, presence and being, the undeniable and unmistakable Divinely-guided power of all that you are to do so. Light just seems to shine away any and all shadows, as it just seems to emanate from your heart and mind, vanquishing all shadows from the past. For right now in this very moment, you have forever and always relaxed your way into a brand new chapter of your life, free, free at long last, feeling fine, wonderful and trusting. Things that once stood in your way, you easily rise above and are polished by, thriving from these things, in fact, as you are now re-identified in your body, emotions, and mind.

You are the mighty one in your life; you keep you power within and feel it budding and building and easily rise above anything and everything, by slowly deep breathing and remaining calm while realizing that a feeling is just a feeling, and a feeling can never hurt you or damage you. For there might be times when you are tired or awake and lively, hot or cold, hungry or filled up, but a feeling can never hurt or kill you; so now more than ever, you are healed, forgiven, forgiving and released, just flowing with life and feeling fine. Whether at home or in a car, outdoors or at the mall or any shopping area, you are just a traveler on a path, and you are now relaxing beyond any and all barriers and rising up to become mighty and flowing through now enjoyable moments into the very best days and night of your life, mastering all past limitations, which now become signs of how powerful you really are, as you master all of these things and become a mighty master of your life, world and circumstances. All things are just right; your breathing, the light, the calmness you bring up and are surrounded by, like a healing and soothing blanket of light. You are flexible and OK; your body and blood flow just right; all is going right; all is working out in Divine order; you are fine, just as you really and truly have always been, truly calm and serene, like a master of olden times. Your stress levels just seem to calm down; like steam from a pipe, they are released and you are relaxed; you are reset and effectively balanced, gentle to yourself and peaceful and easy and serene, like every past moment of serenity you've ever had is coming back to mind and even deeper, to a profound sense of feeling. You simply trust in life and beyond believing, just now know the secret, that life is truly taking care of you and you are free of struggling and worry; instead, you are powerfully lighthearted, cheerful and peaceful, centered and in your zone of tranquility, free of over-thinking, calm, centered and relaxed, truly now knowing what those words mean on a deeper level of feeling. Free of over-focusing on your breathing, your correct response to breathing is a calm and deep, relaxed flow of breath. Free you are, and you remain, free forever of over-analyzing; your life just seems to flow in a new and better, functional harmony, as your powerful and always-working-in-your-favor subconscious mind is now being left to work out the details, and you just seem to thrive. In fact, you are being braced up and supported by every past victory, triumph, breakthrough and success you've ever had and all of that profound energy, which seems to flow through your blood now, activating your inner hero to emerge and become doubtless and certain that all in your life, all in your world, all that you know is now supporting you and is working out supremely in your favor. Trusting in your life, you know, deeply and truly, you are safe, you are serene, and you are rising above any and all limits from the past chapter of your life, into the new and forever powerful and supportive chapter of your life; for only the very best happens to you, and you are easily able to deal with all of the rest, in clever and fluidly, adaptively, supportive and skillfully successful ways.

## Overcoming Panic

Each and every thought, each and every feeling you're having, each and every action, each and every reaction, begins to adaptively fortify you and strengthen you, allowing you to breathe slowly, as a calming life- supporting, foundationally rebalancing life-sustaining breath, is calming you, centering you and is balancing you, as you flow, float, and relax your way through, over and beyond, any and all old barriers that ever once stood in your way, as all of those barriers just seeming to melt away now, as you now, are feeling so deeply and truly recalibrated and supported, by newer and better heroic thoughts, feelings, memories, experiences, actions and reactions, in body, emotions, mind and even spirit, so very supported, you now just easily know, and truly forever feel that you are now and forever living in a brand new chapter of your life, safe, liberated, strong, and free, absolutely self assured and free of any and all things that ever worked against you in your life. You now foundationally re-identified and free, so liberated, so serene, so sure, that you just simply know things are getting better and better and better. Slowly and steadily breaking through here, you are and you remain, your breath and your heartbeat, remains slow and steady, easily under your life enhancing and self-supportive control, truly and emphatically trusting in your world and your life, almost as if someone from deep, deep inside of you right now, permanently and forever, has reset a dial, a switch, a thermostat, or a computer of some type, forever foundationally recalibrating you. Almost as if in fact, someone has opened a valve from deep, deep inside of you, draining off and far, far away from you, any and all distrust, any and all fear, any and all doubt, any and all anxiety, any and all stress, any and all panic, in truly breakthrough, life-supporting and amazing ways. In this wonderful new chapter of your life, you are adaptively and unstoppably rising to the very top and breaking through here, as your mighty inner hero, the part of you that rises up and always breaks-through, the doubtless part of you that is capable of saving children from great danger, like a fire, is now rising up and actively working only in your favor, allowing you to break through here unbeatably and unstoppably, shining your inner light of heart and mind, your courageous inner wisdom, your inner knowingness, into all things from previous chapters of your life that ever once stood in your way, that were shadowy, staticy, and imbalanced, vanquishing all those things completely and forever, as a new day unstoppably dawns in this new and forever chapter of your life. You are truly feeling and knowing you are adaptively and flexibly, amazingly and with the skill of a mighty hero, both bold and mighty, breaking through here, so even in advance you are cleverly setting up every thought, every feeling, every action, every reaction, to fall into place and support yourself, while dynamically allowing yourself to trust in life and in each and every circumstance you might find yourself in, as you are and as you remain, and as you are unstoppably creating, most especially when you're driving, even if you are driving alone. Almost as if the inspiration and knowledge of professional drivers is merging both now and forever into your consciousness and out into the world around you, with new, precise, effective skills and talents; for what they know you know, what they do you do, you're now just doing fine. Whether you're traveling far away, or at home, in a car on the street, the highway, or even a bridge, your calming and trusty, steady breath and soothing, regular, life-supporting heartbeat, are amazingly allowing you to flow over, around, through and beyond any and all old and useless, now released, healed, released, reset and forgiven, obstacles that once ever stood in your way within the previous chapter of your life.

You now, so comfortable and happy in a brand new chapter of your life. Your spirit and your mind, now open to limitless inspirations and possibilities of your breakthrough healing success here most especially, when taking the test, you so calm, you're so peaceful, you're so serene, you now, such a master of your reality and your world, your mind like a well-tuned super computer, working only in your favor in precise, steady, calm, and measuredly effective, self-supporting ways.

You know it's almost like a jumping back over the years to the age of twelve years old, free, calm, balanced, serene, on top of the world, creating a better choice, fine and free, so through the ages of twelve, thirteen, fourteen, fifteen, sixteen, seventeen, eighteen and beyond, you remained free and have been free, mighty, calm, peaceful and serene your whole life, always doing better and better, always wonderfully well.

## Overcoming Panic

Each and every thought, each and every feeling you're having, each and every action, each and every reaction, begins to adaptively fortify you and strengthen you, allowing you to breathe slowly, as a calming life- supporting, foundationally rebalancing life-sustaining breath, is calming you, centering you and is balancing you, as you flow, float, and relax your way through, over and beyond, any and all old barriers that ever once stood in your way, as all of those barriers just seeming to melt away now, as you now, are feeling so deeply and truly recalibrated and supported, by newer and better heroic thoughts, feelings, memories, experiences, actions and reactions, in body, emotions, mind and even spirit, so very supported, you now just easily know, and truly forever feel that you are now and forever living in a brand new chapter of your life, safe, liberated, strong, and free, absolutely self assured and free of any and all things that ever worked against you in your life. You now foundationally re-identified and free, so liberated, so serene, so sure, that you just simply know things are getting better and better and better. Slowly and steadily breaking through here, you are and you remain, your breath and your heartbeat, remains slow and steady, easily under your life enhancing and self-supportive control, truly and emphatically trusting in your world and your life, almost as if someone from deep, deep inside of you right now, permanently and forever, has reset a dial, a switch, a thermostat, or a computer of some type, forever foundationally recalibrating you. Almost as if in fact, someone has opened a valve from deep, deep inside of you, draining off and far, far away from you, any and all distrust, any and all fear, any and all doubt, any and all anxiety, any and all stress, any and all panic, in truly breakthrough, life-supporting and amazing ways. In this wonderful new chapter of your life, you are adaptively and unstoppably rising to the very top and breaking through here, as your mighty inner hero, the part of you that rises up and always breaks-through, the doubtless part of you that is capable of saving children from great danger, like a fire, is now rising up and actively working only in your favor, allowing you to break through here unbeatably and unstoppably, shining your inner light of heart and mind, your courageous inner wisdom, your inner knowingness, into all things from previous chapters of your life that ever once stood in your way, that were shadowy, staticy, and imbalanced, vanquishing all those things completely and forever, as a new day unstoppably dawns in this new and forever chapter of your life. You are truly feeling and knowing you are adaptively and flexibly, amazingly and with the skill of a mighty hero, both bold and mighty, breaking through here, so even in advance you are cleverly setting up every thought, every feeling, every action, every reaction, to fall into place and support yourself, while dynamically allowing yourself to trust in life and in each and every circumstance you might find yourself in, as you are and as you remain, and as you are unstoppably creating, most especially when you're driving, even if you are driving alone. Almost as if the inspiration and knowledge of professional drivers is merging both now and forever into your consciousness and out into the world around you, with new, precise, effective skills and talents; for what they know you know, what they do you do, you're now just doing fine. Whether you're traveling far away, or at home, in a car on the street, the highway, or even a bridge, your calming and trusty, steady breath and soothing, regular, life-supporting heartbeat, are amazingly allowing you to flow over, around, through and beyond any and all old and useless, now released, healed, released, reset and forgiven, obstacles that once ever stood in your way within the previous chapter of your life.

You now, so comfortable and happy in a brand new chapter of your life. Your spirit and your mind, now open to limitless inspirations and possibilities of your breakthrough healing success here most especially, when taking the test, you so calm, you're so peaceful, you're so serene, you now, such a master of your reality and your world, your mind like a well-tuned super computer, working only in your favor in precise, steady, calm, and measuredly effective, self-supporting ways.
You know it's almost like a jumping back over the years to the age of twelve years old, free, calm, balanced, serene, on top of the world, creating a better choice, fine and free, so through the ages of twelve, thirteen, fourteen, fifteen, sixteen, seventeen, eighteen and beyond, you remained free and have been free, mighty, calm, peaceful and serene your whole life, always doing better and better, always wonderfully well.

# Overcoming Separation Anxiety – Children

You are feeling so very relaxed, so very peaceful, so very calm, right now. And as you are so relaxed, you are feeling so very calm, so very comfortable, you are now memorizing this as a way to be, a way to live and as a way to feel very calm yet strong and steady. You are held together, supported and taken care of by everything in your life. You are ready to be a part of your life and you find newer and better ways to live and to enjoy yourself, taking part in everything enjoyable your life will bring you. You know that people will come and go from your life, but that those same people will return to you, coming back into your life, caring for you, taking care of you, being there for you, most especially your Dad and even more especially your Mom.

You are taking better care of your self-pushing out of your life, thoughts and feelings that made you feel upset or made you feel bad. You are absolutely and unstoppably determined and truly able to feel good, even feeling great, knowing you are moving into a better place in your life, feeling more self-supported at school, better taken care of, feeling the thoughts and strengths of your parents, your Dad and your Mom. Everyone's OK, everyone's doing fine, both you and them. You might even begin to feel safe, strong, better, calmer, more confident, more together, much less easily upset, much less easily scared, so much less upset by outside events. Instead, in fact, you are truly so very much more sure of yourself, so very much more cool, so very much more calm and collected and so very much more peaceful, so very much more easy and comfortable. You forgive all past moments of upsetment and move on from them powerfully, because you deserve to, so you relax deeper and now you do. You think to yourself, isn't' there a better way to think and to feel and then you'll come up with it, and you will think and feel better.

You feel each and every day like a hero, like you've may have seen on seen in a TV show or a movie, who can rise up and get bigger than anything and everything that has ever stood in your way in the past, because you are beginning to believe in yourself, trusting in your life, in your world, in your family and in your friends and in each and very helpful and kind thought you choose to create in your mind to improve your life. You are trusting in the way you feel, the way you think, the way you trust that life is always taking care of you. It's almost like you've restarted your life all over gain, feeling fresh, new and better, all better, all new, all improved, all taken care of. You deserve to be happy, memorizing this feeling of relaxation as a way to be, a way to live, a way to be happy, a way to enjoy your life, your school, your friends, your life, so much more calm, so much more taken care of, so much ore re-thought about, so much more relieved, so much more peaceful, so much more connected to all people and things you like and love. Peaceful, quiet, still, able to handle anything, being a part of the fun of life, so much more balanced, encouraged, secure, calm and balanced because you can and deserve to. So you relax, after taking just a few short deep and slow steady breaths and feel great! You think of yourself and your life in new and better ways, feeling those new and better ways becoming a part of you. You've rethought yourself, because you are a kid and you deserve to be happy and feeling great and this only gets easier and better each and every day and night. Your powerful mind is working on this, while you're awake, while your are asleep and even while your are dreaming to improve your life and to take better care of you forever and in ever new, even surprisingly better ways, amazing, surprising and impressing every one, most especially even you. Each and every night and day all of you is ready to feel better in each and every way. And all of you is willing, ready and able to win at this, relaxing into this and succeeding at this, right now and only getting better and better, now and into your happy future.

## Overcoming Social Fears

Now relax even deeper, deeper and deeper on each and every breath, just allow yourself to relax. And as you relax, you allow yourself this pure moment of inner peace, a pure moment of inner calmness. And in this moment, you allow yourself to appreciate all of you, all of you, even the parts that are more challenging to love, and the parts that you truly and most easily love in a most complete way. In this pure moment, you allow yourself the true knowing that you are enough, yes you really are and that just being yourself, is just fine with you, and it's really just fine with all of those who meet you, because deep, deep inside of you, you are whole, calm, comfortable, and complete. In each and every circumstance from your past, you were enough, you did actually fit in, and as you relax, you are calm, you are comfortable, you are at peace, and you are enough, in each and every way. It really doesn't matter if the world understands you, or if they appreciate you, because beginning right now and for the rest of your life, you truly and very deeply and very powerfully appreciate you, all of you and that's really all that matters. And as you relax, you allow your communication skills and self-expression skills to flourish. And all that you have to say, all that you are just flows from you, powerfully and expressively, with focus, ease, poise and grace. You are calm, at peace and focused. You trust in yourself and your decisions, for you are enough, and all of you is life affirming, life supporting, and your self- supporting choices are correct. You are one with yourself and your life, and you take pride in that. You let go of all ideas and symptoms of struggle, just letting that go slowly and yet forever, letting it drift away, drifting away, drifting far,

far away, relaxing into a masterpiece of a life that you gently and boldly create. Now and in each and every moment, you are remaining adaptable, calm and at peace. You are in a place of calm yet powerful determination about all that you wish to accomplish and all that you will accomplish, achieving with poise, ease and grace. And even as you relax right now, the limitless and wonderfully dynamic power of your subconscious mind is working whether you realize it or not, and is coming up with five new, positive, and very powerful solutions and strategies to the situations and things that had once caused you stress in the past. And these solutions and strategies readily activate into your life, whether you realize it or not, into each and every moment of your life, liberating your life, liberating you, easily allowing you to create the masterpiece of a life you've always desired and deserved, bringing it right here into the right now, in every aspect of your life, physically, emotionally, mentally, and spiritually, in each and every way, beginning right now and for the rest of your life, now and forever!

## Overcoming Terrorism Panic and Post Traumatic Stress

**Note:** You must be a qualified and certified Clinical Hypnosis professional and have a written note of authorization to perform this or any other complementary hypnosis session from the attending physician, psychiatrist, psychologist, etc., no exceptions.

You are so very calm, comfortable and relaxed each and every night, finding newer and better ways of relaxing your previous day's away and putting all of the days cares and events up on a shelf. Today took care of you, just like every other yesterday, and tomorrow will do just the same, in a powerful and unstoppably Divinely-guided and protected ways. And you feel so increasingly sure and certain of this, surer than anything you've ever experienced in your life. You find newer and better ways to trust in yourself, your world and in your life and the Divine protection life has continually brought to you. When anything ever feels too big, you let go and give it to God to handle. You sleep peacefully right through the night, allowing yourself the gift of a peaceful and deeply healing and soothing night of rest. You awaken each and very morning after having a calming and deeply soothing, relaxing night of sleep. You are feeling calm, emotionally balanced and fortified, calm, comfortable relaxed, breathing just a few deep and steady breaths, which immediately allow you to instantly balance yourself. You are safe, calm and secure, Divinely-protected, guided, taken care of, worry-free, balanced and relaxed. You are trusting in all that your life brings you, finding forgiveness and balance. In fact, I wonder if you even yet realize how easy this is going to be for you to do, as you find newer, better and calmer ways of living. You feel so calm, so balanced, so free, so liberated, so moving on, so stable, so untroubled by thoughts that once blocked you, just flowing like a mighty and unstoppable over, around and through any blockage, you so free, so happy, so emotionally balanced and harmonized, finding and creating new ways to trust in life and to better support yourself with every thought, every feeling, every emotion and emotional response, and reaction, just relaxing out of, away from and through, just letting go of any and all thoughts and feelings that once stood in your way. You become and actually feel, beginning to forever truly know, that you are mightier than any all past blockages, feelings or hurtful reactions.

You are just flowing and moving on into a newer and happier, brighter and better chapter of your life. You'll hardly ever be thinking what if, but if you do, it will be in reaction to wondering what if your life is so filled with joy, hope and ease. You feel reassured, heartened, glad, comfortable, releasing anything and everything that was ever uncomfortable. You are powerfully and effectively blockage-free, struggle-free, peaceful, calm, balanced and relaxing your way into a happier life. As you take your life back and feel this newer, brighter and better chapter of your life starting, filled with joy, hope and ease and comfortability. You are feeling not just like your old self again, but so much better than that. With each and every breath you take and with each and every steady beat of your heart, you are more calm, more balanced and more relaxed, happy to be alive, and happy to thrive.

## Overcoming Trichotillomania (Hair Pulling)

**Note:** You must be a qualified and certified Clinical Hypnosis professional and have a written note of authorization to perform this or any other complementary hypnosis session from the attending physician, psychiatrist, psychologist, etc., no exceptions.

All old and completely unhealthy and unpleasant and unhappy and undesirable repetitive behaviors and ways of acting are and have been, pockets of resistance and struggles to you. They are ways of struggling and resisting your life and your embracing your most precious gift, your life and how you embrace your life. And now by further relaxing, you are allowing all of those pockets to completely dry up and to evaporate, both now and forever, blowing away from your life. Now instead, even better, you allow a more balanced, calmer, happier, easygoing, un-resistant way of life to develop, one in which you relax, trust, flow, are in harmony with yourself and with your forgiveness, of all past issues, that had once, in some unpleasant past chapter of your life, stood in your way of leading the kind of a fulfilling life, you deserve. Right now you relax even deeper, you release, the force of your forgiveness is powerful, very powerful, completely unstoppable, growing and getting stronger and more powerful, more adaptive, more healing, allowing for greater wholeness and harmony, each and every day and each and every night. For in this moment only getting stronger, better and more powerful, a new balanced healthier chapter of your life has truly begun, whether you realize it or not, allowing you to thrive and heal, in truly amazing ways. There is nothing to pull out of you, or to pull out of your life, or your past, since all of your life, past, present and future is there for you to enjoy, to learn from, to move comfortably forward into. There is no moment, no experience, no thought, no feeling, no emotion, no sensation, no energy or anything at all, that you would ever have to pull out from yourself or from your body, your emotions, your thoughts and mind, or your life in any way. So just relax deeper and deeper now. As you relax, you relax into happier and more gentle ways of being. Even your hands, can be elsewhere, touching your life, touching the world, creating, shaping, but your hands are absolutely free of hurting, free of pulling at, free of gnawing at, free of pulling out, everything and anything you once found unpleasant, for instead and even better, you are completely releasing, forgiving and healing, forgiving and releasing, and moving on from everything and anything, that once had you hurt or in pain. You relax deeper, 3, 2, 1, its over, it's gone, you've succeeded, you move on and you've unstoppably won!

You begin to take better care of yourself and you find pleasure and happiness by leaving your hair alone. Each and every time you've accomplished this, you give yourself a reward. Whenever you go to pull your hair, your arms feel heavy, heavy, heavy, heavy like cement, heavy like lead. Any area they may go to touch without thinking, feels hot, very hot, uncomfortably hot, like a very excruciating sunburn. You are and you remain, free of touching your hair, most especially when you are stressed, you may go to play with your hair, eyebrows and eyelashes, but this time, this day, both now, always and forever, only getting stronger and more and more powerful, you are forgiving your past and living your life, you feel that everyone you care for is caring for you, loving back, giving you the kind of admiration and respect you deserve. Any and all old abuse and patterns of abuse stop, right now, completely forgiven, absolutely forgiven, only getting easier, more powerful and better. Anytime you even might slip into the old unpleasant ways of yesterday, you stop your heavy hands and silently in your mind only, you yell out to yourself, louder than you've ever heard, STOP, STOP, STOP! And then instantly, you STOP, both easily and completely. I really even wonder if you even yet truly realize how easy this is going to be for you to STOP, move on and begin a happier, healthier better way of life. You see yourself with a beautiful (head of hair, set of eyebrows and lashes) like a model or a movie star on a magazine cover. All and everything that ever once had you do this, is something you've now moved on from, away from and its over with, because you've now made that decision and that only gets more and more powerful, each and every day and night, each and every second, with each and every beat of your heart and each and every breath that you take. You know you can do this, so you do, you did, its done, you deserve it, you can you will, in fact, you do, you have.

---

## Releasing Fear and Anxiety

---

You are most assuredly, unstoppably and miraculously moving into a newer, better and brighter chapter of your life, as optimism builds, you sharply refocus, your clarity now begins and just builds and builds. You calm down, forgive, heal and trust in your life as you are and as you easily remain powerfully free of things that once ever stood in your way. You have moved on, you have relaxed through and beyond any and all barriers, both real and imagined, trusting in the fact that your life is polishing up while allowing you to unstoppably thrive, in potent ad powerfully effective ways. As you relax, you release all barriers and blockages and move onto higher, better and more wholly centered places in your life. Feeling calm, serene, centered, at peace, you are easily able to handle anything. You are growing and glowing while basking in the luxurious energies of confidence. You are thriving, steady, feeling free, even feeling mighty.

You are re-molded, reidentified correctly and powerfully, so comfortable, so safe, so centered, so sure and completely secure at home, in your house. And just like the sun coming up each morning, just like it has done each and every morning, you trust in the steadiness of your life and of this path you are now and forever living. While at home or even outside your home, you know you are safe, secure and serene, easily able to rise up and to adapt in all events and circumstances, just like you've always done. You are so inspired right now, liberating only your very best and simply activating your inner hero. Gone are the things of the past that once stood in your way. You have forever vanquished them, having moved on. Certain, sure and mighty, you are reidentified into a newer and brighter life, a brighter and better chapter of your life. You are powerfully forgiving and releasing everything that ever stood in your way, just sweeping it aside from your life and powerfully moving on. You are feeling free, free at long last, released from the bonds of the past, things of the past are just simply things of the past. Things from your childhood are simply just memories from your past. Fears from your past now are gone and you are completely free unstoppably and undeniably right now. Forever you are freed, as if someone from deep, deep inside of you has reset a switch, a dial, a computer or a thermostat of some kind, all things begun anew, reset. So highly effective and successfully focused, reinforced on each and every breath you take and on each and every heartbeat, you are now forever free and it's only getting easier to be forgiven, released as you are easily and effectively moving on from old and past things are now and forever released, like: (list) fears of leaving the house, fear of fire or structural damage, you are so much stronger now and have taken strides forward, so calm, comfortable and clear you are and you forever remain.

Just now, a powerful and new supportive thought comes upon you now: life is actually taking care of me. Yes really it is, I trust in life and those who love me, most especially how I better and better love myself. I am moving on and feeling more whole, centered and complete. I now deep breathe slow and steady breath and easily overcome outdated and vanquished feelings of being overwhelmed by bills and possible repairs to the house, as I forever calm down, succeed easily at all of this, completely and creatively trust in my life and how things have always seemingly worked out for the very best. I am centered, I am whole, all is working out in my favor; all is OK and only getting better and better. I forever learn to acknowledge my accomplishment, forever free I am and I remain. free of ever again being overwhelmed by the responsibility any new accomplishments might incur.

I easily overwhelm all things that once ever stood in my way. I take control of any and all thoughts and feelings by slow and steady deep breath, my heart rate calms down, I relax all over and feel comfortable, powerful and mighty and I relax, I thrive and I feel great. I trust those around me. I forever and unshakably now resolve that my spouse is perfectly capable of handling homeownership. All of life works to support me and my feelings, my supportive thoughts, I am strong, I am dynamic, I am clear, I get this and all other jobs done. My imbalanced and distrustful days of being a "control freak" are now and forever over. I forgive any and all past things that every stood in my way, all thoughts, all feelings, all disappointments, all distrust and leave in their place, rather I create trust, appreciation, love and respect for myself and trust in the talents and supportiveness of others, moving beyond old limiting beliefs, to a powerful and forever place of knowing, and centeredness, resting comfortably in refuge of my knowledge, this brand new, creative, mighty and powerfully supportive chapter of my life, that begins right now and only gets stronger and better and better for me. For all things about my home are safe, I am secure, I can handle anything in stride, just as I've always done, I share responsibility with spouse. I am loved, I am calm, both me and my life are just great! I deep breathe, I relax, I trust, I am mighty, I win!

## Removing Anxiety and Stress - From Past Abuse

**Note:** You must be a qualified and certified Clinical Hypnosis professional and have a written note of authorization to perform this or any other complementary hypnosis session from the attending physician, psychiatrist, psychologist, etc., no exceptions.

You have unstoppably moved into a newer, brighter and better chapter of your life. The past is the past; you are determined to liberate your inner hero and to become mighty over things that once stood in your way, rising above and moving into a brighter and better chapter of your life. All abusive people, places, things and events are now being filed away into the past and are unstoppably given less and less importance over yourself and your life, not because I say so, but because it's the nature of your own powerful and dynamic mind to do so. And so it is. You are powerfully relaxing and gaining newer and more powerful perspectives on who you are and what your life is to be about. You are becoming mighty, brighter, better and more powerful, more adaptive and amazingly more successful at releasing past traumas, almost in fact feeling polished and better, having grown up and moved on, all things uncomfortable from your past meaning less and less. You always knew that traumas from the past would one day, more and more, mean less and less. Right now and only easier and better, healingly and adaptively moving on into a brighter and better life, most especially in spite of anything that has ever happened to you. You are re-conditioned to see and to even truly know that you are moving on, forgiving and letting go of any and all past abuse situations, seizing a newer and more real sense of personal power, so much more easily able to rise to the very top and to begin anew, in a brand new and more powerfully mighty, dynamically more loving, self-supportive and healing chapter of your life. You learn to let go of harsh judgments you once put upon others, or even upon yourself, because you are feeling so much better, more effective, more dynamic, more and more relaxed. You begin to realize that the only power others have over you is the power you give them; in this new chapter of your life, you are keeping your power to yourself and thriving, flourishing and winning from this newer, more healthy and peaceful place from deep, deep within you. Powerfully, fully ready, as if in some sort of starting gate, you go forward into your life now, striding beyond any and all past mental and emotional abuse. You are FORGIVEN, RELEASED, HEALED, ENERGY BALANCING, MOVING ON, moving easily and ever onward from any self-destructive patterns of anger, or hatred, so much better at taking care of yourself than that, as your powerful and effective mind just allows you to move forward into a brighter and better way, a better and more supportive day and night. You were a survivor, and now, more importantly, you are a person who thrives and lives. You are freed from the past, free, free at long last, finding newer and better ways of becoming and remaining happy and content. Regardless of what might pop up, you are adaptive, fluid and feeling fine, in the clear, determined to deep breathe, then calm down and relax, finding a newer sense of inner harmony, balance and at long last peace, as your perspective changes in your favor to support you and make you feel fine. You keep your power base steady and balanced, free of the opinions of others; in fact, what others think of you or how they've tried to control you is, in fact, none of your business. You know who you are; you know what you do, you are free of condemnation, from others, and most especially from yourself. You learn to adapt and to not play old games, to move on and to teach, instruct and explain better at home, guiding and maintaining a level of dignity, keeping your position as moderator, teacher, guide and loving, even sometimes corrective, parent to your children. As a way of teaching them self-respect, you teach them to listen to you as you remain emotionally detached, and correct, guide, and remaining forever free of any emotionally-charged games. It has been said the best parents are not their child's friends, as they maintain the wisdom of keeping an upper hand and are free of emotional equal-ness. You are very rapidly evolving into that sort of wonderful parent, liberating your very best parenting skills out and into your life.

## Stress and Anxiety Relief

You have unstoppably moved into a brand new chapter of your life, feeling like you have arrived and are living in a newer and more supportive place - for each and every thought, each and every feeling, each and every action and each and every reaction, is now just simply getting more and more supportive, as you now and forever believe in yourself, trust in yourself and in your life and all that it brings, absolutely taking better care of yourself. Both now and forever you realize you are whole, you are enough and you are doing just fine, while finding, cleverly creating, truly and powerfully living and actually knowing better ways of feeling calm, peaceful and serene; most especially knowing and living from all parts of this when around other people and even friends. You are breathing calmly and deeply, feeling tranquil and clear, in thoughts, emotions, body and mind, even if upset or challenged in some way, you are supremely trusting in your life, breathing deeply, blowing off any and all of the old bad stuff from the old and past chapter of your life, feeling clear, drinking plenty of refreshing life giving water, happy to be in your skin. You are learning to take things in stride, like the master of your life you now are, all things are in proper pace and moderation, finding the proper pace and place in your life, finding and thriving, achieving and living in proper harmony, rising above old fears and doubts, and learning that life is truly taking care of you, you are just doing better and better in your life and in your world, easily achieving thoughts of positive thinking, bestcase scenarios and what if things only better and better, better things happen, life just filled with promises and better and better things, in fact, your very thoughts and feelings are magnetizing better and better things into your life, these inspirations, always take hold of your mind. In fact, you might just come to know, both now and forever, your thoughts are improving in your favor, your feelings are more and more supportive and working in your favor, even bodily functions, supporting you in the very best of ways, in each and every feeling and thought. For now you are reinvented, rejuvenated, reconditioned, all of this only getting more and more honestly powerful and clever, clear, focusing only upon the very best, rising up and rising above, healed, released, forgiven, breaking though, right now and right here, even if it just seems to be happening all around you, truly finding peace and approving of yourself, and finding better and better ways to love yourself. All things and energies that have ever worked against you are now and forever turned back upon themselves, to reduce, remove and completely eliminate those negative and destructive energies and limitations, removing and eliminating difficulties, while opening up your heart and mind and magnetizing only the very best of experiences and people and events into your life. For you are beginning to not only believe in yourself, but to know whom you truly are as someone worthwhile, someone deserving to be here, your powerful and dynamic subconscious mind now creating clever pathways, methods and strategies to breakdown the barriers that have ever stressed you and to move you forward, feeling whole, deserving, better, complete, just doing better and better, being a more supportive and loving friend to yourself. Free now you are and you remain, of any and all things that have ever stood in your way, feeling calm, balanced, restored, balanced and relaxed. You know, it's just like someone has reset a switch, a dial, a thermostat or a computer of some kind from deep, deep, within you allowing you to become and forever remain breaking through here, calm, balanced and stress free, feeling fine about whom you are and how you are doing, like your whole life has been reset and rebalanced and you are cleverly succeeding, just doing anything and everything it honestly takes to feel better and better, calm, balanced and stress free, your powerful mind having made a powerful, working in your favor and effectively adaptive decision to break though here, always working in your favor, while you are awake, asleep and ever dreaming, you are and your remain, doing just fine, feeling fine, redefined and doing better.

---

# Extras – Anxiety, Panic, Fear

NOTE: This is a section of additional suggestions I've written for various sessions. As with the rest of this text, please read and select or adapt the suggestions that apply to your client (patient) to fit their specific needs. By using this section, you are agreeing to pre-reading, rewriting, adjusting and adapting these suggestions to individual and specific needs.

**Anxiety Extra -** Rather than finding new things to be stressed or upset about, you are truly finding newer and better ways of rising above any and all stress and just deep breathing and relaxing your way through, beyond and past anything and everything that has ever stressed you in the past, making these moments right now, the clearest, easiest, and best so far in your very life. You are finding inner strength and support by going within yourself to deep breathe, slow and steady, powerful, healing breaths and now knowing your correct response to any and all formerly stressing or anxiety-producing challenges is to deep breathe and relax your way through them, in a brand new and polished chapter of your life, trusting in life and truly knowing you are supported, most especially when: in any restaurant while waiting for the food to be served; most especially when: you have to do things seemingly not for benefit to you in some way, like going somewhere you don't want to go, but determined to relax and to enjoy the ride or experience anyway. The only opinion of you that matters is your own; you are cutting yourself a break and are bound and determined to be upbeat, forgiven, released and fine, and so you are now and forever moving forward, freed at long last, even if people are looking at you. What they think of you or not is none of your business, and you are easily and smoothly moving along and beyond any and all old barriers into the most supportive of times ahead, truly and deeply feeling a new and abiding sense of trust and the calming embrace that this does, in fact, truly bring to you. You are fine, feeling fine, doing just better and better, like someone from deep, deep inside of you has reset a switch, a dial, a computer, or a thermostat of some kind, allowing you comfort, power and supportive thoughts and feelings in this new and better chapter of your life. All things, including health, are just fine. You are allowing yourself right now steady calming breath, which is relaxing you and drawing you beyond any and all old blockages into the brightest and best vistas of your life. Any and all things that once challenged you, you are now and forever easily and powerfully mightier than, as you always have been, only even more so now. You are calm, you are safe, you are taken care of and you now know this, it's just getting easier and better. You are sturdy, you are calm, you are safe, you are taken care of, you are sturdy, forgiven, balanced, healthy, whole, calm and supported. You are safe, serene, and so very comfortably in your zone, and all of this and in your own powerful and precise way, it's only getting easier and better, sometimes mightier than each and anything that had ever stood in your way, most especially yourself, just getting out of your own way and breaking through here, doing fine, feeling wonderful, knowing you are calm, breathing deeply, feeling serene.

**Beating Travel Panic – *Extras* -** You are finding newer and better ways of feeling good, even great, (name locations) at home or wherever You are no matter near or far, whether near your home or far from your car, there's always a way home for you. After just a few short and deep, steady breaths, you are feeling calm, balanced, harmonized and relaxed, in fact, truly relaxed all over. You are feeling unstoppably upbeat, calm, balanced and relaxed, like someone from deep, deep inside of you has drained off any and all of your old panic from the now dry reservoir. All of your thoughts work to support you. You are now trusting in life, free of ever needing a safety net. You are and you forever easily and effectively remain, calm, balanced and relaxed, deep breathing supportive and calming breath, deep breathing, releasing and flowing away from any and all thoughts that ever caused you any discomfort. You are draining away and now effectively removing all thoughts that ever stood in your way, you are feeling calm and comfortable for as long as you have to be anywhere you are. You are now safe and forever free, just like when you are nearby your car, but regardless of whether the car is there or not. You can go anywhere if you have your car and you can comfortably go anywhere you have to go when you are not with your car as you now know this whole world is now your home, you are am important part of it all, you deserve to be here and you are supported by this in new and more profound ways. You find yourself taking little steps, each leading to new destinations and brighter horizons, even long car rides, and you are even feeling so mighty, so much ever stronger, so much more powerful, you might gain more and more success with your ever expanding courage, drive and determination or you might even one day possibly move to a new location to be with loved ones or travel to (name locations) having fun with your loved ones. You are doing ever increasingly well, feeling fine, better and better, trusting in your life and your world and all that you travel to, feeling fine and supported, trusting and supported better, each and every day and night.

**Nail Biting – Extra -** You always knew your nail biting days wouldn't last forever, so now they are powerfully over. You are and you powerfully and amazingly remain, calm, balanced and free of old patterns of the past, in a newer and better chapter of your life, most especially if there is or might be times of being under a lot of stress.

You are, and you powerfully and amazingly remain, calm, balanced and free of old patterns of the past, in a newer and better chapter of your life, most especially if you are or might be studying for a test or while you are taking a test, you choose to treat yourself better than the old ways, and now so you do.

You are, and you powerfully and amazingly remain, calm, balanced and free of old patterns of the past, in a newer and better chapter of your life, most especially if you are or might be worked up emotionally, relaxing, deep-breathing steady and calming, life-giving and balancing breaths, taking better care of yourself. You are, and you powerfully and amazingly remain, calm, balanced and free of old patterns of the past, in a newer and better chapter of your life, most especially if you are or might be really upset, angry or frustrated. You are forever free now, free from ever biting without even knowing it, for even if you did, your hands would feel heavy, heavy, heavy, like lead. They would taste disgusting, and you'd notice all of this instantly and refuse to do it. You are now forever free of old nail biting habits and have moved on. You are just doing so much better and better; I wonder if you even yet realize how easy this is for you, and you have unstoppably moved into a newer and brighter, better chapter of your life.

**Stress Eating** - You are finding newer, better and improved ways to create and maintain self-control at any and all moments of your life, most especially after a long and stressful day, choosing in your favor to make the very best choices for yourself. You are powerfully free of doing anything that ever stood in your way, most especially like drinking wine, just growing up and moving easily beyond that and moving on beyond eating unhealthy choices, and beyond overeating in any way, as you exercise good judgment and use proper portion control. You know what's bad for you and easily find ways to say no when you have to, feeling better and more dynamic, upbeat, adaptive and capably inspired. You find yourself now and forever drinking more water and getting some exercise, bringing your exercise goals down to levels of ridiculous ease, feeling fine and content. You know you need to change and tap into your motivated and powerful, dynamically inspired inner strength, improving easily and treating yourself right, just as you know you should. All of your impulses drive you forward to better and better ways of living, acting and reacting. You are feeling inspired by every past victory, triumph and breakthrough you've ever had. You are finding a new joy in life, a new way of releasing stress, perhaps by just deep breathing, making time for yourself, enjoying your Hypnosis reinforcement by enjoying the deeply soothing relaxation, which powerfully calms you, stills you, balances and restores you, readying you for all that life will bring you, as you powerfully and forever flow and dynamically succeed.

# LEARNING ENHANCEMENTS

# Better Public Speaking For Teachers

In these moments of deep and soothing relaxation, your body, your mind, your emotions, in fact all that you are, is now memorizing this soothing, calming and comfortable relaxation state as a way to be, as a way to live, as a way to react, as a way for you to relax beyond any and all old barriers from your now done and finished previous chapters of your life, as a mightier, more enhanced, more brilliantly polished you, more courageous, and free flowing, free of ever second guessing or over-thinking, is both now and forever enhanced and completely in the moment, reconditioned, liberated, strong, and mighty now beginning to emerge, unstoppably and truly, as you now know this, foundationally from places deep, deep inside of you. You are now recalibrated into a better life and way of living, speaking and presenting, feeling wonderful about any such experiences as needed, truthfully, in the most amazing of ways you are unstoppably breaking through here.

In front of any audience, your breathing now calm and relaxed, your correct response to any and all stress is to deep breathe soothing relaxing breath, bathing in relaxation, as your skin gets and feels comfortable, your heart strong and relaxed reassuringly, beating comfortably, your stomach relaxed almost as if you are inhaling and exhaling life-giving golden-white sunlight through your naval as your stomach is relaxed and comfortable and your back is relaxed as well. Amazingly and truly, as it is now a time for you to rise to the very top, in this brand new and unbeatable chapter of your life, all things that ever once stood in your way, are now being released and it feels wonderful to be so alive and free. You are releasing any and all old and unneeded, useless and undeserved patterns of second-guessing yourself, both known and unknown to you, as your creative, clever, and adaptive mind, is now unbeatably working in your favor to support you, in brilliant, true, and absolutely effective, unconditionally adaptive, amazing ways. You both now and forever remain in a place of supreme knowing, knowing who you are and what you have to present, easily and effectively sharing and expressing, your confidence while truly feeling completely enhanced, re-calibrated, re-tuned and reset. All actions, all reactions, are all now completely supportive and balanced emotions, are undeniably activating supportive and harmonious success and goal-oriented thoughts, all energies now reoriented to a more unlimited place, foundationally from deep inside of you, completely supporting you in the truest and most amazing of ways, because the job must get done, and just as in all times from your past you have always gotten it done, liberating personal success from places from the deep, deep inside of you, that are completely self-supportive, as you trust in the very true fact that a brighter and better you is now unstoppably unfolding and emerging; for the greater the stress might possibly have once been, the more focused, calm, precise, cool and collected you become.

For most assuredly now and forever, your adaptive and always working in your favor, clever creative mind, whether you yet realize it or not, is setting up highly effective patterns and rhythms, even clever strategies of brilliant and amazing success, as your new vibrant and vital better way to live and experience just so right, and you feel so wonderful, comfortable and calm, centered, serene and peaceful. As if speaking in front of children, youngsters, and students with open minds, thirsting for knowledge, the knowledge you have to share with any audience, even playfully and having fun, enlightening, explaining, and illucidating Any and all points with any group, young or old or even mixed. For truly you are there to enlighten, enliven, and motivate, the teacher that you are active and coming forth, foundationally from deep inside of you, is now heroically, unstoppably, undeniably, cleverly and even adaptably, now profoundly rising to the top, and even merging, with your mighty inner hero, right now and whenever most needed. The part of you that is capable of saving children from great danger, like a fire, is now unstoppably rising to the very top, joining and becoming one with all that you are. Whenever you're ready to speak to any audience, you are empowered like a legendary hero of olden times. Whenever you must speak in public in any form, in all the essential ways, you recognize or perhaps just realize that you are there to enlighten, enliven, illuminate, share information, educate and to get your points across, perhaps sharing experiences, points and the most valid parts of who you are, worthy and deserving, as you now truly recognize and realize, that deep down the vast majority of members of the audience, are secretly rooting for you, cheering you on, even sharing their very best energies even fueling you, joining with you, their strength is your strength, all of this just driving you forward, and ultimately bringing you the success you deserve, as you are remaining cool and calm in front of them, as the important and valuable ones there are truly supporting you and encouraging your well motivated and focused, easily, skillfully, and dynamically liberating true and complete success. From deep inside of you, you now know your audience is interested in what you have to say, and what you were there to present.

Just like a performer polished from years of experience in front of audiences, your correct response to stepping in front of an audience of any age just as you do with youngsters that you teach, is to relax, to rise to the top, play and have a bit of fun, feel like you're fitting into your zone of comfort, just as comfortable as putting on a comfortable old pair of shoes or an old sweater, as you allow yourself a moment of feeling activated to speak, to share, to express, making eye contact with the friendly members of the audience, as if having a conversation, with two or three of your closest, dearest old friends, experiencing only comfort, joy and ease.

As you know there are people there, in fact truly, the vast majority of the people there, are cheering you on in spite of and more importantly because of, a very small minority of somewhat negative individuals in the room. Focusing in on only the positive people, most especially your motivated self, truly you are becoming one to some degree with their consciousness, which is completely supportive, caring, appreciative, and setting off a chain reaction of support for your success here, while you are automatically deep breathing slow and comfortable, steady, completely supportive breath. Your energy correctly shifting into just the right register for you to experience complete success with ease, almost as if it's happening on its own, as if it has already happened, and you are there to witness it, or perhaps just having liberated skill and success while cleverly and easily bringing it right here in to the right now, almost as if flying a plane with active automatic pilot. You now enhanced by every past victory, triumph, breakthrough, and success you've ever had, almost as if in any moment when you must speak in public, someone from deep, deep inside of you, has actually in your favor reset a switch, a dial, a thermostat, or a computer of some type, instantly kicking you into the right register, the right modulation, the right speed, the right volume, easily pausing every five to seven minutes to change energies with any story or presentation, as your personalization of an idea or an insight, or to share a joke of some kind, almost it's truly as if you have been polishing yourself into a greater level of brilliance and performance skill, and have been breaking through and succeeding right now at this for an additional five years, ten years, even sixteen years down the road.

It has been said and it has been written, that what other people think of you is none of your business, in your mind what is truly important is the valid and true fact that you are feeling good about yourself, you will get to have fun any time you must speak in public, even now looking forward to it as it is so easy and effective for you, feeling comfortable and better about who you are and making all public speaking moments truly valuable and enjoyable, triumphant experiences. You are relaxing beyond any and all old barriers from previous moment and chapters of your life, into this brand new chapter of your life, as your mighty inner hero is now turning back upon themselves, any and all negative thoughts, any and all negative feelings and now silly fears, any and all negative expressions or negative audience spin. Completely and absolutely replacing now gone and forever easily vanquished uncomfortable moments, thoughts and feelings with only positive, fulfilling and self-supporting, only getting easier and better, thoughts, positive, fulfilling and self-supporting, only getting easier and better, feelings, positive, fulfilling and self supporting, only getting easier and better, expressions, positive, fulfilling and self-supporting, only getting easier and better, audience interest and participation. as you smile glowingly, inwardly as vital and budding new self-confidence is flowing and building up all around you. You now truly knowing, and appreciating, even gleaming with dynamic inspirational energy in abundant limitless supply, as if unstoppably inspired by new and profound supportive and encouraging thoughts, feelings, emotions, inspirations, actions, and reactions, all of which are part of your arsenal for success here, unbeatably breaking you through here, as you are and you remain, more confident, more clear, more self-appreciated, as a better you, is unstoppably rising to the very top, once and for all, getting out of your own way, while allowing yourself to breakthrough here unbeatably. Not because I say so, but because it is true. For beyond belief, there is faith, and beyond faith you simply know you are in a place of complete empowerment, liberation and freedom in all of this, rising only to the very top, realizing and appreciating and living new and better days, as a more determined, more motivated, more self-starting you, is now unstoppably emerging into the very best chapter of your life, just as if you have stepped forward to realize a dream with twenty years worth of knowledge, experience, talent and ability. So right now in this very moment, you are doing better and better, all of this becoming easier, deeper, more powerful and profoundly true, more than any other time in your life, and more. Overpowering any challenge presented while creating higher impact and greater results in your favor, as well as in the favor of your audience, each and every time, you perform this with correct and inspired results achieving relaxation technique on your own.

Speaking in public and oral discussion now just as easy as the ideas are written down on paper for you. Whether busy or calm, you rise to the top easily overcoming and or overwhelming any and all challenges presented to you, now cleverly and adaptably, and the most truly effective of ways, forever free of feeling, being in any way overwhelmed.

At the end of each and every day, your thoughts are unwinding, calming down, you relax, as you begin to realize, recognize and trust in the very true fact, that today took care of you, and tomorrow will do just the same, just as any and all yesterdays have done before, so not only is it OK to put today on a shelf, to relax and unwind at night as your body, emotions and thoughts calm down for a wonderful night of deep and profound rest, becoming more relaxed and centered, as you put your head down on the pillow, close your eyes, and go to sleep, just as you have done thousands of other times in your life, all getting easier and better, as you were skillfully and effectively even effortlessly reorienting your thinking to become challenge-oriented and problem-free, for the greater the challenge, the more mighty and focused, clever and creative you become, as you are forever easily rising up to meet, easily defeat and overwhelm any and all challenges, problem-free, challenge-oriented, failure-free, either choosing rather only to learn or succeed. You present your case, you stand up for yourself, you are valid, you are vital, essential, you were meant to be here, so you share and express more easily, finding better ways to do this on each and every breath and heartbeat, confident, clear and free, certain and sure you are in a brand new chapter of your life, and so it is, and so it remains, you doing wonderfully, forever, and always.

# Irish Ceili Dancing
# Test and Performance and Teaching Management

From deep within you and from all that you are, you are confident, very, very confident, as your mind relaxes and liberates from all that you are, your greatest abilities, memory, graceful movements, ease, poise and gracefulness.
You know the music playing during any music test, and you are easily able to accurately name the tune, the type of dance, the timing, the number of bars to the step and the number of bars to the set. Your mind is becoming more relaxed, more relaxed, focused, more focused, and as it does, you respond in perfect knowledge, harmony and rhythm.

You are confident and you successfully perform all that you do, as always, in a professional manner to a room of people, who you now truly know secretly wish you to unlimited success, any and all hard shoe dances you are asked to perform, with ease, poise and grace, liberating the greatest dance ability out from the unlimited power of your body, emotions, mind, spirit while instinctively adjusting as needed, through your smooth-flowing and balanced, graceful body, skillfully and wonderfully well.

You are always able to confidently and successfully perform in a professional manner to a room full of strangers, who deep down wish you unlimited success, any and all soft shoe dances you are asked to perform, with ease, poise and grace, liberating your greatest dance abilities out from the unlimited power of your body, emotions, mind, spirit while instinctively adjusting as needed, through your smooth-flowing and balanced, graceful body, skillfully and wonderfully well.

When asked to perform any and all parts of a particular hard shoe dance, you are easily able to perform and completely confident in all of your abilities, to execute all and any dances, perfectly, even if another dancer is dancing at the same time doing different steps, because you are acutely focused and flowing, acutely focused and aware of your own performance, performing with poise, ease, the perfect amount of power and grace.

You learn easily, with your mind absorbing like a sponge, remembering and recall easily, and perform all required any and all hard shoe dances by or even before December first. Any and all of these dances are known to you, you have known them for years, for they are second nature to you, they are a part of you, you are one with them, they liberate from you.

You learn easily, with your mind absorbing like a sponge, remembering and recalling easily, and performing any and all soft shoe dances by or even before Dec. first. Any and all of these dances are known to you, you have known them for years, for they are second nature to you, they are a part of you, you are one with them, they liberate from you powerfully and easily.

You are able to dance all of the dances to the correct timing and beat of the music supplied to you, at any time, including test time, with poise, ease and grace.

When asked to perform any or all parts of a particular soft shoe dance, you are confidently able to execute all dances perfectly even if another dancer is dancing the same dance at the same time doing different steps, you are confident, and you are successful.

You are easily able to confidently break down any step the judges ask you about, and effectively communicate and teach the steps to any volunteer with patience and success; your students are receptive, supportive and friendly, wanting to learn.

You are able to hum the music, know and communicate the timing, teaching the students effectively and with all of the right words so that the students execute the newly learned steps to the satisfaction of the judges; you are confident of this.

You have no critics, only supportive and nurturing people who have your best interests at heart are there; you are performing for appreciative colleagues and students and audiences.
You are easily able to memorize and analyze, recall, any and all dance movements. You are able and confident in your ability to recall and easily access all figures, all parts, to the body, the number and the position of the dancers, and all of the music that's danced to and the type of dance.

You are easily able to answer any and all questions on any written part of the test, while you are teaching any students the Ceili dances. You are able to relax and allow yourself to recall any information on any written test, you relax, you deep breathe and you recall! Your breath activates your memory recall and all of your abilities! Your train of thought and memory are easily activated, as you breathe, you remember all that you are to know, whether a question is written or orally presented. You are beyond any intimidation from another person, you are a professional, you are focused, clear, precise, you are zoned in, you succeed in fact not only do you feel this in every fiber of your being but you know this all pervasive truth from places even deeper inside of you as well. You liberate your inner power and all data stored in your memory and body, you are truly and deeply empowered as never before. You are fully empowered in every way. You rise above all pitfalls and you are limitless in your abilities, you are succeeding easily with poise, talent, ease and grace. You are precise, flowing, you are one with your unlimited success.

Your mind has and continues to absorb all the information, learning easily and powerfully, learning in the best ways, the ways most natural to you, and you use your time and energies, constructively and wisely, liberating success into all that you do. You easily liberate all of the talent and knowledge already contained within you, from your spirit and subconscious mind, easily and very dynamically.

You visualize all parts of each dance, allowing the dance to flow through you from your spirit, your mind and through your body, proudly, enthusiastically, and happily, for all to see, impressing even yourself! You remain calm, clear and focused no matter what the circumstances, you flow, like the eternal ocean. You are greatly motivated to study, to succeed, and retain and recall all knowledge. You are positive and happy in your studies, now and forever, even while taking an exam of any kind, you relax, you have fun, and you succeed. No matter what, you are calm and serene. All of your teaching and any of your performances, bring joy to all who participate with you, and experience you performing in any way. You use your teaching certificates, that are already yours, liberated into the right now, from passing an exam, for the most beneficial and greatest good for society and the world, you light up and bring great joy into the world with all that you do!

# Learning Enhancement - Activation

Now relax even deeper, and as you do, you imagine, notice or even know that a new confidence and a take-charge attitude of success is truly emerging from deep within you. And right now, you choose to rise above, take and utilize all of your inner power and act confidently, confidently taking and passing all necessary tests and exams, with certainty, clarity, ease, strong and sharp focus, even stronger mental recall. Right now, you truly allow yourself to flourish, in thought, in word and in deed, and in fact, you succeed, of course you can and you do right now. You relax right now and you truly realize that you have never ever failed, you have either learned or have succeeded. You truly know that failure is false, failure is an illusion, failure is unreal, because in fact you always succeed. But right now, you are so relaxed and so deeply focused and you are succeeding, succeeding as never before, because you are confident, clear, sharp, focused and in your zone, you are empowered as never before, meeting and succeeding at, even exceeding all of your goals. All that you do and all that you actually are, is about success, your limitless success. You are success!

You see yourself, your forever emerging self- succeeding and passing, now realize it, you know it, for this is truly you. Taking a test in a relaxed, clear and confident manner, you are glowing both inside and out with confidence and total recall, in knowing confidence, powerfully self-assured, you are feeling good all over and in every way. You feel good physically, emotionally, mentally and even spiritually, because you are truly supported by your knowledge, you are truly supported by your ability to reason and you are supported by all that is your life. You feel strong, because you are strong, confident and very capable. In this vision, think about seeing yourself, you've passed. You've succeeded. See this future you, you know this future you, this is in fact who you are right now in the most important ways and in each and every way. This you stands tall, is strong and is smiling both on the inside and even on the outside, smiling with a warm self-assured glow of confidence and success, with a warm and a very confident heart. You are successful, you have succeeded, there is only this option. And you right now, liberate this vision of you, right here, into the right now, from now on and from this moment forward, you are one with this vision, you are one with your success and you are in harmony with yourself and all that you have learned and with all that you can reason. You are truly proud, confident, capable, comfortable, relaxed, strong, fearless, and courageous. You live in dynamic ways, forever free from all former symptoms of struggle, which are gone from you and your life, forever. You are now one with your future and you accept and own your limitless inner power and you really live your life, courageous, motivated, able and able to remember and to think and reason, you are motivated, and you embrace success in the most amazing ways, for you realize you are the power in your life and you utilize this power, in limitless ways, benefiting you and all whom you help, use all that you are to open up in the most complete ways all that You are in each and even moment.

## Learning Enhancement – Confidence

You are becoming sure of yourself, so very sure, so very certain, so very steady, perhaps even in fact, fearless, both inside and out, you feel your confidence building, building, building, you are feeling the feeling, the embrace and the support of each and every time, even anytime, you have ever had a victory, breakthrough, triumph and powerful yet unstoppable success, coming upon you now. You are relaxed, you are determined you are calm; you are relaxed, you are powerfully and unstoppably determined. You remain powerfully, comfortably, effectively and supportively calm, balanced in and in your zone. You are free of any needing to tell yourself anything, because you are becoming so very sure of yourself, you are calm, steady and relaxed, easily succeeding; you are calm steady and relaxed, easily succeeding, even while you are thinking about it or even talking about it, you are relaxing into your very best potentials and opportunities. You are truly in fact, becoming problem-free, challenge oriented, in spite of the thoughts and feelings of others, or even of yourself, most especially of yourself. Your mind, after just a few deep and steady breaths, clears, opens, becomes focused and laser-beam pin point precise, working completely and absolutely, all information and thoughts are just flowing smoothly and precisely, accurately and clearly, just effectively flowing out, allowing you to understand the system, in your favor, to allow you to pass, to thrive to succeed, to gain, to win, to triumph and to unstoppably succeed. In fact, you've never been so sure of anything in your life, all of your very best is coming to the forefront. You relax into a better way of living and being and all of your very best comes right through, just as it's always done at times when you needed it most. All of your very best comes to your mind when you need it, most especially in a calm, balanced, peaceful, correct and precise way, after just a few short deep and steady breaths, most especially and effectively when it's time for a class or a test in (name subject e.g. – math). You feel calm, whole, balanced, able and relaxed, most especially when it's time for a class or a test in (name subject e.g. – Spanish), most especially when it's time for a class or a test in any (name subject) science. You feel calm, whole, balanced, able and relaxed, so confident that everything and any thing you've ever heard or studied will come back, in just the right ways for an answer or an inspiration, relaxing you and assuring you that you'll move on to the next grade (step or classification), so you can move on into a bright and happy, supportive and lucrative future. You relax, and rather than your old habit in your past of once getting nervous, even better, right now in this brand new and improved chapter of your life, a new and better habit and way of reacting emerges, where you allow yourself to thrive and succeed, just like you are fully understanding the system better, you now feel you just know how to get there, so you do and you are more able, more confident and more sure of yourself. You find better ways of handling strict teachers, you are finding newer and improved, calmer and better ways of handling yourself. You are feeling safe, confident and secure, seeing and thinking of those teachers as guides into a happier, healthier, brighter life, knowing that regardless of circumstance, they are there to help you, and you are now accepting any and all challenges they might present to you. You relax and trust in your life as a great and bold adventure, where you are supported, by living better, thriving, succeeding, enjoying your life and all new experiences to their fullest capacity, even new surroundings are places for you to explore and to learn from. And with your newer and calmer, growing, glowing, self-sustaining confidence, you go boldly onward, believing in yourself, truly and absolutely creating a better learning and success experience for yourself in new and powerfully amazing ways.

## Learning Enhancement - NASD 7 Test (Stockbrokers License Exam)

You find yourself mentally peaceful, serenely relaxed, comfortable, as a knowing and glowing confidence, is now in bracing all that you are, this unlimited and inspirational energy is powerfully and dynamically spreading throughout your heart and your mind, and throughout your body, and beyond, you are glowing inside and out, feeling wonderful, in this time of calm and knowing glowing confidence, gentle yet all pervasive ease, you are and you remain forever freed of ever being stressed over the test, as a matter of fact, you are almost powerfully energized while rising to the top, having powerfully liberated your inner hero to powerfully, cleverly, and adaptively break though here; you are unbeatable, you easily and forever vanquish all challenges before you as you are now and forever mightier than any challenge before you, most especially this test, a proof of how powerfully aligned and dynamic, how ready for anything you actually are. Rather than shrinking, you are the one who is the winner here, your empowerment and your thoughts expand, liberating your inner winner, inwardly and outwardly into the outside world around you, you feel and actually are strengthened, fortified, driven forward, bigger and better than any and all challenges before you, as you ambitiously take on and welcome any and all challenges, because you can, you do and you are driven and strengthened by the energy of each and every past victory, triumph, breakthrough and success you've ever had. Things you once considered a problem on now cleverly rethought to be a challenge, as you powerfully rise up to meet and beat, your mind so clear now, so precise and effective, you are easily remembering all the formulas, easy trusting your first impressions and answer, free of reading into anything, but easy able however to reason it out, as you now understand the lay of the land and the way the system works.

Yes, you are doing it; you are succeeding here and you are practically Divinely-guided, sure of yourself, you are failure-free, you have learned and now succeed, clear, sharp and focused, fearless and mighty, you personal inner power is back inside of you now and you are as a hero of olden times, rising to the top, and thriving, some might even say, this time is the charm, for it is and you are serene in your knowledge, knowing you are sure in having done the work and studies, actually knowing more than you realize, easily able to recall, perform and remember, just flowing on unbeatably, and like a mighty warrior or athlete, focused, in your zone here, rested, just a few minutes of Hypnotic rest the same as a few hours of powerful and life-changing sleep, you now and forever re-identified as a mighty and unbeatable success here, or simply just passing your test. This time is your time, you are sure, you are safe, you win, this is the time, you knew you'd do it, it is here, like you've already done it, it's yours now, because you knew you'd do it and you seize this moment.

Notice the soothing and calming, steadying rhythm of your breath relaxing you and focusing you with laser-beam-like precision, fortifying you, as you effectively and cleverly relax beyond any and all old barriers from the past, into a new and better chapter of your life, a breakthrough chapter of your life, where you achieve and are unbeatable, redefined as flexible and adaptive, rising up to successfully meet any and all challenges. The greater the challenge becomes, the more relaxed, confident and focused you are and you remain, unstoppably determined and ensured of unbeatable breakthrough, skillful success, sensing and feeling from deep inside foundationally restructured, confident, sharp, and clear. You are and you remain most assuredly clear, and whether you realize it or not, your now-always-working-in-your-favor, subconscious mind, is developing blockage-free strategies for success, inspirations, a building and budding can-do spirit, which unstoppably allows you to cleverly, easily, and dynamically break through here, while you are awake, while you are asleep, even while you are dreaming happy dreams, your whole focus driving you ultimately toward breakthrough and unbeatable success here. You now an unstoppable force of super-motivated ultimate success. You want this, you are doing and have done the studying and the work, your years of experience and expertise expertly guiding you as a harmony of heart and mind, a comfort, of precision and ease, are now most assuredly, liberating the ultimate success you now deserve to enjoy and now embrace it and make your own. As in previous chapters of your life, you may have once found excuses and reasons to avoid studying and taking the necessary steps; it is now time for you to take all of the necessary steps, to seize the moment, and give yourself the gift of success you now deserve to liberate, master, make your own and enjoy within each and every moment of your life. Of course you can and so you do, and so it is. Liberating future success bring it right here, into the right now. You effectively stepping up to seize this moment, making this success your own, embracing and activating this ultimately successful you, the you now are. All other challenges becoming easier for you, including not only studying for this or any test, but also the Series 63 and 24 tests as well.

Relax deeper and further and just imagine a time in your life, when you felt brimming with wonderful knowing and glowing confidence, self-assuredness, in a better rhythm and harmony, on top of the world, and just knowing, you were going to succeed and break through unbeatably as all things were working out in your favor unstoppably. See who you were then merging unstoppably with who you are now, becoming one with the feelings, sensations, and memories of that harmony, as the new you stepped forward to seize the moment confidently. In a knowing, glowing confidence, you are and you remain, liberating ultimate success. You're even looking forward to taking a deep breath and exhaling in and then hitting the button at the end of the test to embrace and recognize the well deserved success you have generated here, making all of this your very own, almost as if you've got the whole world in your back pocket, or perhaps a just sitting on top of the world or maybe just even having passed a test, with flying colors. Dynamically achieving these goals, one of your top priorities, you are most assuredly giving yourself a well deserved gift of success here, succeeding not only for yourself but for those in your life that you love as well, but you are especially succeeding for yourself here. You begin to trust in your instincts, what feels right first on the test is generally the correct answer; you feeling so carefully guided and precise, you're trusting in your first response free forever of ever over-analyzing any question, your first impression generally the correct one. You're trusting in this, and allowing it to work in your favor wonderfully, precisely, effectively and unbeatably. You are also relaxed and focused enough to understand that you are fully capable of reasoning out any more challenging questions that might arise, based upon your years of expertise, your vast amount of studying You understand the lay of the land, while being able to effectively reason out any and all potentially challenging questions on any test. You now permanently and forever, self-assured, self-confident, and effective and precise, with powerful better memory and recall, it all just seems to flow, in a brand new chapter of your life, breaking through, all things and any things that ever stood in your way, you now know, all challenges are easily mastered by you as you are rising to the top, unbeatable, super-focused, and determined to break through here. You begin to effectively refocus every thought, every feeling, every emotion, every action, and every reaction, to learn to relax while focusing upon, grasping and seize your will deserved success. You know a better life and a better way, failure-free, challenge-oriented, thriving, only learning or succeeding, these now your only options.

You begin to skillfully and dynamically create an improved, even masterpiece, of a life you deserve and now unbeatably create as an achiever, treating yourself better and wonderfully well, free forever from ever smoking cigarettes post-test, just as if you are forgiven, released, and healed, into a brand new chapter of your life, unbeatably one in which you are skillfully taking better care of yourself in each and every respect and regard, doing only the very best for yourself here. You believe and you achieve, and beyond belief and beyond faith you simply know; you're making this happen and it is yours right now unbeatably, truly, all steps necessary being taken, ultimate success and breakthrough options now yours magnificently. This time of course, you win!

## Learning Enhancement - Overcoming School Fears

Now relax even deeper and as you do, you imagine, notice or even know that a new confidence and a take-charge attitude of success is truly emerging from deep within you. And right now, you choose to rise above all limitations from your past and focus only on what's best for you, your future and your future limitless success. For beginning right now and for the rest of your life, you have truly decided to take charge of your life, to rise up and do what you know is really best for you, right now and in your future, bringing up and utilizing all of your inner power. You take charge and act confidently, and you always act and perform confidently, always taking charge and succeeding in your life, most especially in relation with learning and with school. You have come to a new realization today, that school trains your mind, expands your horizons, paves the way for your brightest future, allows you to truly rely on yourself, and allows you to really take care of yourself and to create the kind of financially secure future you deserve to have for yourself.

It really doesn't matter what your past emotional reactions to school were or what you once thought, because instead right now, each and every day, and in each and every aspect, you are determined to succeed. You are succeeding throughout all that is your life and succeeding most especially in terms of you laying down the foundation for your future success. You deeply and truly know, what other people may think of you is none of your business so you continue to build an even stronger foundation of self-reliance, self-confidence and self-esteem. The only opinion that really matters about you is yours and you begin each and every day and each and every night to like yourself, to trust in yourself, you take better care of yourself and you really begin to love and appreciate yourself, since your relationship with yourself is improving day by day, night by night and moment by moment. You really begin to appreciate your best qualities, because that really who you are You reidentify yourself as a person who is fair, honest, strong, clear, confident, motivated to succeed, energetic and very capable, because that's really who you are deep down inside and really what you are about. You can actually feel that old unwanted energies from your past, just lifting up, lifting up off and very far away from you. And what fills you up now is a feeling that I can do this, I have the determination to succeed because I accept all challenges and because I can and I am willing to impress myself, just to show myself that I can! And this makes you smile, both inside and out.

You relax right now, and you truly realize and recognize that you have never failed; you have either learned or you have succeeded, you are in fact now and forever failure free. You truly know that there is no such thing as failure, because in fact you always succeed. But right now, you are focused and you are succeeding, succeeding as never before, because you are confident, clear, sharp, focused and in your zone. You are empowered as never before, meeting, succeeding, and often exceeding all of your goals. All that you do and all that you actually are, is about success, your limitless success.

You see yourself, your forever emerging self-succeeding and passing, you now realize it, you know it, this is only getting stronger and better, for this is truly you. Taking a test in a relaxed, clear, confident manner, you are glowing both inside and out with confidence and total recall, in knowing and glowing confidence, you are feeling good all over in every way. You feel good physically, emotionally, mentally and even spiritually, because you are truly supported by your knowledge and your ability to reason. You are in fact supported by all that is your life. You feel strong, because you are strong, confident, focused and very capable. In a vision, think about seeing yourself, you've succeeded. See this future you, know this future you, this is who you are right now in the most important ways and in every potent and amazingly wonderful way. This you stands tall, is strong, and is smiling both on the inside and even on the outside, smiling with a warm self-assured glow of confidence and success, with a warm confident heart. You are successful, you have succeeded, there is only this option. And you right now, liberate this vision of you, right here, into the right now, from now on and from this moment forward, you are one with this vision, you are one with your success, and you are in harmony with yourself and all that you have learned and with all that you can reason. You are truly proud, confident, capable, comfortable, relaxed, strong, fearless, and courageous. You live and thrive in dynamic ways, forever free from all former symptoms of struggle, which are gone from you and your life, forever. You are now one with your future and you accept and own your limitless inner power and you really live your life, courageous, motivated, capable and able to remember and to think and reason, you are motivated, and you embrace success in the most amazing ways, for you realize you are the power in your life, and you utilize this power, in limitless ways, benefiting you and all whom you'll one day help, you use all that you are to open up in the most complete ways all that You are in each and even moment.

# Learning Enhancement - Passing an Oral Exam

You are finding yourself calm, balanced and relaxed, finding yourself slowly and deliberately deep breathing your way past any and all useless, empty and unwanted fear and doubt, into greater and greater states of relaxation and flowing skillful success, even without realizing it, most especially whenever you need it most in an exam situation. In fact, all week, any week, most especially just before your exam, you are calm, balanced and relaxed, trusting in your life, trusting in your skill, trusting in your knowledge and embracing your success, making success your very own, as all correct, needed and in-demand information is just easily flowing from your mind, as needed, through your words, thoughts and expressions, in correct, flowingly adaptive and in very precise amounts. So when it's time to take and then master your exam, you are solidly and adaptively there, thoughts flowing and fluid, adaptive and precise, knowing all that you need to, performing with skill, pose, ease, perseverance, determination and success. In fact, all of those who are present are there to support you and are rooting for your success, and truly urging and encouraging you onward to the glory of your success. They are on your side, urging you into greater and greater levels of success; you are embracing your success, you are making it your own right now.

Your breath and breathing patterns are calm, deep and steady. You are calm, balanced and relaxed, feeling so very comfortable, so right in your success building and you are creating your perfect power zone, easily and successfully being able, through correct mental and mind associations, memory patterns, inspirations and activations, to be clear, precise and able to recall and remember, expertly able to understand the system and to reason out any and all correct answers to any question or case, in slow, clear, deliberate and precise fashion, just getting it done properly and in your own perfection.

You trust in your life, trusting in your abilities, remembering and recalling easily all that you've studied, as you remember, recall and perform amazingly. You are feeling dynamic, rising to the top, fearless, bold and courageous, activating the feelings, energies, strengths and right actions of every past victory, triumph, breakthrough and success you've ever had, feeling truly mighty in the face of any and all challenges, problem-free, challenge-oriented, blockage-free, freely flowing ever onward and even feeling unstoppable, even looking forward to the experience, your chance to shine through, having done the work, having had years of experience and now liberating your well deserved reward of your success, claiming it, making it your very own, right here, right now, presenting the case to the examiner clearly, fear-free, body and emotions powerfully calm and working in your favor, motivated, at just the right mental and verbal pace. Even if you might not be completely sure of the correct answer, you are firmly, foundationally and truly remaining at ease, able to reason it out, by your understanding of the system and absolutely ready to take on the next challenge, in a calm and paced manner, rising to the top, relating to the examiner as a colleague, just as if you are pleasantly giving or hosting a consultation, only allowing your very best and most confident self to shine through, dynamically, sparklingly and brilliantly. You are calm, you are balanced, you are relaxed; you remain calm, you remain balanced, you remain relaxed, doing all that it takes, whether you realize it or not, you are speaking deliberately, clearly and slowly, in bold, precise, confident ease; easily liberating and any all victory, triumph, breakthrough and success, memory, method, recall and reasoning ability, with skill, confidence, poise and ease, making these moments your very own, in truly and even surprisingly powerful and skillful ways, impressing and amazing everyone, most especially yourself, feeling a warm and confident glow inside and out, from your heart and mind, getting all that it takes, done adeptly and successfully, in rewarding and powerful ways.

# Learning Enhancement - Passing Tests and Exams

Your mind is now open and you are open to new and more powerful possibilities, more and more both you and your mind are now open to limitless possibilities of success. Yes, you can succeed, you can thrive, you will succeed, you will thrive, you've done your work, even better than you realize and recognize that you are supported from your very powerful and dynamic subconscious mind, the automatic part of your mind, is storing all of the needed necessary information, that you need for you to relax, recall, perform and to powerfully succeed. And as you relax, your mind is open, clear, very deeply relaxed, sharply focused and open to have easy access to any and all information you might require, easily accessing all clever and creative thinking and reasoning patterns you might need. You know and trust in the fact, that you deserve to pass, you can, you will and as an important gift to yourself and of limitless benefit to others in your future, you realize that you can relax into passing your exam, and that you truly deserve to pass. You deeply and truly recognize, you deserve to pass and you will by relaxing and recalling and remembering and creatively reasoning, utilizing the logic of the system you've learned, you pass and succeed, with poise, ease and grace. You easily live all of these truths. And as you relax even deeper, you feel so comfortable, so peaceful, so at one with this, you are actually beginning to feel completely unstoppable. You are completely willing to put aside any and all things you once had used to stand in your way of this limitless success, you've relaxed out of that and into a new and better way of living and succeeding. You are right now and you remain, calm, relaxed and you recognize, you are prepared. You are talented, you relax, and you always allow yourself to mentally step back a bit and surrender to the fact, that your mind is always working in the most beneficial ways, always revealing all of the correct information and best impulses, always brilliantly allowing whatever might be needed to come to the forefront of your thoughts, as you might need it, with complete ease and success.

You know you've done the learning, all the work, heard what has been taught and you realize and deeply recognize that you actually really know more than you even thought. So your mind operates precisely, effectively and successfully, amazing and impressing everyone, most especially even you. One day very soon, perhaps even later today, you'll find you've passed! It might be that you go to your mailbox, you see an envelope, results from your test, your official notification. You open it. You've passed! These results are an extension of how much you are willing to give to yourself, to benefit yourself, to take care of yourself and brighten your future, in the most beneficial ways. Your passing score is a powerful part of how much better each and every day and night you are taking care of yourself, allowing only the most beneficial improvements in your life to become a part of your world. Truly, in this and every moment, you are making your life, a place of peace, a place of joy and beneficial support, creating the masterpiece of a successful life you deserve. Congratulations! You succeed.

## Learning Enhancement – Passing the Police Promotion Exam

You are filled with substantial resolve and self-assurance regarding the upcoming exam; you are in fact truly feeling fine, confident and secure with a great and growing sense of talent, ability, memory and recall. You are finding newer and better ways of being motivated. It's just like tapping into the memories and energies of a past time when you took charge, thrived and succeeded. You are now creating an easy time of focus, comfort and success for yourself by concentrating on the material, which you are reading and enjoying. You are so motivated, so focused, so laser-beam like precise, in ever thought, feeling and action that you effectively take. You are seeking new reasons to study and succeed, for yourself, for your family and for your friends, most especially for yourself, as you deserve to, focusing on the goal, winning the richly deserved prize, easily able to make time to concentrate and study, finding yourself now easily creating the time by doing all that it takes. You are feeling truly unstoppable. You are feeling so energetic, so upbeat, so motivated, so ambitious, so easily able to succeed and even more so, just as soon as you begin to study the material. You know want to take your exam, an opportunity to shine. You are succeeding and passing, you are truly interested. In reality, you are deserving, motivated and doing all that it honestly takes to make the promotion list, you are a winner, you are unstoppable, activating the energy of every past victory, triumph and success you've even had or imagined, feeling truly, in reality and in fact, in substantial ways, you are becoming one with those inspirational energies that drive you forward to an impressive and amazing success, your success, this time, right here and right now. Your success, so well deserved, so well earned, is yours now by all that you do, not because I say so, because it's the nature of your own powerful and unstoppable and successfully powerful and inspired mind, calm, balanced, supportive emotions, energized by the power of your eternal spirit to do so, now truly seeing yourself and reidentifying yourself and the (name rank- e.g. – Lieutenant) you deserve to become, live to be and now unstoppably liberate into the reality of your life, right here and right now. You are there and this is yours right now. You are so very easily motivated now and becoming so very interested in all that you have to learn, spurred on by your own passionate desire to learn and to prosper, to thrive and to unstoppably succeed for your family, for your loved ones but most especially for yourself. You find yourself easily setting aside and creating the time it takes to succeed, all the time just seems to be there for you to do all that it takes right now. You bring your study goals down to levels of ridiculous ease, stay, just going on to study for just 2 or 3 minutes, almost like you where just wondering about something you'd like to look up. But then most often, you are easily exceeding those goals whenever you need to, as you study onward. You are strong, focused, clear, procrastination free, active, super motivated, sharp, laser-beam like, sharply focused, ready to win and excel, ready to claim your prize. You take a better pace, you learn, you read, you remember and recall, easily and successfully doing all that it honestly takes, skillfully, absorbing, remembering, truly enjoying the process of enriching yourself, taking your time to get to the end, easily and effectively observing and remembering all and any of the key points. You are easily finding newer and better ways to rise up to meet and excel at any challenge, including facing down any presented written questions, as you rise up and conquer them. You are now forgiving and releasing the past and any and all of its uncomfortable blockages, you are feeling so very calm, peaceful, at ease, so very sure of yourself and all of the work you have done and are continuing to do, so in your zone, free flowing, almost serene. You are easily allowing and trusting in new and better first impressions that just freely flow. You are understanding the answers and now dynamically activating better memory and recall, in laser-beam like precision and also with great confidence, amazing skill and effectiveness, in a calm yet determined manner, activating an understanding of the system and how it works, effectively allowing your years of knowledge and experience to allow you to correctly identify any and all answers that you might need to reason out or reason to, even if it might seem unfamiliar, as you are glowing in a new, better and profound confidence. You are so focused, so in your zone, whether at home and when in class, so upbeat, so ready for this, so excited to bring yourself and the ones you love, the kind of success you deserve to enjoy and now liberate, bursting forth into your life and into their lives right now. You are calm, taking the test like a pro, like a master, calm, balanced and relaxed, tapping into all of your very best moments of wonderfully relaxed success. In fact, you are feeling so absolutely determined to succeed by doing all that it honestly takes to thrive and succeed, so peaceful and ready, you are feeling on top of the world, truly now enjoying this experience, making the most of it, as it allows you to make the most of your life and enjoyably and easily, powerfully, readily, confidently and clearly, you succeed, tapping into the energy of all past victories, triumphs and success, you are in fact an unstoppable force.

## Learning Enhancement – Passing the Police Sergeant's Test

You are powerfully finding newer, more interesting ways to find things fascinating, taking a genuine interest and effectively finding newer pathways of easily concentrating on any and all certain subjects. You are fascinated and interested in doing all that it takes to succeed, free and unblocked, so right now you do! You have made up your powerfully and highly logical and effective mind to find newer and more effective ways of overcoming old habits like procrastination; in fact, you'll find yourself easily and effectively focused, paced, motivated while creating newer cycles and rhythms for skill improvement, memory retention and recall than you ever did in the past: strong, effective and sure of yourself now and into the future in the forever lasting and only-getting-stronger chapter of your life. Your memory, ability to recall are now activating, almost as if someone from, deep, deep inside of you has thrown a switch, reset a dial, turned up a thermostat or activated a master computer of some sort, easily allowing you to perform, remember, recall, understand, trust in your first instinct to answer any and all questions, even plot out beyond what you've studied the correct answers; like you understand the lay of the land, allowing any and all memory to flow smoothly, evenly, effectively, correctly and precisely, in the right and correct fashion, as you win, thrive and succeed, not only for yourself, but for those whom you love, but most especially for yourself. And like a well-paced, long distance, world class marathon champion, you are using the power it takes to thrive, to effectually accomplish, and get to the end, with interest and fascination, effectiveness and ease. Just like when studying, when your desire to succeed, coupled with your passionate desire to get ahead, works in effective combination to focus your body, emotions and mind, guided unstoppably by your spirit, to allow you to thrive and succeed with skill and interest at this, proudly tapping into the very best motivation and skill from each and every one of your past moments of victory, triumph, breakthrough and success. Yes, you can do it! Just like others before you have, as you have effectively tapped into all of their skill in the most highly effective ways.

## Learning Enhancement - Series 6 NASD (Stocks & Securities) License

Your powerful and always-working-in-your-favor mind is now confidently and unstoppably working upon highly effective ways of creating precise and proficient ways of succeeding at the tasks at hand, allowing you to confidently succeed. Your mind is powerfully storing, sorting and easily and effectively retrieving any and all necessary information as needed, whenever needed. You are also powerfully understanding and acclimating yourself to the lay of the land, so you will be easily able to reason out any and all needed information. You are finding and easily providing better, more enhanced and easier methods of retaining product information and converting it to knowledge, by relaxing and allowing it to just come to you, after just one of 2 deep and slow, steady, relaxation breaths. Your mind is now open and clear, absolutely ready to understand what is being said whenever you read didactic texts, truly enjoying the experience, unblocked and free thinking. Your focus is precise, laser-beam-like focused; you are so easily focusing on the task at hand, distraction-free, even empowered and strengthened in places where distractions once arose. Your mind is now unstoppably working in your favor, as you are easily applying the knowledge to all you do, gain and glean, both correctly and effectively. You are finding and creating newer and better ways of simplifying key terms to make them more digestible for comprehension, even using memory aids, just like being back in school, to make all things work out powerfully and fulfillingly in your favor.

## Learning Enhancement - Studies and Homework

You know you are a smart student, but now even better, in addition to this, you'll want and need to be more responsible with any and all homework and any and all assignments that are given, completing them with ease, precision and clarity. You now find you are powerfully believing in yourself, since you know that by recognizing, efficiently utilizing and activating your very best talents and abilities, you can effectively allow yourself to do anything you need to do or get done. You are absolutely and unstoppably determined to succeed in life, doing all of the correct and honest things that it takes to succeed. You are set aside time for what you are really and truly interested in, doing all that it takes to believe in yourself, trusting in yourself, easily overcoming your shyness, you are feeling bold, driven, focused, sharp, easily able to communicate and ready to get the job done. You find newer, better and more precise ways to study, to get the job done, easily able to succeed, easily, successfully and correctly in precise ways able to get the job done to improve your study habits and boost your grades. You are feeling more and more sure of yourself, relaxing into greater and greater levels of success, becoming outgoing and succeeding more smoothly, overcoming laziness and doing all that it honestly takes to thrive and succeed. You are easily able to focus on your studies, making, creating and finding the time to study as many questions as necessary even finding the time to easily and effectively study the _____ (amount of) questions per day required to pass the _____ EXAM. You are creating a foundation and a base of strength, you are creatively inspired to create thriving success, in spite of and because of any and all challenges you once may or may not have had to pass, you even thrive and amazingly, unstoppably succeed. Your goals come down to levels of simplistic and ridiculous ease, as your mind is now active, thriving in precise and functionally correct ways and expanding, as you find newer and better ways to thrive and succeed. You are finding newer, enhanced and powerfully effective ways of setting aside time for study and committing to a time frame for study. Relax and breathe, your biggest strength is having complete and total devotion, even inspired and limitless commitment to studying for the test. A mountain now becomes an easily surmountable hill for you, as you commit yourself truly and relax your way into total focus and total concentration, right there in your zone, in harmony, tapping into the energy of those of who have successfully gone before you and passed. Their habits become your habits; their triumphs, breakthroughs, victories and successes, now becoming and remaining your triumphs, breakthroughs, victories and successes. So you are feeling this new and unstoppable energy, build, building, building, it's building like a giant reservoir of unstoppable, commitment, a strong foundation of strength, courage, drive, determination and passion as you take this new, reinvented, more correct and highly effective roadway to success. You easily find that both your mind and your powerful, highly effective and now supercharged subconscious mind can, will and in fact does understand all that it need to, creating better memory, method and recall. The past does not equal the present nor the future, your future is one of ever growing improvement, success via knowledge, via commitment, creating ease, precision and unstoppable success. This is a different day and time, and this time you will succeed. You feel and you are truly and powerfully free of any and all negative past experiences, forever free of stumbling, failure-free. You now effectively either learn or succeed, or just even thrive; all past challenges are now polishing experiences, and your light of knowledge and wisdom shines ever true. All of this forever and most especially whenever your repeat this enjoyable exercise, fosters you into remaining crystal clear and sharp during the exam with 100% recall and retention. You stay focused and free of any and all distractions, hindering tendencies and blockages from the past, easily finding yourself coming back to centeredness even if you are interrupted. In fact you are becoming laser-beam like precise, balanced and relaxed, finding newer and better ways of scheduling, as your ability to concentrate just builds and builds. You are really feeling so calm, so relaxed, so motivated, finding newer, better and easier ways to organize and concentrate, especially when studying. All of this is truly paving the way to a brighter future and life, the kind of life you deserve and now effectively create. You are easily able to focus upon and to absorb, anything and everything you need to, developing a new and powerful interest in the work you are accomplishing, staying right there and succeeding with ease and success, struggle free, wandering free, struggle free, so focused, so calm so powerful and so relaxed, while at home or in class. You are truly finding that your correct response to any and all stress is to relax your way out of it and into a brighter, happier, healthier and more prosperous way of life, even if you are feeling stressedout or any discomfort, you simply find newer, better and more precise ways to rise above old blockages and succeed. You powerfully reset you mind now, correctly thinking, "I can do this, so I focus, I succeed and I do." You begin to re-identify yourself and begin to re-think, truly coming to know as a deep and profound personal truth, "when I am studying or in school, I am always finding newer and better, more successful ways of creating a new interest or focus on what I'm doing." And as your stress levels stay in check and after a few short deep and steady breaths, you even find that can effectively can relax your way through anything and everything, succeeding at any time you need to. You are focused and remembering things easily, you feel enlightened, calm, smooth thinking, peaceful and serene. You are easily able to concentrate and even better, easily able to focus, becoming fully functional and balanced. You are anxiety-free, feeling the stress and discomfort levels fall, finding yourself easily able to slow down and calm down, easily regaining balance, purpose and calm, peaceful and focus. You are easily thriving, succeeding, doing all that it takes and you win! It feels so great!

## Learning Enhancement- Fire-Fighters Promotion Exam

In this moment of truly deep and profound rest and relaxation, you are inspired and have come to truly know, now only better and better, that truly, absolutely and surely, right now begins a brand new and better chapter of your life. Gone are the blockage and frustrating ways of the old; gone are the ways of blockage and hindrance; gone forever is any and all thoughts and feelings, responses and actions, even reactions and adaptations that ever stood in your way as this newer and breakthrough moment of your life now begins. You know, it's almost like someone from deep, deep inside of you has reset a switch, a dial, a computer or a thermostat of some kind, or simply just opened a valve of knowledge from deep, deep inside you somewhere, allowing a newer, brighter and better you to emerge unstoppably right now, most especially in spite of and because of older and unpleasant moments, as you are just powerfully and vigorously flowing unstoppably beyond any and all blockages with the skills and talent of a pro. In fact, you are now, blockage-free, skilled and just doing better and better; in fact really, you are doing just fine, doing all that it takes and getting it done. You've always known it was time to step up and move into the next echelon in your life, to move upward and onward, seize these moments of your well-deserved success and make your promotion reality, not only for yourself but for your family and those you love and those you shall one day command and guide, and save the lives of – so even better, right now is that moment, a moment of power and a moment to seize.

It's time to step up and to take charge and to find inspirations and reasons to do anything and everything it honestly takes to break through and put all other business and distractions of old aside and study, blockage-free, barrier- free and so you do. You are now thinking about feeling those inspirations, feelings and aspirations of every moment in your life when you made success your very own, feeling that energy and right now experiencing only your very best and most shining moments in your life; in fact, truly, the energy of every past victory, triumph, breakthrough and success you've ever had is upon you now, unstoppably and undeniably activating the energy of your mighty inner hero, the part of you that knows no doubts, no bounds and no limits and just breaks through here, right now and unstoppably, truly the part of you that is fully capable of saving children from a car wreck or a fire, and perhaps has, to mightily surface here. You now, right here, better, redefined, that old fogginess from the old and past chapter of your life, just lifting up and off of you, gone and gone forever. You are clear, sharp and optimistic, disciplined and interested, you now, redefined and are now easily and dynamically overpowering and showing down the ways of old, bigger and mightier than any old, useless and now forever finished ways of procrastination from the previous chapter of your life, making and investing the time in your future and your success right here and right now, to study and make and take any and all strides necessary to unbeatably accomplish your goals and succeed here with better memory and recall, inspired, guided and understanding and a knowledge of the lay-of-the-land and the way any and all materials and systems just seem to logically lay out, and to just break through here and win, succeeding and passing, like it's already happened and you've already done what it takes, stepping up to the plate and making it yours, because it's time to do so and you are the one right now, right here to do it, well and you are doing it unbeatably. You just like an invincible and unstoppable test-taking pro, what they know, you know; how they work, you work; how they pace themselves, you pace yourself, in the calm and empowered ways, rhythms and strides of a master test-taker and feel and have come to truly know you are so in your zone, like a hero of old, you are practically Divinely-guided to unbeatable success, inspired, strong, creative, and adaptable, seizing the moments here, making them yours, feeling calm and wonderful; success and all that entails is now yours. You make and take the time and study, because you want to, truly interested and succeeding here in even surprising ways. All things you need to know seem easily at your disposal, at your fingertips, at your dynamic command; you so very calm and deeply breathing soothing and focusing breath; all of this just illuminates, unblocks and frees you, just guides your way, unblocks and unlocks your inner wisdom and real knowledge before, during and even afterwards.

Whether it's any topic at all, you so ready to take this on, you so prepared, doing and having done all that it takes; it feels like the whole regimen is in your back pocket, or you are just on top of the World, or you are just very simply succeeding at being and remaining interested in recalling, remembering and performing and at optimized and peak efficiency, even doing surprisingly well, trusting in your first answers, free of over-thinking, getting it all skillfully and correctly done, fulfilled, completion! Whether it's anything, you unbeatably rising up to meet and beat any challenge: most especially: incident command manual system, just succeeding and breaking through, knowing your way and just getting it done; collapse of burning buildings, you are just succeeding and breaking through, glowing in knowing confidence; fire / emergency size up and evaluation, just succeeding and breaking through, understanding and skilled, from any and all past moments in class and at work; fire / emergency management: procedures, tactics and strategies, just succeeding and breaking through, with skill and ease, calmly, easily and unbeatably, paced and relaxing beyond old barriers and blockages; communications, just succeeding and breaking through, relaxed, calm and in so very much your zone, focused and just doing fine; fire prevention, just succeeding and breaking through, with skill and ease, soothing breaths; personnel management and supervision, your wise and knowing inner leader of men, now activated; cfr, just succeeding and breaking through, with able and comfortable, emergency response plans, creatively and adaptively; your knowledge from years of experiences with hazardous materials and how to deal with them; coordinating training bulletins, regulations, as you skillfully and decisively, make sure and insure to budget your time, at just the right pace, as all of this is just seemingly yet amazingly and dynamically coming together, just the right rhythm time to have sufficient amount of time for "in- basket," organizing your in-basket materials, allowing you to take the time to get the answers right, just like you've been doing this for years. In fact, you are and find it just right, relaxing before, during and after the test and while driving / traveling, so in your zone, so focused, deeply and soothingly powerful and steady breaths, guide you way had still you, even making you feel upbeat and able; you just know, this is your time and your time is a break-through, your time,

This time, you creatively, honesty and adaptively and fluidly succeed. You now know, yes truly know, you are reconditioned, re-calibrated, reset, and glowing, flowing and breaking through! You are surer of this than any moment in your life, all of this just getting easier and better on each and every breath and heart-beat.

# Learning Enhancement- LSATS

You are readily and powerfully allowing your powerful and always active, now working only in your favor, subconscious mind to easily attain, remember and recall, retain and deliver all things that you read, hear, see or feel, verbatim and with great speed and accuracy, as if someone from deep, deep inside of you has truly, effectively, cleverly and dynamically, pushed a button or has activated a switch, a dial, a computer or even turned up a thermostat of some kind, easily allowing you access to any and all information that you might need at any and all given times or at some point in your life. Any and all information just seems to be flowing from your always-active subconscious mind right into your conscious mind, whenever you need it, for easy and effective access. As this is done, your energy upgrades to the next and most potently powerful level and as your energy brightens, as you brighten, every bit of the old and unwanted fogginess lifts and is drawn away, just like when the sun so very easily washes away the morning fog and dew in its golden-white brilliance, as you truly and unstoppably become and unstoppably remain and truly and effectively are upgraded, brightened; each and every one of your thoughts, each and every one of your memories, and each and every bit of your recall, intensified and enlightened. Relaxed, calm and empowered you are, you feel, you become and you remain, most especially just after a few slow and deep, soothing and steady breaths, as any and all stress, doubt or uncomfortable patterns of the past simply lift off and vanish from you, whenever you need this. You allow a moment for pause; you stop trying so hard; you simply just relax, from down deep down inside, from the very core of whom you are, as all necessary information comes back to you, flowing every onwards as needed, anytime, any place, anywhere, and how you need it, always trusting your first instinct, in the most precise, intense, fluidly adaptive and most correct of ways. Trusting in this and allowing it, you easily and dynamically succeed, easily rising to the very top, happy and smiling on the inside. Deep within the recesses of your powerful and dynamic mind is everything you've ever heard, learned, thought about, felt or remembered. Your mind is more powerful than any and all of the very best and most powerful computers ever invented. Any and all information is easily accessible; your mind, relaxed, ready and open to recall, remember, perceive, achieve any and all things you require of it. While you are awake, while you are asleep, even while you are dreaming, your powerful and always active mind is now creating, whether you realize it or not, new and better mental associations, effective strategies, and even pathways, for you to learn, recall, remember and optimize performance from, brilliantly, adaptively, fluidly, clearly and precisely, in even, balanced, and dynamically effective ways, amazing and impressing everyone, most especially you, and you come to trust in this, rely on this, activating only your very best, at any time you need it. You are so sure of yourself and your ever increasing success, that you easily remember, retain, recall and perform your very best throughout all the subjects you've studied, easily able to remember all the things you've learned, in correct and proper speed, just the right rhythm and pace, like a champion marathon runner's precise pace. All things are just seemingly flowing easily and free of effort, just flowing and thriving, in proper proportion, your mind functioning like a fine-tuned machine, as you are precisely and correctly completing any and all diagrams and logic games, with dynamically activated confidence and brilliance. All of this you are taking in stride and at just the right pace, trusting in your knowledge and skillfully succeeding, unstoppably succeeding, reconditioned at a higher functioning rate of breaking through, at just the proper pace. Your mind is so very, very clear, functioning like a fine-tuned machine, active, at ease, articulate, clear, calm, unstoppably effective and relaxed, so in your zone, dynamically and surprisingly able to absorb the meaning/main idea of the readings. You are free of over-thinking and over-analyzing your answers, reading and comprehending clearly, carefully and precisely, powerfully trusting in your first and best impression, while skillfully navigating any and all questions, even trick questions, with knowing and glowing inner and outer confidence, calm, relaxed and determined, stress-free. You are comfortable, rested, super-dynamic, well-rested, vigorous, lively and super-focused, truly and sincerely trusting in all that you have studied and accomplished, skillfully relaxing beyond any and all barriers from the past chapter of your life. In this chapter, you are liberated, safe, blockage-free, and succeeding, powerfully and unstoppably breaking through, RIGHT NOW, that you know and all that is even in the back of your mind, now easily graspable, and functional, all things at your disposal, working in your favor as needed.

All of your powerful mind and consciousness are now powerfully being reconditioned to respond in clear, active and precise measure, always achieving optimum results. This powerful mind of yours is even now working in effective and dynamic ways to further be able to recall people, names, faces, and dates of events as needed, historically and otherwise. You can and you are able to read books, and other forms of literature, with relative speed while accurately retaining the information presented; your precise mind storing any and all modes necessary for you to liberate and to then achieve greatness in all that you are focusing upon. So successful, so sure of yourself, you are on top of the world and doing all that it takes to honestly succeed; all thoughts, feelings and actions you might feel, think about, respond to or adapt to, now only working in your favor, creating a limitless tidal wave of ever increasing success, effectively washing away any and all past blockages, easily forgiving them and any and all negative judgments, on each and every breath you take and on each and every beat of your heart. Just like remembering a song, or a melody, you are easily able to recall all that you need to, sure of your ever-increasing success, you are unstoppably improving, as your life is now improving in your favor.

# Learning Enhancement- NASD 7 Success

You find yourself mentally peaceful, serenely relaxed, comfortable, as a knowing and glowing confidence energy is powerfully and dynamically spreading throughout your heart and your mind, and throughout your body, and beyond; you are glowing on, feeling wonderful, in this time of calm and knowing glowing confidence, gentle yet all pervasive ease, forever freed of ever being stressed over the test. As a matter of fact, you are almost angry, rising to the top and have powerfully liberated your inner hero to powerfully, cleverly, and adaptively break though here. You are unbeatable, you easily and forever rise to the very top and vanquish all challenges before you, as you are now and forever mightier than any challenge before you, most especially this test, a proof of how powerfully aligned and dynamic you are. Rather than shrinking, you are the one who is the winner here, liberating your inner winner, out and out into the outside world around you. Strengthened, fortified, driven forward and bigger and better than any and all challenges before, you take on and welcome any and all challenges because you can, you do and you are strengthened by the energy of each and every past victory, triumph, breakthrough and success you've ever had. Things you once considered a problem, now a challenge you powerfully rise up to meet and beat; your mind so clear now, so precise, you are easily remembering all the formulas, easily trusting your first answer, free of reading into anything, but easy able, however, to reason it out, as you now understand the lay of the land and the way the system works. Yes, you are doing it; you are succeeding here and you are practically Divinely-guided; sure of yourself, you are failure free. You have learned and now succeed, clear, sharp and focused, fearless and mighty. Your personal inner power is back inside of you now; and you are, as a hero of olden times, rising to the top, and thriving. Some might even say, the third time is the charm, for it is and you are serene in your knowledge, knowing you are sure in having done the work and studies, actually knowing more than you realize, easily able to recall, perform and remember, just flowing on unbeatably, and like a mighty warrior or athlete, focused, in your zone here, rested, just a few minutes of Hypnotic rest the same as a few hours of powerful and life-changing sleep. You are right and only getting stronger, more adaptive, and fluid, more successfully, both now and forever, re-identified as a mighty and unbeatable success here, or you are simply just passing your test. This time is your time, you are sure, you are safe, you win. This is the time, you knew you'd do it, it is here, like you've already done it. It's yours now, because you knew you'd do it, and you seize this moment.

# Learning Enhancement- Passing the Bar Exam

You are breathing deeply, calmly and slowly before you take any exam, most especially the Bar Exam. You are just relaxing and releasing to be at the very top of your game, trusting in the fact that you've done the work, and you are truly and absolutely confident and absolutely ready to rise to the top right here and now and be at only your very best, trusting in your knowledge, in your inner knowing, activating wisdom, even easily able to rationally or instinctively reason or reason out answers, while trusting your first instincts while allowing yourself to flourish, as if almost Divinely guided. As easily as something might be forgotten, it can be remembered. You are easily allowing yourself Ah-ha moments of remembering, recalling and activating memory and knowledge while allowing yourself to succeed. You are ready to win; you are ready to thrive. You are ready to completely rise to the occasion and win most unstoppably, almost as if you've already done this before, just liberating your future success into the right here and now, and you are just easily doing this again, now feeling and knowing that before, during and after the exam, you are braced up, strengthened, fortified, motivated and driven forward by each and every past moment of victory, breakthrough, triumph and success you've ever had. So right now, you are easily rising to the top, clear, confident and strong; for when you trust in your life, when you know the truth of your success, beyond any and all limitations, as you do now, you are unstoppable, unbeatable and a conqueror over this and any and all challenges, most especially this exam, each and every morning, afternoon and evening, more and more fluid, effective, efficient and adaptive, upon each and every calming, soothing breath and on each and every steady heartbeat. You breathe deeply and regularly, and think to yourself, truly knowing as a deep and powerfully personal truth, I know the truth, so I am relaxed, I am calm, I know this - I unstoppably succeed. Like a mighty river flowing powerfully down the side of a mountain in the springtime, which easily flows over any and all obstacles, you are flowing every onward into the rest of your life and in powerful, precise and glowing effective success. Just like a boulder in that stream, you are being polished by all your knowledge and experience. Your focus just becomes easier and easier, better and better, with laser-beam-like precision, while energetic or most especially when you are or might be tired, at the beginning, end or even most especially during the middle of the exam, you are active and energetic, ready to win here, seizing the day, making it your own, effectively and actively taking on all challenges and insured by those whom have gone before you, almost like what they know, you know, so you know! Just a deep and soothing breath brings your energy back up and with your ability to skillfully perform now fully active; your memory, recall and glowing and warming self-confidence are super-activated, almost as if someone from deep, deep inside of you has activated a switch, a dial, a computer or a thermostat of some kind, easily allowing any and all knowledge to rise to the top, whenever you need it, and it's easy, not because I say so, but because it's the nature of your own powerful and flexible, truly successful mind and spirit to do so, so you just do! You are sure of yourself, finding newer and better ways to thrive and succeed, almost as if a blanket of invisible calmness is luxuriously embracing you, allowing you to be, to become and to remain, calm, balanced and relaxed, truly and easily confident and trusting in all that you know and in all that you've done to skillfully and effectively succeed. Your ability to trust and succeed is now active. You've activated your inner hero to come out and to win unstoppably, effectively and easily, willing to be sure of yourself. Sure of yourself, you are an unbeatable and unstoppable force. You are sure and certain that all things are working out in your favor. I wonder if you even yet realize how easy this is going to be for you? As you are now easily smiling on the inside and on the outside - glowing and brimming with confidence and ability. Even if tired, you are now gaining the ability to focus on and to see the important details in any and all questions. You are relaxing through any and all obstacles, taking your time, finding your pace, leading the way, wining your race. You are doing it, you've done it, you are winning at this, seeing in your mind's eye that you've done it, feeling just as you would after knowing you've passed, making this well- deserved victory your very own, moving into a brighter and better day and life for you and all of those whom you love, but most especially for yourself; you win and win glowingly, brilliantly, and powerfully.

## Learning Enhancement- Passing the MCATS

You are readily and powerfully allowing your powerful and always active subconscious mind to easily attain, remember and recall, retain and deliver all things that you read, hear, see or feel, verbatim and with great speed and accuracy, as if someone from deep, deep inside of you has truly, effectively, cleverly and dynamically, pushed a button or has activated a switch, a dial, a computer or even turned up a thermostat of some kind, easily allowing you access to any and all information that you might need at any and all given times or at some point in your life. Any and all information just flowing from your always-active subconscious mind right into your conscious mind, whenever you need it, for easy and effective access. As this is done, your energy upgrades to the next and most potently powerful level and as your energy brightens, as you brighten, every bit of the old and unwanted fogginess lifts and is drawn away, just like when the sun so very easily washes away the morning fog and dew in its golden-white brilliance, as you truly and unstoppably become and unstoppably remain and truly and effectively are upgraded, brightened, each and every one of your thoughts, each and every one of your memories and each and every bit of your recall intensified, and enlightened. Relaxed, calm and empowered you are, you feel, you become and you remain, most especially just after a few slow and deep, soothing and steady breaths, as any and all stress, doubt or uncomfortable patterns of the past simply lift off and vanish from you, whenever you need this. You allow a moment for pause, you stop trying so hard, you relax down deep and all necessary information comes back to you, anytime, anyplace, anywhere, and how you need it, always trusting your first instinct, in the most precise, intense, fluidly adaptive and most correct of ways, trusting in this and allowing it, you easily and dynamically succeed, easily rising to the very top, happy and smiling on the inside.

Deep within the recesses of your powerful and dynamic mind is everything you've ever heard, learned, thought about, felt or remembered. Your mind, more powerful than any and all of the very best and most powerful computers ever invented. Any and all information is easily accessible, your mind, relaxed, ready and open to recall, remember, perceive, achieve any and all things you require of it. While you are awake, while you are asleep, even while you are dreaming, your powerful and always active mind is now creating, whether you realize it or not, new and better mental associations, effective strategies, and even pathways, for you to learn, recall, remember and optimize performance from, brilliantly, adaptively, fluidly, clearly and precisely, in even, balanced, and dynamically effective ways, amazing and impressing everyone, most especially you, and you come to trust in this, rely on this, activating only your very best, at any time you need it. You are so sure of yourself and your ever increasing success, that you easily remember, retain, recall and perform your very best throughout all the subjects you've studied, easily able to remember all the things you've learned scientifically, including (name subjects) Biology, Calculus, Chemistry, Genetics, Physics, Anatomy / Physiology (starting from year X, almost like you are jumping over recent years and bridging the gap most effectively), and in all other areas, all of your consciousness now powerfully being reconditioned to respond in clear, active and precise measure, always achieving optimum results. This powerful mind of yours is even now working in effective and dynamic ways to further be able to recall people's names, faces, and dates of events and numeric configurations, historically and otherwise. You can and you are able to read books, and other forms of literature with relative speed while accurately retaining the information presented, your precise mind storing any and all modes necessary, for you to liberate and to then achieve greatness in all that you are focusing upon, so successful, so sure of yourself, you are on top of the world and doing all that it takes to honestly succeed, all thoughts, feelings and actions you might feel, think about, respond to or adapt to, now only working in your favor, creating a limitless tidal wave of ever increasing success, effectively washing away any and all past blockages, easily forgiving them and any and all negative judgments, in each and every breath you take and in each and every beat of your heart. Just like remembering a song, or a melody, you are easily able to recall all that you need to, sure of your ever-increasing success, you are unstoppably improving, as your life is now improving in your favor.

# Learning Enhancement: Better Studying, Testing & Exam Results

You find yourself just simply and effectively pacing yourself with proper rhythm and speed, finding your own natural pace and just taking the perfect and the proper winning, self-assured pace that allows you to always unbeatably win the race, this race, making it your very own. Slow and steady, in just the right rhythm, having all the time you need, just like everyone else who has succeeded before you; what they've done, you successfully do, and it's easy. You are finding this easy; you trust in life; you have the time you need and know you've done the work, memory, recall and understanding here; it's just so simple and easy, almost second nature for you. You are triumphant at this; you win, you thrive and you succeed for yourself and for those you love, but most especially for you. You break though and you win. Worryfree, confident, and calm you are, you remain, while cleverly relaxing your way past any and all barriers, as you now win. This is yours to master and so you do; you are most unstoppable at all of this.

You relax, you truly know, recognize and trust in the fact, that everything you've ever heard, read, thought about, seen and been a part of is stored within your powerful and unbeatable subconscious mind, so the moments in the past chapter of your life of forgetting what you just read are now and forever over; your memory is now razor-sharp, precise and working in your favor, and you trust in this important, success-instilling fact. So just like a powerful and precise computer, you remember, recall and perform like a pro, so skilled, so precise and succeeding, you are and you easily and simply remain.

Even if an answer to a question is or even might be challenging, your correct and actual response is to relax, take a deep, soothing and calming breath or two, as you powerfully and easily unblock, unlock and open up your mind, which relaxes you and now works in your favor; the correct inspired answer just comes to you. You are forgiving and releasing all that once ever might have stood in your way as you just trust in your initial first choice. Free of reading into the question, your instincts are correct and you succeed at this; all thoughts, feelings, actions, reactions, emotions, and experiences, any and all things, now are working in your favor, as you pass, win, thrive and succeed at this. You are now relaxed and allowing the unstoppable, inspirational energy of every past victory, triumph, breakthrough and success you ever had to come down upon you and to drive you ever onward; with the power of a hero, you are succeeding and breaking through here.

You easily know the answer; you trust in this and you succeed. It's all coming back to you now, just coming to mind whenever you need it. It's just there, and you use it to win here, so focused and successful, in knowing and glowing confidence. Like a long distance runner, like a master test-taker, you find your rhythm, reading the question slowly and carefully, like reading a story to a child. You relax all over, you easily and dynamically comprehend, think of the correct answer, know the correct answer. It comes to you effortlessly and correctly and rationally; you reason it out and succeed succinctly and correctly. All of this is just getting easier and easier for you, for I wonder if you even yet realize how you are so powerfully and surely are becoming a master at all of this, just like the dozens of times you've practiced before. Powerfully and unshakably re-identified, now you are. You are focused, calm, serene, unshakable, so focused, so in your zone, so beyond the past, in a better and more professionally focused chapter of your life. You have the calm serenity of a focused professional, calm, unshakable, remarkably precise yet adaptive, so easily able to find the right answer, easily able to reason it out, thinking like the test-makers do; what they know, you know, and use to your ultimate advantage here. Just thriving and succeeding in knowing, growing confidence, you now and forever emerge as a successful winner at this and in all that you've ever set your powerful and unstoppable mind to.

## LEARNING ENHANCEMENT: Taking and Passing A Typing Test

You know, this is the last time you'll be taking this test, as you are completely deserving and unstoppably determined to rise to the very top, because as you just know, you are relaxing here right now, you are also relaxing powerfully beyond any and all limiting old barriers, both known and unknown to you, from the now over and previous chapter of your life, with precise grace and ease, re-identified, free, liberated and safe from the previous chapter of your life, unbeatably in a brand new chapter of your life. Right now, you are reconditioned to become completely effective, super motivated, easily moving beyond the what's the use mentality, just letting that go while unstoppably and powerfully you are moving into an inspired, better chapter of your life, unstoppably, achieving limitless success in all of this, your best and only option, you now the mighty one. In fact, truly, it might even seem as though you're five to ten years down the road, you've already passed this test, for the power is within you, and you're keeping your inner power alive, focused, effective, inspired and active. You are embraced by energy of higher unstoppable success. In fact, you may even feel as though you've got it under your belt, just as if you have been on this job for five or ten or even fifteen years now, perhaps as a supervisor, perhaps as a trainer of other people; their skill, focus, patience, calm, balanced, stress-free feelings are activating all the inspiration and limitless talent that teachers have, is now rising to the top, bubbling up and over within you. What the pros know, you know; what they do, you do; how they succeed, you succeed; for truly and unstoppably, you are breaking through here, focused only on the task at hand and your success is at hand here, right here, right now, as any and all stumbling from the past, is now considered by you a real and valuable learning experience that you've gained from, in both break-through strength and momentum while now harnessed as a pivotal point of your inner power to break you through mightily, in knowing, growing, glowing confidence.

You know you have learned, you have gained, you're breaking through, all of your experience has taught you to be more steady, precisely and sharply focused, calm, successful and unstoppable, striding beyond each and every imbalance in the now-over past you once experienced. In fact, the previous chapters of your life, you know, have strengthened and fortified you, so right now, only getting stronger and better, mightier and more powerfully effective, to the point where you have unstoppable inspiration and momentum, you truly recognize that you are rising to the top, making success your very own, blossoming forth into a brighter and better day. You are and you remain becoming one with your success, as your mind and fingers are all working in perfect harmony, in correct and precise skillful fashion and speed with the fortifying embrace of soothing and steadying breath, effective focus and liberating precision, in profound freedom as you now are forgiven and released unstoppably from the past. In fact truly, you are now in a brand new chapter of your life, all things just falling into focus and into place, almost as if in fact, you have been practicing and succeeding at typing for thirteen, fourteen, sixteen, or even seventeen years. It's almost as if, in fact, someone from deep, deep inside of you, has reset the switch, a dial, a computer, or a thermostat of some kind, allowing you to remarkably maintain speed and accuracy, while keeping your focus, with a laser-beam-like precision, as you rise to the very top, just wanting this and making it happen, easily succeeding, trusting in your instincts, your mastery, which you are now making your very own; your mind, eyes and fingers, just knowing what to do, as it all just seems to pour out of you. All of this now is breaking you through here, unstoppably and unbeatably. You are a new remained certain ensure, you know you were waiting at this. In fact, your mighty inner hero, that powerful and unlimited profound part of you, that you truly are deep, deep down inside, the part of you that is capable of saving children from great danger, like a fire, is rising up on your behalf right now, to remain unbeatable, unstoppable, with precision, accuracy and speed, calm and steady breath, focused forward upon the task at hand, feeling so right, so profoundly with in the zone of success, as you want now making this yours, so steady and in your zone, steady and calm, adaptable and successful. Deeply and truly you are now properly and effectively reorganized, powerfully and accurately strong and mighty, as a person who's unbeatable at this. You rise to the top, this time you enjoy success, as you are certain, sure, and steady, so of course you can, free of the past, you are and you remain problem-free, challenge-oriented, completely focused and absorbed in the moment, absorbing the moment, of your success, as each and every breath is slow, steady, and calm while each and every heartbeat, slow, steady and calm, every thought, feeling, action, and reaction, is now unstoppably working in harmony and only within your favor, to focus you, to activate every mastery skill, and talent you have, to amazingly and unstoppably and unfailingly, break you through here, making your success your only option, as you rise up to meet any and all challenges being presented here, by a great deal, for the greater the challenge, the more focused and effective you become, and that strength is only growing stronger, and stronger, and stronger on each and every breath and heartbeat, while you're awake, while you're asleep, even while you're dreaming; all of you now reoriented towards winning here, and so you do, and so it is, and so it becomes yours, as you are winning here unbeatably. Smiling from deep, deep inside you, it feels so good to win at this, and so it is, and is forever, you were a winner, and it feels great to be a winner.

## Perfecting Your GOLF Game
## Golf Performance Suggestions -1

Relax, relax, relax, and as you truly realize that all of you right now is deeply and powerfully relaxed, you are relaxed in body, emotions, mind and even spirit. Now, imagine preparing yourself and rising up to meet any and all challenges that your golf game can bring; it could be a challenging course or opponent or maybe you have just even decided to challenge yourself, it doesn't really matter. Because right now, instead of reacting like you once did in your past, your energy has gotten stronger and you've made a new commitment, a commitment that you are sticking to, a commitment to remain, relaxed, calm, energetic, strong, confident, clear, easily able from the limitless power of your winning determined mind, to always allow your best talent, skill and ability to visualize and flow to emerge from its deepest places, while playing your own game for yourself. You are and you truly remain focused and in your perfect and most comfortable zone. You are comfortable, focused, relaxed, calm and secure, your equipment is in good order and is adjusted just the way it should be; just right to suit all of your needs. You are prepared both physically, emotionally and mentally, you are absolutely ready to thrive, your talent is emerging from you, like water from an underground stream you are flowing, strong, relaxed and unstoppable. In fact what the top pros, the most powerful experts know, you know. How they flow, you flow. How they play, you play. How they think, you think. How they feel, you feel. How they adapt, you adapt. How they are creatively and successfully inspired, you are creatively and successfully inspired. How they visualize each move, each and every stroke, you in the most powerful and profound ways, deeply and truly know and perform like, powerfully as well. Its almost like some unstoppable current of talent is flowing through you, you know this and it feels just great! The golf course is one of the most comfortable places in the world for you to be.

Now just imagine, just for a moment, a possible stressful situation that may arise, such as the weather, the actions or words of another player or course conditions, but even as you do, you remain relaxed, you really relax even deeper and deeper, you are really just relaxing through all resistance, which you now and forever truly and really know is the correct response for you and you start seeing yourself react to these conditions in a cool, confident and undisturbed way. You are relaxed, calm, comfortable and in control, rising up to meet all obstacles as challenges, you are unshakable, in your perfect zone, calm and cool, in your perfect zone, and you are prepared and eager to begin. Now relax and allow your mind to review easily and without effort your entire game, both movements and strategy, from start to finish. Relax, recall and allow for all of your experience to come forth from you into your body and into the world around you, as a confident energy, and you see what it is you need to do in slow motion. (Pause). See it in as much detail as you can. You played a perfect game, and now review all of the perfect moves you made, feeling the pride and exhilaration that is yours right now. (Pause). And review all the strategy you used. (Pause). This perfect game, can be played again and again, imagine yourself relaxed, clear, confident and successful, reaching your goal. You have reached your goal, you have reached this goal and you can go on to other goals whenever you like. Now just imagine how you feel during your perfect game, imagine that confidence and ease, you were focused and strong; imagining yourself begin again, take a few deep relaxation breaths and in slow motion see every action, feel move in the most positive, thriving and beneficial ways. (Pause). See yourself act and react, moving perfectly, in a wonderful confident flow, every muscle in harmony with your thoughts, see and relax into your strategy, see yourself moving perfectly, see every perfect move just flowing from you and now notice how you feel, you feel relaxed, at ease, strong, alert and clear-minded, your vision is sharp, your reflexes flow and are just perfect, you feel great, you feel like you can smile on the inside and even on the outside, ready to take on the world or at least just taking on the golf game with success, poise, tranquility, plenty of energy whenever it is needed or required and now see yourself rising up and concluding and winning this challenge, you feel pleased with yourself and every correct move, every proper movement is imprinted into your subconscious so that you can repeat your perfect game over and over like a film, now go back and once again replay the sequence in your mind and this time at normal speed, imagine the sequence from start to finish. (pause) And see and even feel all of this in great calmness and comfortable detail, in great detail, imagine making all the right moves and playing a terrific game, playing a terrific game, the best game you ever played.

As you do this, you are calm, comfortable, confident, relaxed and you can even imagine feeling the guidance, wisdom and inspiration of every great golfer who has gone before you, their breakthroughs, victories, inspired insights and successes, somehow now, are your breakthroughs, victories, inspired insights and successes. And each and every time you repeat this exercise, you just get better and better, even in yet unimagined ways, and you smile inside, for you always choose to relax through any and all stress, unblocking yourself and liberating you and your best effort into your best game at all times. You recognize that relaxing through any type of resistance allows you to easily and most successfully to accomplish any and all of your goals. Your concentration is relaxed, yet abundantly clear, sharp and powerfully focused, without any effort on your part, it just flows, your unstoppable more unlimited abilities are powerfully focused like a laser-beam, dynamic, powerful and strong. All that you are right now is relaxed, clear and confident, there you are right now, succeeding, with each and every breath that you take, your confidence flourishing, in wonderful ways. You breathe, you relax and you allow for limitless energy to emerge from within, amazing and impressing everyone, most especially even you; you truly feel like you've got the whole world in your hip pocket or at least that this game is in your pocket and it will be one of the very best, only getting better and better, because, you are now and forever, congratulations, you succeed, you thrive, you accomplish, you win!

# Perfecting Your GOLF Game
# Golf Performance Suggestions - 2

You take the pressure off. You relax into your swing. You relax into your game. You stop trying. You relax into it and flows. When you are golfing or even when you are not golfing, your powerful and effective mind is now finding new and better ways to improve your game, in truly profound, amazing and powerful ways. You know from deep, deep inside, as a real and deep, powerful personal thought, the effective and potent fact that love will always find a way. Your love of your golf game is now expanding from deep, deep within you to find new, improved and better ways of playing and improving your game. Your love of the game is transcending all limits, flowing over around and through any and all past blockages allowing your swing to flow, accurately, correctly, dynamically, precisely, as you relax into your game and improve in as yet unimagined ways. The golf course is one of the most comfortable places in the world for you to be.

Your body and your muscles flow, as you just relax into this, you thrive, and you succeed, amazing and impressing everyone, most especially you. The long clubs are now new friends, an accurate extension of you. They are allowing your very best energies to flow, all of your past moments of victory, breakthrough and inspired success are now allowing you to thrive and succeed.

As you relax deeper, you now imagine or I wonder if you yet truly recognize and realize, that the inspiration of all of the pros, and all of their past moments of victory, breakthrough and inspired success are upon you now are now allowing you to thrive and succeed, allowing you with their help to move on, unblocked, focused, willing, relaxed, totally able. What they know you know. What they do, you do, so you do and it feels great, flowing, easy and great. Now your swing and back-swing comfortably elongates (or shortens). Everything for you now just seems to flow, flexible and flowing. You are able to use the long tee, you get beyond the tee, relaxing into this, just flowing in body, emotion, mind and in spirit, moving on, you feel so very good now, confident, capable and able. You feel frustration leaving you now, like some sort of valve has been released, releasing the steam of past frustrations, allowing new and better satisfaction, gains, wins, pleasure, fulfillment, and happiness to be yours. And all of your life works to support you in this, every thought, every feeling, every action, while you're awake, while you're asleep, even while you dream; you are effectively, flowingly, and precisely mending, healing and improving this. You've begun a newer and better chapter of your life today. Re-identified, reinvented, released moving on, you fell and truly now know, getting only better and better, you are an unstoppable winner.

# Sales Force Motivation - Stock Brokers

You are powerful and mighty, having relaxed your way into a brand new and more powerful and ever-growing, more empowered chapter of your life, freely flowing easily and powerfully beyond any and all phone fears. You are mighty, powerful and what you have to share, sell and do is important; you are dynamic and redefined, willing to do all that it takes to get your message across, most especially whenever you are or might be dialing the number. So whenever a person answers, your newer and better reactions, thoughts, ideas and feelings, are to breathe calmly, feel balanced. You get so upbeat, motivated, so clear in what you have to say and express that you stay on the phone and share your very best, from your heart and mind with the person you have contacted, and get all of your points across clearly, confidently and with skill, poise and ease. Your relaxed, inventive and skillful mind is clearly feeling calm, balanced, relaxed and in your zone, both inside and outside, now creatively finding newer and better ways of believing in yourself, trusting in your life and thriving, just tapping into the energy of each and every past time, when you were and are actually just wound-up pitching someone on the phone and were very good. You are re-defining yourself in your mind, with each and every breath and each and every heartbeat, while you are awake, asleep or even dreaming; you are dynamic, bold, courageous, freely flowing, all words, thoughts and phrases, just flowing out in just the right ways, all things now working as they should, making some nice money, just like in past times, allowing yourself to live your lifestyle well. Even now, it's time to get back to work and it's just happening, not because I say so, but because it's the nature of your own unstoppable mind to do so; your concentration, so focused, so precise, so recharged, so laser-beam-like in its precision and effectiveness, feeling wonderful. You are so on track, easily and effectively achieving surprisingly powerful beneficial outcomes, for when you believe in yourself you can do anything and amazingly and thoroughly succeeding, you are extremely persistent and diligent, while you are on the phone, super-confident and optimistic as if you know for a fact the stock will triple in a week. You are truly and definitely loving it, doing all that it takes to thrive and succeed at this, and becoming easily and enjoyably addicted to pitching to the point where even when you are home or if you are bored, you will pick up your phone and start calling people. You are finding easy, powerful and unstoppably effective ways of getting to the point of pitching a minimum of 10 people a day. Bright, bold, brilliant, re-conditioned, liberated and re-organized, shining brightly. You are truly unstoppable.

# Sales Force Motivation

Now, relax, relax, deeper and further, relax. And as you relax, this happy and powerful relaxation, your relaxation is doing something amazing, it's beginning to bring up good feelings, good feelings are beginning from deep, deep inside of you, almost like you've been guided and inspired in some powerful and life changing way, in fact, you are beginning to notice a new and powerful feeling of powerfully renewed inspired optimism, a new and powerful feeling of drive and determination is beginning, unstoppably emerging and spreading like a warm glow, throughout your entire body from deep, deep inside of you and you know, you just truly know, a new and more successful, more effective chapter of your life has unstoppably begun and it feels great!

You recognize from deep, deep within, that success in any area of your life requires and even demands, skill, determination, perseverance, step-by-step organized planning that just seems to flow and then activates your limitless abilities and inspired sense of resolve to creatively succeed. So you make up your mind, you can and you will and even better, at all future times learn and succeed. You now relax even deeper on your next exhale, you feel almost as if, truly, that your abilities to be and remain, well paced, well ordered and to recall, to remember, to communicate, to express and get your point across smoothly, efficiently, and effectively is being tuned up, turned up, being activated, in powerful and precise and amazingly successful ways. In fact your attitude is upbeat, confident, clear, optimistic, powerfully creative and completely effective. For in this moment, the inspired and successful power of your dynamic mind is working, your unstoppable and optimistic can do attitude is activating, is growing, stronger, ever stronger, for you, clearly are feeling absolutely inspired to succeed in amazing ways, tapping to the limitless well of your past successes and learning experiences, from all of the energy of all of your past triumphs, victories, breakthroughs and successes.

You are the one who can effectively sell, get the job done and fantastically provide into the equation, the most valuable asset you can offer anyone, you! You believe in you. All of your years of experience and the valuable lessons you've learned from your life are now being tapped into, coming to the forefront, easily and successfully accessed at any moment. In fact, it's almost like someone has reset, from deep, deep within you, a switch, a dial, a valve, or a computer of some kind from deep, deep within you somewhere, all of your very best to come out into the world around you in skillfully guided and inspired harmony, allowing you to powerfully and truly, believe in yourself, to bounce back, to have the correct answer, easily and successfully able to draw upon all of your past experiences and knowledge. You feel proud, you have a right to be proud of yourself and the work that you do, you are proud of the priceless and valuable service you provide. You relax, and you let the very best aspects of yourself come out into all that you communicate, since people need to hear what you have to say, for your service to them provides an invaluable service for their family and future safety. And you come across likeable, substantial, capable, able to guide, you're there to serve, people think of you as one of them, one of the good guys!

Energy sells but passion persuades, both your energy and passion are being powerfully turned up, almost as if someone from deep, deep inside of you has reset or forever turned up, a switch, a dial a computer or a thermostat of some kind, activating newer and power powerful energy in correct amounts to get the job done in the most precise and inspired effectively successful ways. You have both the energy and passionate talent to success and to easily flow over, around and through any and all obstacles, both thriving and succeeding in incredible ways. In fact, you now feel so relaxed, so calm, so upbeat, you truly feel like you have the whole world in the palm of your hand. You are confident, inspired, creative, successful, talented, experienced, getting better each and every day and night in all moments of your life, able to accomplish everything and anything you set your mind to doing, being all that You are allowing only your very best to emerge. You are completely and truly capable, clear, confident, strong, powerfully guided, sharp and strong, both accessing and providing only the very best, valuable, making the most of each and every moment, upbeat, able, confident, bouncing back, achieving, well-paced, well-ordered, allotting time and effectively planning and managing the asset that is your time, better and better, pacing and planning out your goals, relaxing into this, easily achieving. You set goals, easily able to achieve all that needs to be done and you easily do it correctly, in harmony and with ease. You feel harmonized. In fact, you're feeling practically Divinely guided. Each and every little step in your life's journey is one more step on your path to profound and complete success. You are doing all that it takes, creatively, to get the job done, and getting it done well! You always provide the very best, your very best, giving it your all! Your ability to communicate even feels enhanced, your communication skills are optimally, enhanced, expressing yourself practically with complete ease, directly, clearly, optimally, smoothly and even diplomatically when it's necessary, to get the job done, completely and effectively, achieving, following all steps, closing the sale, in a better place, in your new zone of creative, inspired success!

Right now, you allow a new decision, a profound and powerfully inspiring new thought for a life changing new day to dawn upon, you have decided to let all of your past roadblocks, that once stood in your way to now completely and absolutely melt away, to just melt away from your mind, your emotions, your body and completely away from your life. They were just a learning experience, free from any and all effect upon you right now, always and forever and this gets only easier, better and clearer, as you repeat this enjoyable form of deep relaxation. In fact, right now, truly, you can imagine and embrace the idea of being problem-free. It's even occurring to you, that you have moved forward, you are successfully problem-free, because, powerfully right now, you've completely decided to become challenge oriented and problem-free. And any challenge, by its nature, is something you rise up to meet, to deal with creatively and to successfully solve, to complete, to overcome and to succeed beyond, in amazing ways, impressing and amazing everyone, most especially you. You so right now, always and forever, you are always failure-free, having the right and proper attitude, correctly choosing to relax your way through any and all stress. In fact, your new, powerful correct response to any and all stress is to relax through it, around it and away from it. You are also now recognizing from deep, deep, within, that you have always learned from what others might refer to as failure, but you let go of failure as a concept in your life. We may succeed, but we never fail. Those experiences have taught you, you've learned from them, really, they've polished you and allowed you to more freely flow, to thrive, to gain, to win and to succeed amazingly, in the most powerful of ways; so right now, you are problem-free, challenge oriented, goal motivated and always either learning or succeeding in amazing ways. You recognize the landscape, you have a better game plan than ever and see the scheme of things, truly finding a new and better inspiration, having learned that every NO, puts you one step closer to a YES! No doesn't mean no, it means I don't understand, explain it better and convince me more, get your point across. You do better, you grow, it is so very motivating, inspiring. In fact and in reality, you are a powerful and yet unstoppable force and it feels great, you feel great, you are great, getting better and more able, each and every day, and each and every night, each and every moment, feeling better, more able, more inspired, while you are awake, while you are asleep, even while you dream. You rest powerfully each and every night, able to calmly relax and you awaken each morning, powerfully happy, enthusiastic, optimistic, hopeful, bright, cheerful-sounding, both inside handout, in good spirit, ready to start each day, as a day filled with limitless opportunities to grow, to gain, to share, to enlighten, to sell, to win, to gain, to achieve, to amaze and to impress everyone, most especially yourself and to creatively and unstoppably impressively and admirably succeed.

And you know from deeply within yourself all of the following deep, powerful, creative, successful inspired truths: I sell a valuable product, I relax and I concentrate, easily drawing upon my training and experience, I get my points across, my words and thoughts just flow, I succeed. Almost like tapping into the thoughts and experiences of those whom have gone before, I am a pro, easily succeeding. I get the job done. I explain and enlighten, with diplomatic ease, skill and confidence. I only stop when I am satisfied in my success. I am a powerful self-starter, I am motivated and focused, a truly unstoppable force. I flow into my life, using all at my disposal, masterfully utilizing any and all of the valuable tools at my disposal to succeed. I believe in me, I believe in my work and what I sell, I know I will succeed with poise, ease, grace and limitless creative truly inspired success. I skillfully direct all of my sales abilities to provide for the future success of those I work with, most especially for myself and my loved ones. I win!

# Stress Management and Successful Career Training Program Completion

You relax, you trust your in life, truly in this magnificent moment of deep and soothing relaxation, now fully knowing that you have relaxed your way into a brand new, better and happier chapter of your life, more easily able and unstoppably confident, feeling this build and build, in endless supply like a giant reservoir and truly knowing this and appreciating that you are truly and in fact easily able to trust in yourself, to recall all that's needed and are powerfully and unstoppably confident, easily able to remember, to recall, to do what's right and necessary to succeed at taking control in your workplace (name workplace) which could lead only to making all the right moves, taking correct action, precisely and at the right times. You are forthright and upfront, you are confident, intelligent and adaptive, you are willing to tell others you may have the need to learn more, in order to become better, as you both recognize and realize that you are hardly the first or even the tenth, that you are in need of learning in more detail and in precise ways to have re-explained, all that it takes to make yourself better at your job and training, asking to have skills reinforced, completely and totally unafraid that telling the teachers in school the skills you are lacking, you want to relearn, to know more, you are making all of the appropriate moves to be only your very best and working within all of the very best ways to accomplish all that is necessary to be the very best, calm, relaxed, balanced, and just after just a few short deep and steady breaths, easily able to calm down, rebalance, reorient, remember and recall, allowing your inner hero to emerge unstoppably, becoming more adaptive, and flexible, even if you may or might be asked to change something in work, you are even fearless, flexible and loose, even if something unacceptable is asked of you. You are easily able to gain and to live from gaining confidence in your performance. You relax, more and more easily able to remember, recall and perform as needed or necessary, finding your creativity enhanced as the system just seems to flow when you relax through any and all stress and imbalance. Your forever and correctly respond to any and all stress from now on is deep breathing your way into success, relaxing through any and all uncomfortable blockages, finding it profoundly easier and better each and every day and night to develop and execute your ideas, finding it profoundly easier and better each and every day and night, to organize schedules, remaining fluent and articulate, believing in yourself, feeling at home in any of your surroundings, making small talk when necessary, coming to trust in the correctness and appropriateness of all of your decisions, for as you relax, you liberate your powerful sense of inner wisdom and guidance. You feel confident, safe and secure, finding new ways of thinking, acting, feeling, believing and truly and forever knowing, you are moving in the correct ways for yourself, so calm, so powerful and so relaxed. You are powerfully and truly forever determined to be successful, unstoppable, completely unafraid, your wisdom coming up in all areas, tapping inner guidance, feeling almost Divinely guided and directed, trusting so powerfully and living from all past moments of breakthrough, triumph, victory and success, taking charge, responsible and acting responsibly, feeling sometimes even mighty, willing to be your very best, always finding creative solutions, in the most effective and most proficient of ways, to act accurately, easily moving beyond all and any doubts of old fears, just moving and flowing beyond them, accepting the guidance and compassion of authority figures, bringing out your very best, like when driving or being inspired by your very best teacher, transcending any and all apparent limits, liberating only your very best, succeeding easily and forever, able to move mountains if necessary, so you do.

## Success for Day Traders

Regardless of event, circumstance or situation, you are feeling powerfully fine and vigorously guided, practically intuitive, so relaxed, so calm, so determined, so in your zone of success and comfortability. You are unstoppably determined and easily succeeding at being and forever remaining, calm, relaxed and yet powerfully and effectively alert and adaptive to market direction. You are focused, strong and guided, thriving and succeeding, successful, you will, you are and you remain effectively disciplined at all times, in the very best and most potent of ways, to create the kind of success you now liberate. You are so calm and in the flow of things, you easily and patiently wait for a trade to set up. Even any possible losses will be managed well and kept small. You will always trade with a stop loss, finding yourself dynamically succeeding at this, in powerful and creative ways. Success remains and will truly and actually will forever remain a gradual process day-by-day, one trade at a time. You are so very comfortable with this, as you relax your way into a newer, brighter and healthier future so focused, so laser-beam precise, in every thought, every impulse, in each and every action that you take, truly trusting in this. You are so in the proper rhythm for success, so upbeat, so encouraged, so willing to forgive and release past blockages, just flowing beyond any and all past blockage and moving on and ready to move into the kind of success you deserve in this a brand new and forever chapter of your life and that you mightily and dynamically create, easily, successfully and vigorously, one step at a time, doing all that it takes to thrive and succeed, in correct, precise, managed, comfortable and flowing ways, so willing, so ready, so able, so flexible, so empowered, so inspired, so balanced, so harmonized, both outside and inside, so correct in all that you do, so sure of yourself, so easily able to rise up beyond any and all doubt, fearless, focused, capable, able, so light and lighthearted, your body, calm balanced, relaxed. Your new and proper response to any and all stress, is to relax your way right out of it into a better and brighter life, way of living, way of feeling, way of health, into better success, thoughts, feelings, ideas, and inspirations, sure of your self, and the precise actions you take, doing better and better, each and every day and night, fulfilling your real and most powerful of potentials, in the very most unlimited of ways.

# Overcoming a Breakup and Succeeding at Taking the LSATS

Your time for crying is over. You've moved on and are unstoppably determined to be and remain happy, whole and healthy, especially when you talk about it or think about it. You trust in the fact that your life is turning out the way it should, all things working out in Divine order. It doesn't matter how or why, you recognize that it was time to move on or it would have worked out so you find contentment and peace from this, truly and forever knowing a brighter future lies ahead, the only reason that really matters, is that it was time to move on, so you happily and powerfully do. You easily move away from engaging in anything demeaning, as you are far too valuable for that, and your self-esteem and knowledge that you deserve a bright and happy future won't ever allow that, like engaging in some obsessive behaviors such as calling him and hanging up and searching for him / her on-line. You let all unhealthy and damaging preoccupations go, you are moving on, taking better care of yourself, doing what is right for you. You find yourself relaxing into a peaceful night of sleep, easily and ably sleeping right through the night, awakening fully refreshed each morning, easily pacing yourself to get all that needs to be done, accomplished, getting to work on time, in a stress-free, precise and confident manner. As a matter of fact, you are treating yourself wonderfully well, you eating habits simmer down and improve, you feel better, you are so super motivated to succeed in life, apportioning your time, doing all that it takes to properly exercise, eat right, study, memorize, remember, and recall, with laser-beam like precision, truly understanding the system, even deciding to have fun and laugh more often, and enjoying the healing effects of laughter. You go out into the world, getting truly better, healthier, safe and strong, allowing yourself to meet new people, in particular men, and find you now find that you are now confident, safe, sure, secure, and relaxed, allowing only your very best to rise up and make you feel great and allowing your thoughts and feelings to attract like a magnet, all the very best that life has to offer. You are allowing yourself to talk to and approach men / women with ease and confidence. And as you relax ever deeper, you find your concentration becoming even greater because you allow it to and it's coming back into balance and becoming clear and laser-beam like precise, in fact your concentration is strong and you have an easy time and great success focusing on tasks at work, studying for the LSATs and focusing during practice tests.

---

# Extras – Learning Enhancements

NOTE: This is a section of additional suggestions I've written for various sessions. As with the rest of this text, please read and select or adapt the suggestions that apply to your client (patient) to fit their specific needs. By using this section, you are agreeing to pre-reading, rewriting, adjusting and adapting these suggestions to individual and specific needs.

**Learning Enhancement: Bypassing Stress Induced Dyslexic Tendencies during Exams – *Extras* -**You stay and easily and effectively remain focused and free of any and all dyslexic tendencies, becoming laser-beam like precise, balanced and relaxed, as your stress levels stay in check. All of you, just after a few short deep and steady breaths, you relax your way through anything and everything, anytime you need to. You are focused and easily remembering, you feel enlightened, inspired and Divinely guided, remaining effectively and precisely calm and smooth, peaceful and serene, easily able to concentrate and even better easily able to focus, fully functional and balanced. You are anxiety-free, feeling the stress levels fall, now completely unblocked, you find yourself easily able to slow down and calm down, easily regaining balance, purposeful and calm, peaceful and focused, easily thriving and succeeding, you win! It feels great!

# HEALTH AND WELL BEING

Also see PERSONAL DEVELOPMENT:
    Get Up and Do It - Exercise Motivation
    Good Mental Health and Suggestions
    Healing Anger and Creating Forgiveness
    Life Improvement: Memory, Money and Success
    Motivation & Relaxation: Creating Balance and Healing,
    Weight and Life Motivation
Also see ANXIETY, FEAR, PANIC:
    Free Flowing Speech - Free of Stuttering
    Free of Skin Picking
    Healing Doubt, Panic and Fear
    Overcoming Dizziness, Fear, Panic and Anxiety,
    Overcoming Fears: Public Speaking Stage Fright. Gaining Self-Acceptance
    Overcoming Guilt, Fear and Shame
    Overcoming Scalp Scratching (Trichotillomania Variant)
    Overcoming Trichotillomania (Hair Pulling)
Also see RELATIONSHIPS:
    Coping With A Snoring Mate and Getting Better Rest – 1
    Coping With a Snoring Mate – Better Rest - 2
    Coping With A Snoring Mate and Getting Better Rest – 3

# Anti-Gagging Response to Dental Work

In order to maintain good, vigorous and vibrant health now as an adult, you know that you need to relax and to allow yourself to truly relax in terms of your dental and oral health. Your body is your most valuable asset and your mouth and oral hygiene are a vital part of your valuable life assets; your oral health is most important to you. Only you can take care of your body and your health. You owe yourself and your body the proper respect of good health. Self-Preservation is the first rule of life.

As an adult, you also know that it is your responsibility to rise above all limitations of the past and to make the most of your life. Beginning right now and for the rest of your life, whenever you are about to take care of your health, most especially your oral health, you shall work in harmony and allow all procedures to work with you and for you, in truly powerful beneficial ways. You will relax all that You are relaxing your body, (relax) you will absolutely relax your emotions (relax) and all of your thoughts (relax) and your spirit, relaxes powerfully in true inspired successful oneness. You will relax throughout all that you are.

As you relax, you relax your throat, really relaxing it, relaxing it calmly effectively and completely. As you relax your throat, you relax from your throat down, including the muscles of your stomach, allowing only peaceful harmony from your throat down to relax and to calm and to soothe you.

And as you are relaxed, you feel like you are cleansed on the inside and even on the outside, because you can feel the old unwanted, and unneeded, useless energies from the past, just lifting up, just lifting up and removing themselves from you forever, allowing them to drift away, just drifting away, far, far away. And as you relax, you feel cleansed, you are cleansing unpleasant past emotions and memories from the past including all past unpleasant experiences as well. Right now, instead you are relaxed and you shall relax, and allow all old reactions and unpleasant memories to drift away from you, completely and absolutely. For beginning right now and for the rest of your life, you are empowered, and free to relax any and all parts of your body and your muscle system as you decide, including your throat and all of its reactions, no matter where or when they came from, even reactions to stress of any kind, no matter where or when they came from, because you are the empowered one and you are mightier than old memories, memories and reactions that have now left you, leaving you now, absolutely, always and forever. All old unwanted reactions you once had, you are now freed from, putting all of them behind yourself, for the reactions you once had as a child or in younger days are now gone and now you do what's proper for your health as an adult. All memories of unpleasant past dental experiences, are just that, only memories, just like a dream, are right now, drifting way, drifting away, drifting away, until your mind and your emotions are now clear and free; YOU ARE FREE FROM YOUR PAST, YOU ARE UNLIMITED, YOU TRANSCEND, WITH POISE, EASE, GRACE and UNSTOPPABLE SUCCESS. YOU ARE NOW A PERSON THAT ALLOWS FOR A CALM and BALANCED LIFE, A CALM and BALANCED BODY, A CALM and BALANCED THROAT and STOMACH, CALM and BALANCED REACTIONS, and AS YOU ALLOW THIS CALMNESS, A PEACEFUL and YET PLEASANTLY NUMBING SENSATION IS YOURS AS YOU DESIRE IT, SHOULD YOU WANT IT.

BEGINNING RIGHT NOW AND FOR THE REST OF YOUR LIFE, you rise above all limiting memories and concepts and labels and responses from the past and the new you, emerges, each and every day, getting stronger and stronger. You easily transcend all past experiences of limitation.

It might be days, it might be months, it might be hours, it might be moments or yes, even right now, but before you relax into any oral procedure, you relax, you deep breathe, very calm, very slow, very steady calming relaxing deep breaths. You relax by breathing slowly through your nose, all that you are and especially the muscles of your throat, feeling soothing elegant relaxation and almost gentle yet powerful and pleasant numbness spreading throughout all that you are. Relax even deeper now and allow yourself to feel calmness flowing through you like a river of powerful and deeply soothing relaxation energy. As you relax, you notice the pleasant and wonderful feelings that emerge from deep within yourself. You assimilate all of the dental assistance and healing and procedures, including X-ray work and all of this becomes a beneficial means to a healthy new you, taking in all and becoming one with all of the beneficial life maintaining properties. You realize by breathing through your nose as needed you relax, you heal and you thrive. And beginning right now and for the rest of you life, you move into a happier, calmer, new and better chapter of your life, for the rest of your life, a healthy and new beneficial time of health and healing. Beginning right now and for the rest of your life you are becoming one with your new habits for health, healing, rising above, transcending your way into new health in every way and complete happy and balanced vitality. You are free from your past, and you are a new, more alive, healthier you, a person who relaxes and enjoys life and truly is empowered in all that you do.

---

# Anti-Gagging Response to Pill Swallowing

---

In order to maintain good, vigorous and vibrant health now as an adult, you know that you need to relax and to allow yourself to truly relax in terms of your physical and medical health. Your body is your most valuable asset and your health and hygiene are a vital part of your most valuable assets, in fact your physical health is most important to you. Only you can take care of your body and your health. You truly owe yourself and your body the proper respect of good health brings. Self-Preservation is the first rule of life.

As an adult, you also truly and absolutely know that it is your responsibility to rise above all limitations of the past and to make the most of your life. So beginning right now and for the rest of your life, whenever you are about to take care of your health, your physical health, even your health emotionally and mentally, you shall work in complete harmony and allow all procedures and prescriptions to work with you and for you in the most beneficial ways. You will relax, your body, you will absolutely relax your emotions and all of your thoughts and even your spirit. You will deeply and powerfully relax throughout all that you are.

As you relax, you relax all that is your body and most especially you relax your throat, just like your body is relaxed right now, really relaxing your throat, relaxing it truly, calmly, effectively and completely. As you relax your throat, you relax from your upper throat down, including the muscles of your stomach, allowing only deep and truly peaceful harmony from your throat down to relax and to calm and to soothe you in every beneficial way.

And as you are relaxed, you feel like you are cleansed on the inside and even on the outside, because you can feel the old unwanted and unneeded, useless energies from the past, just lifting up, just lifting up and removing themselves from you forever, no matter where they came from, absolutely allowing those unneeded energies to drift away, they are just drifting away, far, far away. And as you relax, and as they are removed and removed from all that is your life, forever and always, you feel cleansed, and you are cleansing unpleasant past emotions and memories from the past including, all past unpleasant experiences as well. Right now, instead you are relaxed, you remain relaxed and you shall relax and allow all old reactions and unpleasant memories to drift away from you, completely and absolutely. For beginning right now and for the rest of your life, you are empowered and free to relax any and all parts of your body and even your muscle system easily, as you decide, including your throat and all of its reactions, no matter where or when they came from in your past, you even relax through reactions to stress of any kind, no matter where or when they came from, because you are the empowered one and you are mightier than any old memories or reactions that have now really truly left you, leaving you, now, absolutely, always and forever. All old unwanted reactions you once had, you are now freed from, putting all of them, each and every one of them behind you, as you are now set free, for the reactions you once had as in your past or in younger days are now gone and now you do what's proper for your health as an adult, congratulations, you have already succeeded.

All memories of unpleasant past experiences, are just that, only memories, memories you are now and forever freed from and just like a dream, they are right now, drifting away, drifting away, drifting away, until your mind and your emotions and all that You are now clear and free; YOU ARE FREE FROM YOUR PAST, YOU ARE UNLIMITED, YOU TRANSCEND, WITH POISE, EASE and GRACE. YOU ARE NOW A PERSON THAT ALLOWS FOR A CALM and BALANCED LIFE, A CALM and BALANCED BODY, A CALM and BALANCED THROAT and STOMACH, AS IT WAS BEFORE ANY OF THIS EVER BEGAN, YOU EXPERIENCE ONLY CALM and BALANCED REACTIONS and AS YOU ALLOW THIS CALMNESS, A PEACEFUL and YET PLEASANTLY NUMBING SENSATION IS YOURS AS YOU DESIRE IT, SHOULD YOU WANT IT.

BEGINNING RIGHT NOW, AND FOR THE REST OF YOUR LIFE, you rise above all limiting memories and concepts and labels and responses from the past and a very empowered chapter of your life truly begins, beginning right now into forever, and this brand new liberated you, emerges, every day, getting stronger and stronger. You easily transcend all past experiences of limitation.

It might be days, it might be months, it might be hours, it might be moments, but before you relax into any experience, you deep breathe, very calm, very slow, very steady calming relaxing deep breaths, you relax, for relaxation is the correct response for you. You relax by breathing slowly through your nose, feeling that wonderful relaxation energy flow throughout all that you are and especially the muscles of your throat, allowing them to release, relax and unwind, feeling soothing elegant relaxation response and almost gentle yet powerful and pleasant numbness spreading throughout all that you are most especially within your throat. Relax even deeper now and allow yourself to feel calmness flowing through you like a river of powerful and deeply soothing relaxation energy. As you relax, you notice the pleasant and wonderful feelings that emerge from deep within yourself. You assimilate all of the assistance and healing and procedures, including medication to heal you that you only derive the most beneficial results from and all of this becomes a beneficial means to a healthy new you, taking in all and becoming one with of the beneficial life maintaining properties. You realize by breathing through your nose as needed you relax, you heal and you thrive. And beginning right now and for the rest of your life, you unstoppably move into a happier, calmer, new and better chapter of your life, for the rest of your life, a healthy, and new beneficial time of health and healing. Beginning right now and for the rest of your life you are becoming one with your new habits for health, healing, rising above, transcending, into new health in every way and complete happy and balanced vitality. You are free from your past and you are a new, more alive, healthier you, a person who relaxes, and enjoys life and truly is empowered in all that you do.

## Anti-Snoring - Anti-Insomnia

Think about it being some moment just before bedtime, you are relaxing and you have put this past day upon a mental shelf. This past day has taken care of you, yesterday has done the same, just like every other yesterday and all past yesterdays have done. Your life has supported you, taken care of you, just like tomorrow will and you truly know this. You trust in all of the ready support that life has given you, that life gives you and continues to give you easily and effectively making this is one of your deepest and most personal truths. So you can trust and relax even further. So now it's time to relax, to release and unwind, in your mind and in your emotions and even your thoughts are relaxing, your breathing is so slow, so peaceful, in a powerful relaxing rhythm, allowing you to relax deeper, deeper and further and further, you are just feeling so sleepy, so calm, so relaxed. You can actually feel you whole body relaxing, almost melting, from the top of your head to the tips of your toes, everything just melting. Now think of yourself laying in bed, you are unwinding even more, just letting go, so comfortably, so lazily, so easily, so effectively, so restfully, just letting go. I wonder if you are picturing just letting go even further or if you are wondering about how completely great you are going to feel in the morning. Upon awakening, you are so rested, so relaxed, so peaceful, so calm, perhaps even successfully inspired, with new ideas and inspirations provided by your dreams, to most powerfully let go of any and all old, unneeded, uncomfortable, stubborn, unyielding and inflexible old thoughts, old ideas, old feelings, old useless patterns or ways of thinking, as you relax deeper and further, that once stood in your way, just letting them drift away with the lightness and comfortability that you are now completely experiencing powerfully, powerfully allowing you to even better live your life, to enjoy your life, being successful in all that you wish to accomplish. Any and all stubbornness from your past just seems to be drifting away from you as well, because as you relax even further and deeper, you are just feeling so supported that you are just trusting more and more. You are even feeling inspired to test just how flexible and cooperative You are just as all that is your life is really just feeling so flexible, cooperative, adaptable, changeable in supportive and success inspiring ways, in the most precisely creative and beneficial of ways, your thoughts, both now and tomorrow and throughout all of your successfully inspired and supportive tomorrows. You are correctly choosing to relax through any and all frictional moments, becoming more and more adaptable, pliant, amiable, genial, supple, elastic, you are becoming just like water, easily able to flow around, through, over or even under any and all challenges, new or old, you are becoming more and more problem-free, challenge-oriented, focused on all opportunities to gain, grow, adapt, learn, relax, release, heal and forgive, releasing all harshness and all of its energy from your past, you have been polished from it, and even better and instead, you have actually gained in the most powerful of ways from your past experiences! During this luxurious night of well-deserved and graceful sleep, you have also powerfully chosen to sleep easily, comfortably, peacefully and deeply, in correct and proper body postures and positions, that will support you and allow you to breathe most easily, successfully, quietly and restfully. This is something you automatically do, as you release and relax, carefree and completely successfully, more and more, getting better and better, easier and easier, each and every night that you rest, in a well deserved rest, from another interesting day, a learning-filled, opportunity-packed day.

You relax even deeper now, releasing any and all negative feelings from your past, absolutely yet powerfully and completely releasing all experiences you've had with frustration, fear, guilt, anger, distain, sorrow, dejection, right now, even better and instead, because you recognize you deserve it. You truly allow limitless feelings and the inspirations of love, life, joy, harmony, bliss, feelings of happiness and contentment, you're so very glad to be alive, you are passionate for your life and for living your dreams, with limitless respect for yourself and for others, admiration, great self-esteem, self-respect, kindness, you relish and cherish your life, your world and those you love, conceiving of yourself in even more new, better more self-supporting ways, unleashing and liberating all of your greatest and best inspired success potentials, free of any and all effort, by just allowing, by just relaxing, just sleeping, truly embracing all that is fresh and vital in all that is life and when you awaken, you are relaxed, comfortable and positively great. All throughout your wonderful and powerful night of rest and sleep, you feel calm, satisfied and relaxed, you are in trust and in fact, calm, satisfied and relaxed, able completely to breathe, easily, freely, and quietly! And you bring with you into your next new day this wonderful calm, satisfied sense of relaxation over into your waking state tomorrow, awakening at your usual time, truly inspired to create the most wonderful of days, feeling wonderful in every way! You are completely and absolutely ready for another wonderful day.

# Becoming and Remaining Alcohol-Free

**Note:** You must be a qualified and certified Clinical Hypnosis professional and have a written note of authorization to perform this or any other complementary hypnosis session from the attending physician, psychiatrist, psychologist, etc., no exceptions.

You are now and forever moving into a new and growing better chapter of your life, facing life right on, dealing with life and effectively succeeding. A place in your life where any and all past destructive feelings, thoughts, habits, ideas and reflexive actions you once used in your past in any way, that could or would ever harm you, are now and forever being unstoppably put behind you, because you deserve a better life and you are unstoppably determined to create it because you are worth it, life is worth it, your life is your most valuable asset and you are more determined, effectively adaptively creative to make this work You have decided to grow up and move beyond drinking and other self-destructive behaviors, like feelings of insecurity and feeling down, easily, adaptively and effectively flowing beyond any and all hurtful or uncomfortable energies, truly and in reality having little or no room in your life for self destructive limiting and damaging patterns, so you are determined to kick them out and to live better. You are relaxing deeper now, you come to a deep and forever true realization, that's it's time to move on, grow up, take charge of your life and right into a better and more powerful chapter of your life, alcohol free, regardless of event or circumstances, beyond and any and all excuses, because you are worth it, life is worth it, you deserve it, the people whom you love deserve it, but most of all you deserve it and now will do anything and everything it take to improve your life powerfully and unstoppably, not just because I say so, but because you are have made an unstoppable and unshakeable, better choice for yourself, that feeling better, alcohol free, pain free, balanced calmer happier and relaxed is the way to be and it's yours right now, only growing better and better, easier and easier, and you are driven to accomplish this. You move beyond old patterns of victim mentality, free of that endless trap, blowing off anger and rage, self destruction and pain, now even better, doing the right things, instead and even better now and forever, empowered, driven, effectively thriving, balanced, moving on, vigilant, super-motivated right now, laser-beam like focused, absolutely determined, unselfishly giving to yourself just only all the self-supporting and life-bringing, life-giving thoughts, feelings, ideas and habits, you will use to create the unselfish and excuse free life you deserve and create, being free of excuses you once gave yourself to fall back into any and all old self-destructive ways, habits and patterns in the past you once used to damage yourself, instead now healing yourself, restoring yourself and balancing all that is your healthy and better, now and forever improved life. More and more alcohol is toxic; it's a poison, as poisonous as drain cleaner is to you. So you've moved on, alcohol is out of your life, now, always and forever. You are problem free, releasing the word problem as a pattern of thinking and behaving in your life, now and forever, you are adapting to becoming challenge oriented, rising up to effectively meet any and all challenges in your life, finding fulfillment, power, strength, courage and the power to adapt, succeeding to your advantage, succeeding at living and at life, alcohol free, excuse free, removing any and all poisons and poisonous things from your life, finding and living a better way, feeling and becoming, healthy whole and happy, rage free, stress free, anxiety free, facing down any and all challenges and this time, you unstoppably win! Your want and desire to do this increases, you are driven boldly and unstoppably you are and have moved on. Your body is a natural factory of all that you need, this natural factory of all that you need is now giving you all of the nutrients and agents, guide and motivated by the powerful and unstoppable power of your subconscious mind, to move you beyond all and any discomfort, to rapidly and effectively heal you in the most amazing and profound of ways, moving you on to a whole, healthier, better, comfortable, pleasantly numb when needed, alcohol free life. Even if you are nervous or twitchy, even if you are shaky, you are determined to ride out the wave and move into a better and more healthy, extended life, drinking plenty of water, washing you out and washing you clean inside, because you are worth it. Deep and slow steady breath calms you and heals you, balances and sooths you, powerfully and effective restoring you, releasing self-created and external stress and doubt, free of fear and free of excuses. You are even creating a very powerful and pleasant numbness whenever, wherever it is or just might be needed. You are and you forever remain, free of being a burden to those who care for you, you are doing better and better, little steps mean a lot. You are and you forever remain, beer free, alcohol free, regardless of event or circumstances, even through major or minor disappointments, at any and all times in your life, whether it's personal or involving other people, whether it's with other people or even if you are alone, you are more important than any excuse, any event or circumstance, it's time to grow up, become a responsible adult and to effectively and successfully move on, effectively taking charge of your life, keeping yourself clean, relying on yourself, doing all that it takes to succeed here, because you are worth it, you deserve it, and you now so every masterfully rising to the occasion, free forever of ever poisoning yourself again, finding things to be upbeat about, calm balanced, deep breathing your way powerfully and effectively through any and all stress, relaxing your way through any and all stress, your now correct response to healing all that you are and now steadily and stably grow in the most healthy ways to forever be and become whole, rising to the occasion because you are worth it, you win. All of your life now improving, all of your life now becoming better and better, all things working in your favor.

You become and you are truly in fact, free from drinking any beer or alcohol without thinking. You are free & completely liberated from drinking beer or any alcohol or wanting to drink in any way because you are or may be: nervous, tense, frustrated, lonely, bored, happy, depressed, angry, tired, anxious or simply because you are with other people, or even if you are alone. I wonder if you yet even realize, for already it's almost like how you can forget a dream upon awaking in the morning, because you are beginning to forget your destructive and deadly alcohol drinking habit & forgetting, forgiving & releasing all of it's past influence & effects upon you from your past, all of it is leaving you now, just drifting away, far, far away from your memory & your life, which is really just fine with you, as you move rapidly and forever into a brighter and better, healthier and more fulfilling and prosperous future.

You are finding new and better ways of supporting yourself and your life, finding newer and better ways of beating stress and dealing with your life. You are free of wanting, craving or needing beer or any alcohol in any way, most especially when you are upset or nervous, free of harming yourself with beer or any alcohol, finding just a few deep and steady breaths to calm yourself down. You are free of wanting, craving or needing beer or any alcohol in any way most especially when you are in a good mood you turn away from beer or any alcohol, finding newer, healthier and better ways to keep yourself going, beer or alcohol free, healthy, happy, safe and strong. You are free of wanting, craving or needing beer or any alcohol in any way, most especially when you are looking forward to something, finding even greater happiness in what you are looking forward to, finding maximum intensity in what you are looking forward to, feeling so much better free of drinking or wanting or craving beer or any alcohol in any way. You've moved on, you've grown up and you are feeling better each and every day, in each and every way. You are free of wanting, craving or needing beer or any alcohol in any way most especially when you are stressed or even if you are having a hard time dealing with certain situations, you find better, more relaxed, more adaptive ways of dealing with your life, easily able to trust in yourself and easily able to get through anything, beer or any alcohol free, craving free, easily and more able to get through anything and everything, free of beer or any alcohol, than you ever did with it. For in a great deal of ways, getting only stronger and better, you have grown up, moved on, into a brand new chapter of your life, craving free, beer or any alcohol free, more easily able to adapt and move on, putting habits of the past that hurt you far, far behind you, most especially when you wish you had what others have or just want something better than someone else's, for you are enough, life is bringing you what you need, you are taken care of and more easily able to be taken care of by life, easily able just after a few deep, deep and powerful steady breaths, you are absolutely sure that those jealous feelings are going away, you are content. And now as a more responsible adult, you actually forgive the past mistaken choice you once made at some weak moment to start drinking beer or any alcohol, forever releasing it from your life forever. You come to truly know, beer or any alcohol and beer or any alcohol drinking is far from being an old friend, it's a deadly enemy. One in which you must and will remove from your life at all costs. And your tastes change, improving in your favor, supporting your health, your life, actually extending your life and your health. Beer or any alcohol begins to taste, look and smell to you like burning rubber, or a glass, bottle or container, filled with dirt, motor oil and old cigarette ashes, uggh, how awful! It might even taste like motor oil or bodily wastes. How disgusting, how nauseating that smell, that taste and that sight! You've moved on, finding balance and harmony in your life. Even if you actually tasted beer or any alcohol, you'd feel sick from it, because you have relaxed your way into a newer and happier and healthier, better chapter of your life, one in which you are better supported, better balanced and harmonized, healthy, safe, free, beer or any alcohol free, feeling better about yourself and your life, so upbeat, so calm, so powerful, so peaceful and so relaxed, a winner in life, having moved on, free and safe at long last.

## Bedtime / Days End Induction

Just put your head back in your chair, close your eyes; just imagine feeling that calming and steady rhythm of your breath, in your own unique way, guiding you so steadily, so very powerfully and gently, so very familiar, and relaxing you, in your own bedroom, at Bedtime, at Days End, at night.

Just imagine it is dark outside now, nighttime, as your body slowly begins to wind down at the end of a long and busy day; your day is done; right now, it's just time to relax and to let go, as the day, this day, your day, has been put upon a shelf; you're done, that day is finished as you begin to completely unwind, let go, and ready yourself for a deep and soothing night of powerful rest. At this moment, there's nowhere to get to, mind and thoughts relax, really nothing to do, except relax, unwind, and let go. Just imagine yourself now, at bedtime in your bedroom, in your favorite comfortable pajamas, so restful and relaxing, surrounded and relaxingly supported by your comfortable and familiar bedtime environment, comfortable and familiar pillows, fluffy while supporting your neck and head, your back melting, just struggling up, into your very comfortable mattress and pillows, and you happily under your blankets, your arms and shoulders just where you like to have them, so very lazily over the fluffy blankets and sheets, while relaxing deeper and further, further and deeper, feeling waves of soothing, and ever stronger, spreading relaxation, unwinding your body from head to toe, as you relax and deeper and further, further and deeper, so heavy, so weary, so relaxed, relaxing, holding your book, the book you so relaxingly enjoy at bedtime, comfortably propped up and easily held by your weary, tired, heavy arms.

Imagine now yourself, so very tired, holding the heavy book, just maybe having lost your place, as your mind is so very tired and just wandering and relaxing so ever deeper, so carelessly, because you're so tired.

Even though you're tired, just open the cover, and turn to page one, lazily scan the page, turning to page two, while relaxing deeper and further, further and deeper, feeling waves of soothing, heavy and weary and ever stronger relaxation, unwinding your body from head to toe, as you relax and deeper and further, further and deeper, so heavy, so weary, so relaxed, relaxing, letting go, on each and every turn of the page. Page two, lazily scan the page, a little harder to do, a bit more blurry and out of focus, turning page two, even a little harder to do, into page three, what is in turn, more comfortably unfocused, while relaxing deeper and further, further and deeper, feeling waves of soothing, and ever stronger relaxation, unwinding your body from head to toe, as you relax and deeper and further, further and deeper, so heavy, so weary, so relaxed, relaxing, page four, while relaxing deeper and further, further and deeper, feeling waves of soothing, and ever stronger relaxation, your whole body, heavier and weary, so very drowsy, so very tired, unwinding your body from head to toe, as you relax and deeper and further, further and deeper, so heavy, so weary, so relaxed, eyes so heavy now, relaxing, just letting go. Relaxing so very heavy so much more weary, just the right thing to do, letting go of the day, relaxing and unwinding, your thoughts lighter and more carefree, more unfocused relaxing comfortably, weary. Letting the book fall now to the side, and relaxing completely, all over, ahh. So familiar and comfortable lying in your bed, just drifting off, heavy and weary, days end, eyes heavy, restful time beginning, Relaxing your body, your emotions, your mind, just ready to drift, and float, and dream, ever deeper, ever weary, so much more relaxed. Restful, warm and supported, just melting, now while relaxing 10,000 times deeper and further, further and deeper on each and every number that I count, as I count from one to twenty.

One, drifting deeper and further, further and deeper, deeper and deeper and deeper. Two, just drifting, and floating, and dreaming. . .

## Bowel Function Normalizing - Overcoming Uncontrolled Defecation

**Note:** You must be a qualified and certified Clinical Hypnosis professional and have a written note of authorization to perform this or any other complementary hypnosis session from the attending physician, psychiatrist, psychologist, etc., no exceptions.

Relax, relax, relax. And as you relax, you know it's time to begin a new and a better way of life; the time has come for you to begin to know a new and healthier way of life and living, so you do and you will, not because I say so, but because it's the nature of your own mind to do so. Of course you've realized and you've always really known, you'd be able to overcome the lack of feeling and sensation when it came to relieving yourself. You truly knew you wouldn't become a grown man and still have these situations happening to you, so unlike a baby, and just like a grownup that you are, so congratulations! Now you are truly and in fact, grown up enough to move into a new, healthier, happier, more improved, personally cleaner and clearer better chapter of your life, where past incidents and accidents have changed, having improved in your life unstoppably for the better. I wonder if you even yet realize how much easier this is going to be, to be so successful, so right, so grown up you are. You begin to pace yourself, relaxing yourself and finding your proper times and your proper body rhythms and cycles of when to go to and utilize the bathroom, when to try, when to know it's time and this just happens automatically, upon getting up in the morning, after lunch, after dinner, before bed, you are easily able to let go, release, liberate, only at the proper times, so you sense it, you feel it, you just know it. Without realizing this, your mind is just working on this, while you're awake, while you're asleep, even while you dream, successfully handling this, making things right, healthy, proper, just better, just right for you. You now stop and take the appropriate amount of time for yourself and any and all necessary functions. It's just no big deal, you are free of all and any old embarrassments, just as you deserve to be.

So as you relax even deeper, you and I both know and realize you have a very powerful mind, a mind capable of great things, both large and small. I wonder if that powerful unstoppable part of your mind that had once been allowing this to happen and working against you, is now willing to work with you, to provide for you in the truest and most powerful of ways, to allow you to rewire, re-circuit, re-balance, re-harmonize, re-circulate the blood flow, re-wire the nerves for proper sensitivity, messages, signals and feelings, allowing for more feeling, in just the right amounts and ways that work for you just perfectly, and each and every day and night, you only get better and better at this, forgiving your past, releasing any and all anger, upsetment, rage, doubt and even fear. So in the most powerful and unstoppably successful of ways, to allow you to regain your sense of feeling and sometimes sense of urgency when it comes to the normal functioning of your body, its needs, its proper and healthy functioning, and with all people and even animals, your need for food, your need to eliminate wastes naturally, just like everyone else's body does, or if you yet realize how truly easy it will be for you to do this, as you begin a brand new, healthier, happier, better chapter of your life right now, and it feels so good, so right, so unstoppably powerful, that you just know, it's underway, it's happening, yes it is, both it and you, are completely healthy and back to normal. You owe this kind of respect to yourself, and you freely give it, you deserve it, you win. Your body is balancing and so is your life, in the most healthy and beneficial ways, that are just perfect for you, almost as if in fact, someone has in fact, reset a switch or a dial or even some type of computer or thermostat within you somewhere, allowing you to comfortably be aware of your new, improved, better, and successful bowel habits and functions, in powerful, successful and amazing ways. You find things even interesting to read while there, maximizing your time while being true to yourself, performing all necessary functions just as you should and just as you need to, as a responsible person, who takes better care of himself. In fact, you are extremely motivated, energetic and unstoppably determined to take better care of yourself, right now, always and forever.

You know from deep down inside of you, holding it in is a losing battle, and yes, if you lose it, they'll know, of course they will, so you do better for yourself. You've decided to become a winner in your life, yes you have, so you find the time, you relax, you let it go, you win! You've decided to tackle your life, head on, you face the facts, and you do what is right and what needs to be done. You are proud of yourself, you are healthy, your body is developing just right, you look good, you deserve to, so you do, in fact, you are just as good as anyone else, maybe even better at some things or maybe many things. In fact, it's like you are jumping over this time in your life, back say, three years ago, before all of this began, in your mind, see yourself as you were back then, blend with the you that you once were, everything was more balanced, you felt your reactions, were at peace, carefree, feeling everything, it was so normal, it is so normal right now, just like back then. You can imagine an energy, like a cooling soothing energy, calming, balancing, re-sensitizing, lubricating, healing, restoring you in the very most complete of ways, but right now it's forever, you are whole, becoming better, healed, back to proper normalcy, intestines balancing, healing, restored, just as healthy and sensitive as they need to be to report all necessary information, just right for you. You think this will work, it will work, it does work, it worked, more easily than you've ever imagined, you succeed, congratulations. Where there is a will there is a way, you will your way, to be happy, healthy, body working well, reporting all that it needs to, you find your own body rhythms, your will, your way is to have a healthy, normal, balanced elimination system, healthy, normal, balanced reactions and regular, healthy, normal, balanced trips to the bathroom to naturally and normally eliminate your body wastes just as you know you should.

You feel good about this, you are so very confident, each and every day, each and every night, this is going to get easier, better, something you are more able to do, just so motivated, just as you once did in your past, almost like your body, emotions, mind and all that you are is moving back in time, practically able to just jump over this unpleasant part of your life, and begin again, begin anew, a fresh start, your fresh start, a fresh, healthier, cleaner, better you, proud of yourself, you deserve this. You feel the attention, admiration and respect of others for you, and their love is something you deserve and something you appreciate, something you have and something you give to them and reflect back in a powerful harmony of support in your life, a soothing, so right "give and take," a flow, so right, so easy, just for you, now even better, even easier, than ever before. You forgive and release the past, powerfully and absolutely and move beyond any and all of its challenges and blockages, powerfully releasing any and all negativity and negative thoughts, letting it go, letting it go, feeling only good feelings from those times, no matter where they came from, feeling fresh, alive and powerful, like you've got the whole world in the palm of your hand or maybe even in your back pocket; you are a success, and a winner, smart, so motivated, just you believing in you, yes you do, a new strength, and a new sensitivity is forming in you and so very able to do what needs doing here, even beyond the opinions of others, regardless of where they may have came from.. You forgive, your opinion matters, you count, you win, you succeed. You see and even feel the love and appreciation of your loving family, the respect and caring of your friends. They feel respect and interest in all areas of your life, the success of all these people is yours also and importantly including the respect and personal interest in your well being and success of your teachers, all people and all things in your life want you to succeed, so you relax, and you do. You have the attention and respect of all these people, and you feel good, you feel lively, energetic, self-respectful, active, brisk, full of life, you are truly capable and powerful, this is easy.

## Comfort and Ease (Pain Management)

Your powerful and dynamic mind has all the power you need to activate comfort and ease, more and more complete comfort and relief. You are breathing easily and deeply and relaxing your way into a better life, calm and balanced, relaxed, more and more easily free of discomfort, most especially in the mornings. You are finding yourself sleeping easily and powerfully right through the night, easily able to fall back to sleep easily and naturally when you need to, slowly breathing deep and steady breath, creating numbness in areas where you need it most. You are finding newer and better ways of becoming and remaining upbeat; you are unstoppably determined to rise to the top and be upbeat, beating this situation, regardless of event, circumstance, feeling, thought or opinions. Each and every morning, you begin the fight anew, rising to the top and absolutely thriving, almost like you are jumping back in time to a time about X years ago, and now and forever moving into a better place of empowerment and realization. You are ripping apart in powerful ways those things that once ripped you apart; you are unstoppably triumphant and winning easily at this.

Things are only getting better and better for you.

## Controlling Tinnitus (Ringing Ears- Ear Noise)

**Note:** You must be a qualified and certified Clinical Hypnosis professional and have a written note of authorization to perform this or any other complementary hypnosis session from the attending physician, psychiatrist, psychologist, etc., no exceptions.

So relax, relax, relax. And as you relax, you are focusing more and more, more and more on how truly and deeply and wonderfully and truly peacefully relaxed you really are and nothing else at this moment really matters, except how comfortable your really are. And in this profound moment, you have chosen to relax into a new truth for a new day in your life. A new and profoundly powerful truth in you life, your world, your universe, beginning right now and for the rest of your life, you have correctly chosen to relax through any and all adversities, any and all challenges and any and all frictions in your life, regardless of how important or even overpowering they might seem to be or how important they seem to have once been. For right now in this moment, you have correctly chosen instead, to empower yourself in the most beneficial ways possible. You relax and really trust in the true fact that your life readily and most powerfully supports you in the most magnificent and beneficial ways. And you always choose to focus upon hearing your own inner wisdom, inner truth, inner voice, relaxing through any and all old stubbornness or resistances, with ease, poise, power and confidence, always finding new and better ways to relax, to heal, to thrive and to prosper in all that is your life. You correctly recognize that the opinions of others are reflections of their truth and wisdom, each word and thought and emotion, is something you can choose to gain from or to let go of, always trusting from deep within yourself that you are always making the correct choices, because you are always either learning or succeeding, in each and every circumstance, each and every day and night, having the very best attitude about all that is your life, you are always trusting in the inner wisdom that has always supported you and allowed you to thrive and succeed in each and every moment and throughout all that is your life. Each and every day and night you are reassured by your own inner guidance and your ability to transcend all and any limits that once appeared within your life, relaxing and releasing those limits powerfully, truly and forever, even better and instead learning to love, to trust and support yourself, in the most promising ways possible.

So from this place of real, true and permanent support, as you relax even deeper and deeper, you begin to think and to see within your mind, a beautiful place, perhaps a beach just before sunset. You are standing on this beach, right by the water's edge, right there in your bare feet, calm, comfortable, relaxed all over, feeling really, really good, deeply and profoundly calm and relaxed all over. You feel the gentle waves by the salt waters edge touching your toes, you imagine the smell and can almost taste the salt air, the gentle breezes touching the rest of your skin, the calming embrace of the warm water as it first touches your toes and the rest of your feet, you feel almost as if, the water is a form of soothing, even healing energy, as it comes in, gently touching and soothing your feet. You can feel an almost magnificent energy, moving up from your feet, calming you, soothing you, maybe almost even healing you, moving up from your feet and moving up your body. As the water recedes again, you can actually imagine, all old unwanted, unneeded, unnecessary energies from your body, draining out and far, far away from you. Your attention, is calm, relaxed and focused, you look out upon the water, you see far away, a ship off near the horizon, yet in another direction, a buoy with a light on its top, marking the waterway for ships. And you look down and see your toes again, embraced by the water. You can feel different ways the light and gentle breezes touch your skin in various ways, how different scents of the seawater seem to you as the breezes blow. And truly recognize how remarkable it is to be able to and how you really can, focus your attention, on whatever it is you wish to notice, or to feel, or even not notice or even ignore. So in this moment and in all future moments, you further realize that you easily and truly have the ability, a power, in a powerful yet very relaxed way, to successfully focus your attention or to even de-focus your attention, on whatever it is you wish to concentrate upon or ignore. And in this moment, you have correctly, really and truly chosen from deep, deep inside of you, to extend this ability to the area of your hearing. That's right, you have within you the ability to tune into a voice, a sound, a noise, or to even powerfully and deliberately tune it out completely

as you wish, whenever you wish. And in this and all future moments, you have
chosen to tune out any and all sounds, any and all noises, both everything and
anything that sounds less than pleasing to you or that has in any way, interfered
with your life or happiness or wellness in any way. You know, its almost as if
someone has in fact, or really indeed, turned down a switch or a dial within you
somewhere, lowering the volume of a sound or a noise that you have correctly chosen
to relax out of and away from. You have relinquished all unpleasant noises and you
are powerfully releasing from your life, or perhaps even tuning to a frequency you
just can no longer hear, a frequency well outside of the human range of hearing, both
now and forever. But it really is of little concern to you, because you achieve true
and limitless success, through the power of your subconscious mind and from the
dynamic healing power of all that you are each and every day and each and every
night. You have absolutely and correctly chosen to tune into all the things that are
wonderfully pleasant to hear, (perhaps the smiling whispers and laughter of happy
and delighted children) and to tune out all the sounds and unnecessary noises,
putting them out of your head and all that is your life, that you are now each and
every day and night, retuned, reset, readjusted, recalibrated, becoming free, free, free
at last, both always and forever. You can actually feel a shift in your consciousness
and all that are your thoughts and all that are your emotions, really just feeling the
old energies from the past, rising up, off, off and far, far away from you, right now,
always and forever. And from deep, deep within your powerful and dynamic mind,
most especially your subconscious mind, you have made a very real, very true, very
powerful, most successful choice, to begin, with each and every beat of your calm,
happy and healthy heart and with each and every breath that you take, to begin to
heal, realign, retune, reset, readjust, recalibrate your sense of hearing, better and
more comfortably, than ever before, better and better each and every day and night,
in the ways that are most powerfully and dynamically beneficial to you, allowing you
to relax, heal and be supported by all that is your hearing, in all the most beneficial
ways possible, daytimes, nighttimes, while you are awake and even while you sleep,
now always and forever!

## Coping with Illness and Medical Procedures

You begin to relax into a better way of living, feeling and thinking. You have
improved your perspective, and improved yourself. You begin to see, feel and always
choose to react to things in the best possible ways, for yourself and for those you
love, but most especially for yourself. And you health is fine, whole and functional;

you begin to trust in life, your body, your emotions, your thoughts, and all that you are. You trust in your choices, realigning from deep, deep within, that you've put the right people around you to support you in the best of all possible ways. All of your medical choices are the correct ones, your doctors are the best, they are the tops, they are capable, you are confident, strong, clear and always rising above any and all limitations in the best of all possible of ways. You also realize now, from deep, deep within yourself, that you have complete control of your actions and reactions. You are unstoppably determined to rise above any and all uncomfortable, unpleasant and unsupportive feelings from your past of ever being (name the emotional feelings they have): overwhelmed, depressed and mad. Instead and even better, you have become unstoppably determined to improve your life, truly relaxing into a brand new healthier and better chapter of your life, redefined, easily able to become and remain: problem-free, completely challenge-oriented, truly rising above with ease, filled with confidence and comfort, you are happy, pleased with this new ability to transcend all past blockages and limits. Forever and always having relaxed your way into a newer, happier, lighter and better, more easy going chapter of your life. You are comfortable and powerfully able, to feel well and to (name what you seek to enable): enjoy the birth of your baby, making friends and peace with your new love and blessing, your child. You do this for yourself and for your baby's sake, so easy, so calm, so relaxed, you rise up, powerfully flowing over, around and through any and all past blockages, as you supremely thrive and succeed. All of your life is now comfortably and forever working in your favor to support you, in all that you think, all that you feel, all that you do, each and every experience, even (name procedures) an MRI, choosing to make all experiences you have, fun, peaceful, calming. You take a deep, deep breath now, and you let any and all blockage go, just go, just drift and float away, analyzation free, you thrive, you succeed you win. You easily and forever flow over and around and through any and all blockage, like a river. . . easily polished, from any and all past experience.

## Eating Veggies - Anti-Gagging Response Suggestions

In order to maintain good, vigorous and vibrant health now as an adult, you know that you need to eat a healthy, well balanced diet, rich in the basic food groups that sustain and maintain your healthy, vital life. You must eat foods rich in nutrients. Your body is your most valuable asset, your body's health is most important to you. Only you can take care of your body and your health. You owe yourself and your body the proper respect of good health. Self-Preservation is the first rule of life. Self-Preservation is the first rule of your life. As an adult, you also know that it is your responsibility to rise above all limitations of the past and to make the most of your life. So beginning right now and for the rest of your life, whenever you are presented with a meal, you will consume a healthy balanced portion of food, consuming a healthy balanced, slowly consumed, slowly chewed and enjoyed food, from the four basic food groups including vegetables, consuming what is put or presented before you, including the foods that you enjoy and especially the foods that your body will enjoy, in order to maintain health and vitality. You enjoy proper, slowly consumed, properly digested, adult-oriented meals, with foods rich in vitamins and nutrients. You enjoy and recognize from deep within this proper diet of adult-oriented foods is necessary for maintaining vibrant longevity and health, long life, foods that will easily help, assist and maintain your body's health, foods that will help you to cleanse yourself internally, cleansing unpleasant past emotions and memories from past eating experiences as well, each and every time you eat, whether you realize it or not. You shall consume all healthful foods, including vegetables, because, in your new habits for health, you put behind yourself, the reactions you once had as a child and self-respectfully now do what's proper for your health as an adult. All healthy foods were put here for a reason, and the reason is to maintain all human life, especially yours. All memories of unpleasant past eating experiences, are just that, only memories, just like a dream, are right now, drifting away, drifting away, drifting away, until your mind and your emotions are now clear and free; YOU ARE FREE FROM YOUR PAST, YOU ARE UNLIMITED, YOU TRANSCEND, YOU ARE NOW A PERSON THAT CONSUMES HEALTHY FOODS, INCLUDING VEGETABLES WITH EASE, POISE, GRACE and COMPLETE RELAXED COMFORTABLITY. BEGINNING RIGHT NOW, AND FOR THE REST OF YOUR LIFE, you rise above all limiting memories and concepts and labels and responses and limits from any and all moments from your past, releasing the past, forgiving it, moving comfortably and powerfully on and the new you, emerges, each and every day and each and every night, getting stronger and stronger, healthier and healthier, only better and better. You easily transcend all past experiences of limitation by relaxing into the right now that is and remains your life.

Before you consume any vegetables, you relax, you deep breathe slow steady breaths. You relax by breathing slowly, all that you are and especially the muscles of your throat, feeling soothing elegant relaxation spreading throughout all that you are. Take a deep, deep breath and relax even deeper now and allow yourself to feel this powerful and unstoppable calmness flowing through you like a mighty, magnificent river of relaxation energy. As you relax, you notice the pleasant and distinctive aromas of the food before you, pleasant and enjoyable sensations, you now really, truly enjoy. When you consume your vegetables, you shall slowly chew the food in your mouth and slowly swallow the food when it is broken down enough to swallow, with each and every forkful, spoonful or mouthful, chewing all foods completely before swallowing, especially your vegetables for good health, knowing the benefit you are providing yourself with each mouthful, with each bite, until your meal is completed. You assimilate and absorb all of the beneficial nutrients and they become beneficial means to a healthy new you, taking in all of the beneficial life maintaining properties.

You release any and all old past traumas, successfully, easily and comfortably. You now realize you can, you do and you will both easily and comfortably breathe through your nose, in between bites, chewing slowly, carefully, comfortably and completely, swallowing easily, digesting completely and comfortably. And you move in to a new chapter of your life, the rest of your life, a healthy, and new beneficial time, beginning right now and for the rest of your life. You are becoming one with your new habits for health, healing, rising above, transcending any and all old past limits, into pronounced new health, vigor and vitality. You are freed from your past and you are a new, more alive, healthier you, a person who eats properly and truly enjoys life, empowered in all that you do. Having risen above, you are unstoppable, feeling so wonderful.

## Female Fertility Activation

Note: You must be a qualified and certified Clinical Hypnosis professional and have a written note of authorization to perform this or any other complementary hypnosis session from the attending physician, psychiatrist, psychologist, etc., no exceptions.

You relax deeper and further and as you relax deeper and further, you feel almost as if, you've just relaxed through a barrier of some kind, for yes, in fact you have! You are actually feeling as though, from places deep in side of you, that you are inspired, you are released and in fact, your body temperature is going up and up, in ways so right, so beneficial, just right for you, almost as if in fact, someone has reset a switch or a dial or a computer console, deep inside of you, raising and regulating your body temperature, both easily and effectively lowering your F.S.H. levels to proper balanced levels, just right for you and even more powerfully, your metabolism is balancing, fully allowing your lymphatic system to detoxify you, powerfully and truly and most amazingly, cleaning and clearing and completely cleansing your liver and digestive organs, in fact, you can really feel the warmth there, feeling that warmth there, a healthy glow, a balanced and better energy, a

golden-white light of unstoppable healing energy, balancing, restoring, clearing, cleansing, and healing you, in the most amazing and truest of ways, in fact, you feel like you've got the whole world in the palm of your hand, just smiling all over, because in fact, you have been re-balanced, and recalibrated, in the very most amazing of ways. And you feel at one with your life, your healing, your balancing, your re-calibration, all of your organs and the highest wisdom of your body, as well as Divine blessings and restoration from above, are working, now, not because I say so but because the Divine within you has willed this and it flows throughout all that You are in unstoppable and profound healing ways. All of the femininity contained within you really truly feels like it's coming alive right now. You menstrual cycle is actually balancing and activating as well, absolutely, you are a powerful fully functioning female. All that is the energy of your pelvis, physically, emotionally, mentally and even spiritually, is coming into alignment, activating as never before and you actually feel better, truly better than you have in years, in fact you are feeling fantastic. In fact, truly, you are getting your body's room ready for the little one you are bringing forth into this world. And you feel at one with all the things you are doing, releasing anything and everything, most especially relaxing and releasing any and all doubt, washing away all old unwanted, unneeded despair, moving on from any imbalance, just letting it all go, in very most powerful and profound ways, releasing anything and everything that needs to move on, absolutely having no room for anything that once blocked you, allowing and truly manifesting only and just, everything and anything that needs to be there. For right now in this moment, you are absolutely and definitely sure, you are relaxing into whole, healthy, balanced, restored, peaceful, calm, Divinely harmonized, well healed, body, life, world, existence, of a fertile body, so right, just ready, for the baby, your baby, that's ready to come along into your life, to make you smile in fact, you've already bonded on higher levels, relaxing into this new better chapter of your life, its happening, only getting better and better, right now, successfully, unstoppably, truly, you are completely certain and of this you are and you remain,
totally doubtless.

## Free of Drinking Wine (Beer or any Alcohol)

You are finding new and better ways of supporting yourself and your life, finding newer and better ways of beating stress and dealing with your life. You are free of wanting, craving or needing wine (beer or any alcohol) in any way, most especially when you are upset or nervous, free of harming yourself with wine (beer or any alcohol), finding just a few deep and steady breaths to calm yourself down. You are free of wanting, craving or needing wine (beer or any alcohol) in any way most especially when you are in a good mood you turn away from wine (beer or any alcohol), finding newer, healthier and better ways to keep yourself going, wine (beer or any alcohol) free, healthy, happy, safe and strong. You are free of wanting, craving or needing wine (beer or any alcohol) in any way, most especially when you are looking forward to something, finding even greater happiness in what you are looking forward to, finding maximum intensity in what you are looking forward to, feeling so much better free of drinking or wanting or craving wine (beer or any alcohol) in any way. You've moved on, you've grown up and you are feeling better each and every day, in each and every way. You are free of wanting, craving or needing wine (beer or any alcohol) in any way most especially when you are stressed or even if you are having a hard time dealing with certain situations, you find better, more relaxed, more adaptive ways of dealing with your life, easily able to trust in yourself and easily able to get through anything, wine (beer or any alcohol) free, craving free, easily and more able to get through anything and everything, free of wine (beer or any alcohol), than you ever did with it. For in a great deal of ways, getting only stronger and better, you have grown up, moved on, into a brand new chapter of your life, craving free, wine (beer or any alcohol) free, more easily able to adapt and move on, putting habits of the past that hurt you far, far behind you, most especially when you wish you had what others have or just want something better than someone else's, for you are enough, life is bringing you what you need, you are taken care of and more easily able to be taken care of by life, easily able just after a few deep, deep and powerful steady breaths, you are absolutely sure that those jealous feelings are going away, you are content. And now as a more responsible adult, you actually forgive the past mistaken choice you once made at some weak moment to start drinking wine (beer or any alcohol), forever releasing it from your life forever. You come to truly know, wine (beer or any alcohol) and wine (beer or any alcohol) drinking is far from being an old friend, it's a deadly enemy. One which you must and will remove from your life at all costs. And your tastes change, improving in your favor, supporting your health, your life, actually extending your life and your health. Wine (beer or any alcohol) begins to taste, look and smell to you like burning rubber, or a glass, bottle or container, filled with dirt, motor oil and old cigarette ashes, uggh, how awful! How disgusting, how nauseating that smell, that taste and that sight! More and more alcohol is toxic; it's a poison, as poisonous as drain cleaner is to you. So you've moved on, alcohol is out of your life, both now, always and forever. You've moved on, finding balance and harmony in your life. Even if you actually tasted wine (beer or any alcohol), you'd feel sick from it, or just be sick about it, because you have relaxed your way into a newer and happier and healthier, better chapter of your life, one in which you are better supported, better balanced and harmonized, healthy, safe, free, wine (beer or any alcohol) free, feeling better about yourself and your life, so upbeat, so calm, so powerful, so peaceful and so relaxed, a winner in life, having moved on, free and safe at long last.

# Healing Past Hurts and Traumas

You shall be free of being overwhelmed by your fantasizing or thoughts, now and forever. For fantasies and thoughts are products of a healthy mind, however, you shall embrace each fantasy and each and every thought, in a healthy and happy way, smiling and confident from deep, deep within, with you completely in charge of your life and you completely in charge of your fantasy life as well, as you have always been in each and every moment. Right now, you relax deeper and deeper, even more deeply than just a few moments ago, and you begin and truly do release all trauma and pain from your past, any memories of the past are like an old dream, just drifting away, drifting way, drifting away, as you relax deeper and deeper, deeper than ever, until all that is your mind and all that are your emotions, in fact, all of you is clear and free. For right now, you live in the true power of the present moment, right now you release all of your entire past and its influence over you that it once but no longer has, for your past has little if any influence over you, now or at anytime in the future. Your past and any damaging influence is less and less important to you each day and in every way, right now you are relaxed and you are liberated. Right now you choose to relax into your life and live and enjoy, by just letting go. Moment by moment, you release your past and any and all of its past limiting pain and influence, for it less and less important to you, it is unimportant to you, so even better for you right now, the brightness of your happy, healthy future is where your focus is and where your best times are, you look ahead to the brightness of healthy and very happy times ahead. You transcend any and all past limits right now by relaxing deeper and further, you rise above it all and you heal, you really, really heal. You relax, you transcend, you rise above, you heal, yes you do, right now and forever! If at any time you need to release any and all pain and any and all hurt, any and all trauma, any and all blockages or pain, you shall easily and powerfully remember and perform the following post hypnotic suggestion, with ease, poise, power, effectiveness, success and grace, with optimum Impact and results, listen carefully and remember what I say.

You must first assume a comfortable body position, free from all activities. Then you will take a slow steady, deep, deep breath, as you exhale it and say release,

release, release. Then another breath, you'll exhale it and say release, release, release. And finally a third breath, and say release, release, release, - - forgiven! In that moment, you will be released, forgive, calm, comfortable, strong, balanced, clear, restarted, rejuvenated, powerfully and unstoppably healed, having truly and powerfully moved on. . And your pain and influence of the past, both real and imagined, will immediately diminish, draining away to nothing. And each and every time you complete this task, it just becomes easier and easier, you get better and better. In fact, truly and in every way, you succeed, free, freed, free at last!

## Hypnosis Healing Activation

You shall now see before you Four gifts given to you from smiling shining unconditionally loving beings from higher realms or planes of existence, perhaps angels or spiritual masters, completely loving, unconditionally loving you in the most powerful of ways. They set these four wonderful gifts before you. You feel rejuvenated and very alive, almost as if, something truly wonderful is about to happen to you. The gifts they bring are a beautiful jar and three bottles. You see before you, one jar and three bottles in any way that is very pleasing to you. In the first jar is a beautiful scented creamy lotion. You now reach out and open the jar, applying this cooling and deeply soothing cream contained within it to the areas of your body that have been once in your past afflicted with any kind illness, discomfort, disease or pain. As you apply this you are allowing this cream, as it is absorbed right into your skin, deeply penetrating your skin and allowing any and all of your pain to more and more become pleasantly and pleasingly numb, slowly melting away, melting away, melting away and as you allow it to do just that, allowing yourself to relax, more and more, deeper and deeper, relaxing and releasing any and all pain and discomfort, leaving any and all pain away, as all of your pain, drains away, drains away, you can actually feel yourself relaxing as any and all old pain becomes pleasantly numb and all places where you put this cream on your skin, relax, release, unknot and unwind. As this cream melts deeply into your skin, you realize that the purpose of this cream is to not only to reduce any pain, which this cream is doing just fine, cooling, soothingly, powerfully, really and successfully, but also its consecrating your body with some kind of healing energy. With each and every breath that you take and with each and every beat of your heart and each and every stroke or movement of your hands, as you see your hands mentally moving across your skin, you allow the pain to melt away and open your body's energy channels allowing the body to heal and release all or any pain, slowly yet completely draining any and all pain away, flowing away like a mighty river or an ocean. All of your life energy now begins to flow and like a steam or like a vapor, all your pain, discomfort and any illness or disharmony, begins to melt away, as you absolutely release any and all pain. You are deeply, deeply and powerfully soothed by this cream, physically, but as any and all of your physical pain melts any, so does all of your emotional discomfort, all pain and any fear, you powerfully release any and all thoughts of discomfort, you can actually feel them going, going, gone, gone away from you and out of your life. And as they leave you, deeply, truly and powerfully, absolutely and powerfully, you are restored by the power of all that you are (and the power of your spirit) and your (spiritual) connection to the greatest healer of all healers, the Creator of all things. Allow this cream to consecrate your body and absolutely and truly, activate your healing. Allow it to soothe you and calm you. This cream destroys all areas of energy disruption and blockage and wiping away all and any areas of energy that might contain darkness, truly and deeply allowing the pathways of shimmering, shining light to open. It allows for true and complete illness removal and for powerful and true energy healing upgrade. It begins to activate and open your natural ability to channel and guide the healing golden-white healing light to move though you freely and easily, activating your true healing ability, powerfully and forever. The power to heal is activating very powerfully within you, right now and forever. Now, close the jar of healing cream, put the jar of cream down, setting it aside just for now, for it is time to move on to the first of the bottles which has been presented to you. As you open the first small bottle that can never truly be emptied, you imagine a pleasant, beautiful aroma, you put this bottle to your lips and drink from it, consuming smoothly and easily, just a small amount of this very powerful elixir from within this bottle. As you do you feel a gentle playful energy that begins to spread down to your stomach and continues to spread throughout all of your body, a feeling of happy excitement, sort of like when you were a kid, with your birthday approaching, happy and building excitement, growing from deeply within you, just unstoppable, growing and growing. This elixir absolutely begins to restore your body, strengthening you and it rejuvenates, restores, balances and invigorates you. It begins to spread throughout your body to rebuild you and to shine healing golden-white light throughout all of you, causing your life force and vitality energies to steadily rise within each part of your body, from each and every system, to each and every organ, to each and every tissue, to each and every cell, to each and every molecule, to each and every smallest particles of you, to each and every aspect of energy of who you are. You can feel its effect on you, in your muscles, in your blood, in your organs, your connective tissues, even in your bones. You relax even deeper, you let out a sigh of relaxation and relief as you exhale, YES, this really is working, almost as if in fact, someone has given your whole being a jump-start. You smile confidently to yourself, you are clear, you are confident and you are getting stronger, because this is working and you just know its happening in the ways that are just best for you. Now that this bottle's contents are working for you, so you can put it down now. You pick up the next gift bottle and you wonder what this one does, those who brought this to you are smiling at you and beaming with pride and love and you can feel, notice and truly even know, you are being supported by them and their wisdom, healing, their timelessness and fearless inspiration, knowing this better than ever before. You open it, it smells wonderful, almost like a beautiful spring day, you take a sip from it, it combines with the energy from the previous bottle and the jar you first opened and it instills within you, a very powerful sense of optimism and very, very powerful relaxed determination. You can absolutely feel this activating forever throughout all that you are and all that is your life. And all of your powerful and bracing feelings of triumphs, victories, breakthroughs and successes from your past, all of the inspiration of any and all of your greatest moments, all of this magnificent beneficial healing energy, is unstoppably flowing throughout you. You are completely inspired, to thrive and succeed, you are calm, relaxed and can and will only succeed. And as this liquid flows throughout you, doing its job in the most wonderful of ways, you just know you are going to overcome and to thrive. Your healing empowerment is endless, free of bounds or limits! You can only be victorious, successful, whole, well and wonderful! And so you are! All of your life is working to support you and you thrive in very real ways as yet perhaps even unimagined! And now that this is a part of you, getting only to be more and more a part of you, you can close it and set it aside. Now you pick up the final bottle, its contents look like a beautiful nighttime sky filled with the most magnificent stars. It smells like a combination of all things wonderful in life, something like the ocean, roses and wild flowers. And now you drink from this as well. And instantly, you feel a surge of power, its connecting you to higher realms of healing in this universe, it is uniting all of these healing substances powerfully within you, you can feel it, an unstoppable smile begins most powerfully from within you. You smile to yourself, this one is uniting and healing in wonderful harmony, all that you are physically, balancing and healing in conjunction with every emotional aspect and feeling you have, balancing and healing in conjunction with all that is your mind, intellect, ideas and thoughts and utilizing as a source of energy, all that is your spirit, completely empowering you to thrive, heal and to rejuvenate, in the most amazing of ways, impressing everyone, most especially you. You are calm relaxed, releasing, restoring, rejuvenating, healing, deeply and most powerfully inspired, relaxed, yet completely assured that you can, you will and you do thrive and succeed. You recognize that you are focused on a brighter future that begins right now. You thank these beings, they smile, their light intensifies and fades, slowly fading from your view, but you really truly know that they'll always be there for you and guiding your healing, for your healing is here, you thrive, you heal, you succeed, you begin anew, calm and strong, focused and doubtless, relaxing into and truly beginning a brand new healthy chapter of your life, recreated, re-harmonized, powerfully assured and powerfully determined and forever inspired. Now, always and forever, so be it!

---

# Illness Management

**Note:** You must be a qualified and certified Clinical Hypnosis professional and have a written note of authorization to perform this or any other complementary hypnosis session from the attending physician, psychiatrist, psychologist, etc., no exceptions.

Relax deeper and deeper and as you do, you allow yourself a new thought, a powerful thought, a thought that will create relaxation and profound improvement in your life. You may be or have been considered ill via a diagnosis you have received, but in this moment, you decide, that you are the power in your life so right now, as you have always done in your life, you are going to rise above being ill, you are going to absolutely rise above being sick, you are going to take all of your personal power back and with each and every deep and steady breath that you take, you will absolutely rise above whatever symptoms you had or felt or had imagined having and you will transcend, release and rise above what limits have been imposed upon you by this condition, in this very moment, to truly and powerfully both save and live your life.

Beginning right now and for the rest of your life, you relax, you rise above, you trust and you support yourself calmly, easily, brilliantly and very powerfully, creating inner and outer harmony in all that you are, your body, emotions, mind, and even your spirit. All old limiting opinions and feelings and stresses and fears from your past, whether they came from you in any way or from the words or actions of someone else, limiting concepts that had once held you back, are just drifting away, drifting away, drifting away, far away, very far away from you. And they are becoming less and less important to you, with each and every breath that you take and with every beat of your heart and in each and every moment of your life, now and forever. Going, going, gone, and gone forever and always. You'll hardly ever think about them and even if you do, it will be in relation to how much better off you are free of them. What is replacing those old useless, meaningless feelings and what is becoming more and more unshakably important, more and more your own, more and more an actual, real and true lasting part of you, is a greater energy, a limitless energy, it is your new greater self-confidence, your new stronger and more powerful self, your improved more harmonized you. You are becoming more and more powerful, more and more dynamic, more and more healed summoning those healing energies from within yourself in each and every respect, and in each and every day. You feel clear, confident, strong, clear, confident, strong and clear. Truly and in fact, you are confident, whole and healing and, relaxed, confident, clear and strong.

Relax deeper and deeper now and allow yourself to see, to picture, to feel, to imagine, think about and or to even know, truly for a fact know as a new more empowered and truly active part of you and your life, a time from your past, a time when you are well, powerful, harmonized, whole well, a time when you felt truly wonderful. You remember a time when you were wonderful in every way, when you just seemed to flow. This time your life is truly supportive, because in a supportive, nurturing way, your life is now better than ever truly supporting you and your health and your healing and each and every aspect of your life and this time, the Universe wants you to truly succeed. Now breathe again and exhale and allow a newer and even stronger image to come into your truly powerful and dynamic unstoppable mind. And in this image, see and really know that a newer, stronger, healthier, more whole you is unstoppably and forever emerging. The energy of this limitless, always successful, empowered you, is merging with you, merging with you and is now steadily becoming one with you, exhale again, as a confirmation and feel this wonderful energetic upgrade becoming one with all that your are, body, emotions, mind, spirit, this is you, being supported by this energy, daytimes, night times and even as you sleep and dream, all that You are all that you do, supports you in your wholeness, wellness and great powerful inner harmony, a balanced liberated you, with positive and loving, life inspiring healthy feelings. You relax, you deep breathe and you allow this new empowered you to balance, harmonize and heal, liberating from deep inside of you, from places deep within of your greatest understanding, fully and truly liberating your inner wisdom and greatest healing. Now as you exhale again, you allow this image to forever merge with you, feel this new, improved, limitless, powerful energy, one with you, now and forever, comfortableness, with poise and ease, relaxed strength and calm grace, becoming one with all that You are body, emotions, mind and consciousness and even the limitless and everlasting strength of your spirit. You are in powerful inner and outer harmony, you feel like you are smiling in the inside and even on the outside, throughout your entire body and life. You are peaceful, powerful, strong and you are always succeeding, becoming in each and every moment, an inspiration to everyone you meet. You surprise, amaze and astound everyone, most especially and permanently you, forever and always, with the beauty of your life and your healing. Now relax even deeper, and experience the very strong, wonderful, supportive feelings of success, ease, confidence, mental clearness and limitless health and relaxed grace, stress-free, liberated, focused, calm and strong. This is you, empowered, strong, in everlasting powerful harmony. You are now merged with the feelings of each and every new success in all that you do. You are supported by your body, by people and by life, because you are vital and valuable and strong, clearly, and confidently, because you can light up the world, with your truly powerful and dynamic mind. Truly, you are truly and unstoppably getting profoundly better and better, each and every day, each and every night and in every moment.

Then you will take a slow steady, deep, deep breath, as you exhale it and say release, release, release. Then another breath, you'll exhale it and say release, release, release. And finally a third breath, and say release, release, release, - - healing, moving on!

Once you have completed this, you will slip into a deep, deep state of calming soothing relaxation, far deeper than you are right now. And your profound empowerment and limitless confidence, your energy and healing harmony will immediately activate. With every breath that you take, with every beat of your heart, your strength builds, you relax and you are freer and freer to live your life, connecting the world and its people, connecting with yourself and your vitality, amazing and lighting up, everyone you connect with, especially in a new and most profound way with yourself and your body's wellness, in each and every moment.

## Insomnia with Parkinson's Disease

You are re-tuning, resetting, and re-calibrating, all that is your brain, each and every thought, each and every feeling and even perhaps yet most assuredly each and every one of your mental pathways to work now, completely in your favor to generate healing, wellness, and balance into a better night's rest for yourself. It's almost like just imagining now that you are comfortably and floatingly walking into a computer room of some kind and resetting your brain computer to work in your favor to insure comfort, ease, peace, balance, centeredness and calming, soothing comfort in each and every way, to insure a calmer set of experiences, thoughts, actions, reactions, as you are completely sure of this, only getting more and more sure of yourself just as you surely relax into this most assuredly and completely, while you are awake, but most especially while you sleep and dream. In the face of any old and uncomfortable reaction from your past, because of any old and uncomfortable, unwanted, unneeded, hurtful or useless patterns or reactions, your newer, better balanced and more improved, more relaxed you, is now responding in specific and more actively and effectively balanced ways to provide you with all of the substances you require or you need to make your life and night's rest a better, more healthy, more balanced, more peaceful, more sustaining, more soothing, more calming, more easy place to live from and enjoy. Even if you do or did wake up, your reaction will be to deep breathe, slow and steady breath, just as if you were breathing in Divinely guided, golden-white healing energy and flowing it into the areas of your body that will be more and more completely soothed, healed and balanced the very most from your healing breath. On each and every breath, you are calming and balancing from deeply within; your breath balances out, restores you, truly harmonizes you in ways just perfect for you while instantly sustaining your heart, blood pressure and blood vessels, sustaining your life force and strengthening your vitality, in ways most perfect and beneficial to you. You can almost just imagine the golden-white energy just flowing through your nose and mouth, and through your entire body, powerfully, unstoppably, in spite of anything and because it can, calming and soothing you all over, deeply, easily, naturally, powerfully and completely. You can almost just imagine the golden-white energy just flowing into your arms, calming, balancing, resting and soothing them. You can almost just imagine the golden-white energy just flowing into your legs, calming, balancing, resting and soothing them. You can imagine the golden-white energy just flowing into your feet, calming, melting them into calmness and soothing them thoroughly, deeply, truly and absolutely. You can really just imagine the golden-white energy just flowing into your hands, calming, melting them into calmness and soothing them thoroughly, absolutely and unstoppably. You really just know, that the golden-white energy just flowing into each and every area or part of your body, brain, emotions, mind, and spirit, calming, melting all of you into calmness and soothing you thoroughly, deeply, truly and absolutely. This flowing and ever-growing calmness energy is persistent, pervasive and ever more effective. Even if you became fully awake, after just a few deep, slow and steady breaths, you will effectively calm down, relax all over, and gently lull yourself back to a comfortable, dynamically succeeding night of peaceful, well-deserved rest, relaxation, and ease. It's almost like waves of calming, soothing relaxation are washing up over your entire being, your arms, legs, hands and feet, so heavy, so calm, so balanced, so relaxed, so balanced, so harmonized, so rested, so restored, so sleepy, so weary, so drowsy, so calm, so relaxed, so unwound, so loose, so limp, so ready for more rest, so at rest, so weary, so drowsy, so relaxed, deeply and truly all over. And whether you realize it or not, with each and every breath you are taking, with each and every beat of your heart, your powerful and unstoppable mind, your calm and balanced, steady and supportive emotions, and your Divinely guided and powerfully unshakable spirit, are now all in harmony, working in your favor, to create and manifest better and better ways of you succeeding at this in clever and creative, sure and unstoppable ways, as you creatively and adaptively succeed at this, in the well-rested, glowing, most certain and precise of ways.

# Irritable Bowel Syndrome And Acid Reflux Suggestions

**Note:** You must be a qualified and certified Clinical Hypnosis professional and have a written note of authorization to perform this or any other complementary hypnosis session from the attending physician, psychiatrist, psychologist, etc., no exceptions.

Now relax even deeper, deeper and deeper, allowing exquisite deep relaxation to flow throughout all that you are; and see in your mind a beautiful scene, a beautiful flowing river, flowing down from an exquisite broad and lovely mountain top, on an early and crisp spring day. Imagine smelling wonderful fresh blossoming wild flowers and trees somewhere nearby, hearing the songs of happy birds in the distance, so very peaceful and relaxing. See or think about this river with all of its wonderful twists and turns from its banks as the snow at the top of the mountain melts down and this nourishing river flows downward, the water of this river flowing, both blessing and nourishing, bringing life to all that it touches, flowing peacefully, easily, without effort - downward, flowing onward forever. Now, allow yourself to think about or see this wonderful nourishing river flowing throughout all that is your body and allow it to become your digestive system, a channel of life that nourishes and supports you. And notice, picture, imagine, think about or even truly and profoundly know, that this river of life, your digestive system, is relaxing, uncoiling, unwinding, releasing all energies of disharmony, imbalance and stress, leaving in their former place, calmness, gentleness, peacefulness, ease, harmony, powerful relaxation, almost as if, you are unknotting various parts of you that forever are unwinding and uncoiling, beginning from right in the area of you belly button and beginning right from the base of your throat.

And as you relax, you truly realize that from this point forward, starting right now and for the rest of your life, your relationship with the digestion of all food and drink are changing and you are releasing all old stress patterns and truly you are becoming free and liberated and any and all imbalances of any kind are really just draining away, day by day, night by night, moment by moment, in each and every way, until they are gone and gone forever. Its almost as if someone has added a comforting liquid or solvent, or some perfect and perfected medicine from the future or perhaps even special protective coating of healing soothing lubrication to your digestive system, a soothing coating of digestion enhancing and supporting liquid is now cleansing and healing you deeply inside as never before. Any and all of the valves within your system have now been recalibrated, they are now functioning in a one way only direction, keeping any and all fluids and solids flowing in the proper direction. And all of these old unneeded, useless unpleasant imbalances from your past are absolutely leaving you now and they are becoming like a distant yet pleasant past memory, something you've risen above from in your life. They are simply past experiences, completely free from all effect on you now. You are now becoming one with your healing and healthy digestive process and each and every day and night you are more and more fulfilled by life. Both your life and you are completely satisfied by each slowly eaten, normal, well-balanced, well digested, moderate meals, making your time of eating a time of stress-free peace. You slow down while eating and allow for proper digestion and health to become one with you once again.

And you are absolutely free from any and all digestive disharmony before, during and after mealtimes, because well-balanced meals, well-balanced, slowly consumed, moderate meals will absolutely more than satisfy your hunger and allowing yourself to comfortably digest easily, naturally, smoothly, properly and happily. Your eating times are now about peace, ease, comfort and relaxation, deep soothing relaxation, most especially throughout your digestive and eliminative systems, because they are more and more deeply relaxed, functioning better than ever before, calm, peaceful, good and proper blood flow, which means both they and you are functioning to sustain all that is your body, emotions, thoughts and all that is your life through good nutrition and calm, comfortable, proper digestion. You will truly find that you enjoy food with comfortable digestion now more than you ever have before, digesting healthily and easily which is really just fine with you. You will now relax and take pleasure in the time that you take to eat and most especially relaxing to digest; you always relax and allow for proper and perfect digestion, savoring this time as never before. You enjoy the tastes and aromas of your food so much more than you ever have before, powerfully and yet always comfortably and naturally digesting, almost as if truly and in fact, someone has reset, recalibrated, or readjusted a dial or a switch, a computer or a thermostat from deeply within you somewhere. You are always comfortable and relaxed before, during and after meals, because you are completely satisfied and comfortable in each and every way, all of your emotional cravings and your mental appetites are powerfully restored and balanced, you are powerfully free and fulfilled. And if at any time you might feel a challenging emotional sensation, you'll instantly stop, slowly deep breathe, count slowly from one to five, and all of those imbalanced emotions, will fade away, disappear, and your body will balance, and you'll feel great. So congratulations, you have truly and absolutely begun a brand new happier and healthier chapter of your life, for beginning right now and for the rest of your life, you relax and with each and every slow and steady breath that your take and with each and every beat of your heart, you succeed. You relax and your empowerment is limitless. You heal, you are getting better and better each and every day, and you are calm and your metabolism actually works to heal you, as if someone has in fact, reset a switch or a dial, a computer or a thermostat from deeply within you somewhere, allowing you to comfortably digest and process food more efficiently and in a healthy way; while your speed when eating is comfortable and moderate, just perfect and just right for you.

Now relax even more and more deeply and as you relax, you allow a new thought for a new day to come upon you, a very new and very true and very powerful thought to begin within you; beginning right now and for the rest of your life, you are beginning a brand new, more empowered and happier and calmer chapter of your life; a newer, comfortable, energetic chapter of your life begins right now, because beginning right now and for the rest of your life, you have moved from the previous chapter of your life and into a brand new beginning. Beginning right now as you relax into this new chapter and this new you, all of you begins to actually flourish, in all that is your thoughts, in all of your deeds, in each and every attitude, in all that is you and right now, most of all you succeed most especially in your very powerful, successful, unstoppable, creative and dynamic mind, flourishing and succeeding throughout all that you are. You feel like you can beamingly smile into all areas of your life because, you, can actually feel the old energies lifting up, off and far away from you, removing themselves from you forever. They are going, going, gone, and gone forever.

You let go of all old unneeded ideas and symptoms of struggle from your past and you let those go slowly and yet forever, letting them drift away, drifting away, drifting far, far away, relaxing right now into a masterpiece of a life that you gently and boldly create, now and in very moment, you are calm and at peace, you are in calm determination, about all that you wish to accomplish, and all that you will accomplish, all that you do in fact accomplish, you accomplish with poise, ease and grace. In fact, your very powerful new thoughts are readily activating into your life and whether you realize it or not into each and every moment of your life, liberating your life and liberating and releasing you, in very aspect and regard, easily allowing you to create the masterpiece of a body and life you've always desired, bringing it into the right now, into every aspect of your life, physically, emotionally, mentally, and even spiritually, in each and every way, beginning right now and for the rest of your life, supporting you in every way, now and forever! You feel like you've got the whole world in the palm of your hand or least take on becoming calm, comfortable and healthier.

# Managing Sadness (Non Chemical) Suggestions – Part 1

**Note:** You must be a qualified and certified Clinical Hypnosis professional and have a written note of authorization to perform this or any other complementary hypnosis session from the attending physician, psychiatrist, psychologist, etc., no exceptions.

Now relax even deeper, deeper and deeper on each and every breath, just allow yourself to further relax. And as you relax, you allow yourself this pure moment of inner peace, a gentle yet somehow, pure moment of inner calmness. And from this calmness, feel the power of your slow and steady breath and the calm yet powerfully relaxing life-giving beat of y our heart. And as you relax, you allow a new thought for a new day to come upon you. And very new and very true and very powerful thought begins within you; beginning right now and for the rest of your life, you are beginning a brand new, empowered and happier, healthier, better, chapter of your life. A newer, more exciting, more harmonious and balanced energetic chapter of your life begins, for beginning right now and for the rest of your life, you have absolutely and unstoppably moved from the previous chapter of your life into a new beginning. Beginning right now as you relax into this new chapter, all of you begins to actually flourish. You flourish in each and every supportive thought, deed, attitude, in body, in deeply calm and peaceful emotional harmony, throughout your powerful and dynamic mind, in all that is your spirit, in fact throughout all that you are. You truly feel like you have the whole world in the palm of your hand because, you, can actually feel the old disharmonious and uncomfortable blockage energies lifting up, off and far away from you, removing themselves from you forever. Your energy turns up and you light up and your light vanquishes all shadows, because the light always wins and your light always wins and from now on, you always win.

You begin to take better care of yourself, re-identifying and redefining yourself, by allowing newer thoughts and feelings of healing, wellness and wholeness each and every day, each and every night, to absolutely build within you like a giant reservoir of limitless energy, allowing yourself to love all of you easily and powerfully, even the parts that that had once been more challenging to love and most powerfully and especially you love, heal and forgive those parts that you truly, deeply and most easily love in the most complete way. In this pure moment, you allow yourself the true knowing that you are enough, yes you really are and that just being yourself is just fine with you. And its really just fine with all of those who meet you, because deep, deep inside of you, you relax and you allow yourself to bring forth the true reality that you are whole, calm, comfortable, loveable, loved and complete, getting better and better, more complete, in each and every moment. And in each and every circumstance or lesson from your past, you were polished. And now you begin to let those moments become, very powerfully in your mind, lessons and understandings. And just like a large boulder in a fast running stream, all of these life lessons have truly polished you, upgraded you, allowed you to shine and showed you how truly powerful you really are in every moment, a powerful, dynamic, sensitive and feeling person. And each and every moment of your life is a new bold opportunity, an exciting adventure that you dare to live successfully and because in reality, you begin to take pride in yourself and in your life and truly start to live, finding and liberating joy from yourself and into your life. Not only did you survive, but even better, right now you truly begin to live, embracing all that is your life, living from and creating all of the very best life has to offer you right now!

It really matters little if the world understands you or if they appreciate you, because beginning right now and for the rest of your life, you have decided that you truly and very deeply and very powerfully appreciate you, all of you and that's really all that really matters. And as you relax, you allow yourself to experience the true understanding, that you are the true power in your life and all that you have ever experienced, felt, pictured, imagined or even remembered has supported you in some way, but now, you choose to support yourself in even better ways, with focus, ease, poise, grace and limitless inspired creative success. And you decide in favor of yourself, to relax even further, to relinquish and release all blockages, releasing everything and anything that has once held you back, from experiencing life to its fullest, including limiting feelings, emotions and thoughts because you are determined to make your life the masterpiece it deserves to be. You forgive anyone, anything and any pain and any and all past painful judgments and memories you once had associated from your past, just letting them drift away, drifting away, drifting, far, far away, just letting it go, letting it all go permanently, always and forever, free of it forever, free at last, triumphant and having overcome it, always and forever. You right now choose instead to love all that You are now and in the past and in the future, amazing and impressing everyone by the beauty of your love, even you.

You are calm, at peace and focused. You trust in yourself and all of your decisions, for you are enough and all of you is in fact life affirming, life supporting and your self supporting choices are correct and just right. You are one with yourself and your life and you take pride in that. You let go of all ideas and symptoms of struggle and you powerfully and absolutely let those go slowly and yet forever, letting them drift away, drifting away, drifting far, far away, relaxing into a masterpiece of a healthy and balanced whole life that you gently and boldly create, now and in each and every moment. You are calm and at peace, you are in a place of calm and growing and glowing determination, about all that you wish to accomplish and all that you will unstoppably accomplish, with poise, ease, grace and inspired, unstoppable, thriving healthy creative success.

# Managing Sadness (Non Chemical) Suggestions - Part 2

**Note:** You must be a qualified and certified Clinical Hypnosis professional and have a written note of authorization to perform this or any other complementary hypnosis session from the attending physician, psychiatrist, psychologist, etc., no exceptions.

You begin to see beyond the surface details and the obvious in your life, for the real truth in life very often lies beyond the obvious, deep beneath the surface and you especially begin to look into the depth of what's going on, so beyond all surface appearances, to see the real truth. So you begin right now to see people for who they really are, beyond what they appear to be on the surface and you begin to see them for who they are inside and you see their inner selves, their inner being and you begin as well to see yourself for who you really are and beyond your surface is a really wonderful, caring, sincere, sensitive person, a worthwhile asset to your family, friends, co-workers and all of those you meet. In your life you love and have been loved, but even better beginning right now and for the rest of your life, you truly begin to know, love and appreciate yourself, in deepest, truest ways. The opinions of others are just that, you are free right now from any and all judgment, any and all opinions, that keep you from being supported in the most magnificent and beneficial ways. You begin to think of yourself as getting better and better each and every day and night, because its what is best for you, but also, because that's a brand new truth in your life and your world. And in your calm yet strong determination, you will have this as an important part of your life. You truly allow the limitless dynamic aspects of all that your are, to heal, while you are awake, while you are asleep and even while you dream, powerfully and dynamically and successfully healing each and every part of you that demands or in any way might require healing, physically, emotionally, mentally and even spiritually. You are healing all hurts, all damage, all scars, inside and out, diminishing the unneeded, healing, sealing, balancing and the disharmony from anywhere in your past is truly becoming less important, because you are truly empowered and motivated each and every day and night, to rise above, and focus upon what's truly important, living your life to its fullest, in the most magnificent, creative, correct and happy ways possible, regardless of any old less and less important limitations from your past, because each and every day and night, you are releasing those in the most powerful ways, amazing and impressing everyone, most especially you.

Each and every morning upon rising from a deeply restful and truly inspiring night of sleep, you feel energized and highly motivated and ready to set out to accomplish new and important things, finding new ways to love, to appreciate and to care for yourself, always giving yourself the benefit of the doubt, always giving yourself a break, always lending yourself limitless support in all that you do, allowing yourself to either learn from a situation or to succeed in new, imaginative and magnificent ways. This includes physical activity and even perhaps exercise, as a way of caring for and supporting yourself on the physical, emotional and mental levels, because exercise, restores, calms and balances each of these parts of yourself. You always remember to relax, deep breathe powerful slow and steady life-improving, relaxation breath, which powerfully clears you, emotionally and mentally, and allows you to focus upon your real truth in your life, higher truth and your greatest purposes in your life, all of this comes together after you breathe just a few deep breaths and all of you rises up and all of you finds harmony, peace and inner fulfillment, from your most powerful inner truths and inner wisdom, always letting your inner light shine throughout all stress, adversity and disharmony, allowing you to find true inner peace, balance and powerful dynamic harmony in any and all moments. You create your life, you create your truth and beginning right now, you allow all that you are to rise above any and all situations, absolutely and completely transcending them, you begin once again to make amazing and powerful breakthroughs, flowing into the very best moments of your life, because you can, because its time and you have absolutely decided that you will and you do, because you create your life, but now you create it in even bolder and better ways succeeding magnificently in each and every moment.

## Managing Sadness (Non Chemical) Suggestions - Part 3

**Note:** You must be a qualified and certified Clinical Hypnosis professional and have a written note of authorization to perform this or any other complementary hypnosis session from the attending physician, psychiatrist, psychologist, etc., no exceptions.

You begin to become and truly feel, mightier than anything that you correctly chosen to see as a challenge in your life, you are the strong and mighty one in your life. You correctly choose to relax and deep breathe quite often each and every day, completely empowering yourself, since you truly know that relaxing through any and all stress and nervousness, while you remain calm, relaxed and balanced, grounded and focused, emotionally tranquil is the best and only choice for you, for you are getting better each and every day and night, you recognize and truly realize, that relaxation accompanied by slow and steady deep, deep relaxation breath, is the correct response to any and all adversity. All adversity, friction and disharmony each and every day and night, wherever it might arise from, are best and most easily handled and healed, by just relaxing, breathing and remaining calm and at ease, easily and truly getting centered, balanced and calm, which becomes easier, and easier for you to do and more and more powerful and meaningful, each and every time you deep breathe and relax, with each and every beat of your heart, and each and every breath that you take, now and forever. You truly begin to recognize, appreciate and live from the greatest power and inspiration that life offers, see each and every day and night, as opportunities, to grow, to learn, to heal, to share, to expand your horizons. Each and every moment is a time to relax and expand your horizons. You are there for yourself, you now recognize that you have always been there and have always supported yourself, but beginning as a brand new chapter of your life, beginning right now and for the rest of your life, you begin to truly trust in yourself and your ability to hold yourself together, to relax through and to rise above and to transcend and move through and beyond and to excel in the most wonderful, beautiful and beneficial ways. You are stronger and stronger each and every day and night, completely flexible, you feel the flow of life force energy from deep within supporting you in the most magnificent of ways. You are vital, real, always getting through in even better and better ways, amazing and impressing everyone, most especially you! Each and every moment, you are letting go of worry, because in each and every moment, you are trusting in your life, your world and your limitless Divine support throughout each and every moment of your life. Your emotions and your mind are calm, you relax, your thoughts flow, you relax and flow in any and every situation, words smoothly express your thoughts and feelings, clearly calmly, because you know that you can, you have and you will, each and every day and night getting and feeling better and better. You truly begin, yes you really do, to trust yourself and in this delightful state of relaxation and trust, you begin to actually flourish, in your thoughts, actions, words, ideas, for it really matters not where any and all old past adversities or challenging blockages came from, in this moment, in this brand new chapter of your life that you've unstoppably begun, you have deeply and profoundly decided, to relax and release your way through the past, just letting it go, finding new, more empowering ways to heal, to love, to grow, to expand your horizons, so you let the past that had once caused you any pain, to just drift away, all of it just drifting away, physically, just drifting away, emotionally just drifting away, mentally just drifting way, spiritually just drifting away, until you are calm, free, empowered, as never before. You are calm and you are completely and absolutely determined and in this truly perfect focus and determination, you certainly will have only success, calmness, creativity, peace, self-expression and opportunities to grow, to heal and to expand your life in the most magnificent of ways. You begin to know, from deep inside of you a new truth, that any and all fear, no mater where it came from, becomes more and more useless to you, because you have decided to rise above it, to relax away from it, to heal it, to even become outrageously fearless, in each and every moment with each and every breath that you take and with each and every beat of your heart, you're getting better and stronger each and every second. You realize that you are here to express what is important to you and your words just seem to flow, because you are here to heal and feel and truly become whole, to communicate. And your words, thoughts and concepts are important and the people of this world need to hear them, understand them and to grow from them. As you speak, you share some of your deepest, most true self, as you hear the words and verbal expressions of another, the energy you have shared is reflected back to you and exchanged in healing harmony, benefiting all of whom partake in it. You are essential, worthwhile and meaningful, your thoughts, concepts, actions and words shape and guide your reality and you are choosing better and better to express and create your life in the most beneficial, amazing, profound and meaningful ways possible, becoming each and every day, an inspiration to both men, women and children alike. And you are able to truly express, create better and better each and every day and night, because, you have truly always known, that you have either, learned, profited, gained from or even succeeded in any and all things that you have undergone or have been a part of, improving each and every moment of your life, refining and redefining and improving all that You are even while overcoming any and all situations, even in a crisis, but most especially now, learning to live and love all that is your life, most especially all that You are all that you will become and all that you will succeed doing with your life, because you are determined to do so, you can and you will, because in your calm determination, you will have success as your only option. Each and every day and night, you relax and let out the real you, all that you are a good person, an intelligent person with a powerful and dynamic, determined and successful mind. And you relax your mind, while thinking or while reading or while contemplating, and allow for the most beneficial creative successful, beneficial, motivational thoughts and inspirations, to come through into all that you do, accomplishing and succeeding, in each and every moment, right now, into each and every moment of your new and successful new chapter of this masterpiece that you call your life. You can relax, thrive and succeed, you let go of all of the most unimportant questions, often leaving some of them for later, or to let them resolve themselves, just relaxing your way through them, because life most often will work them out given enough time, so you trust in this. And your time is limitless and your life is always working out for the best. Its OK to have wacky thoughts, because the wackier they are, the better and more you will learn to relax through them. You are always safe and supported by your meaningful life and you're learning and your life schooling is training your mind and all that You are to heal, to learn to grow, to heal others, certainly activating and liberating your greatest healer within, to come out into the world, to thrive and support yourself and others as never before. You realize from your powerful and successful dynamic mind, that anything and everything you have ever studied in life, concentrated upon, read or heard, is deep inside of you and with just a few short deep, deep profoundly inspiring relaxation breaths, you can remember, recall, retrieve, and even access, anything and everything, even creatively and logically thinking and figuring out, bringing forth, anything and everything that needs to be there. You are worthwhile and people are inspired by all that you share, most especially by all that you are and have to offer.

## Overcoming a Shy Bladder

Note: You must be a qualified and certified Clinical Hypnosis professional and have a written note of authorization to perform this or any other complementary hypnosis session from the attending physician, psychiatrist, psychologist, etc., no exceptions.

Relax, relax, relax. And as you relax, you know from powerful places, deep down inside, that truly, it's time to begin a new and a better way of life. You've made this decision, and now you're cleverly, adaptively and forever sticking with this. It's just so easy for you. You know right now that the time has come for you to begin to know, heal, break through and live from a new and healthier way of life and living, relaxing deeply now and releasing any and all unpleasant blockages from the past; just relaxing, relaxing, relaxing and releasing, you will and so you do, not because I say so, but because it's the nature of your own mind to do so. Of course you've realized and you've always really known, you'd be able to overcome any feelings of need when it came to relieving yourself. Your proper and correct response to any and all things that ever once stood in your past is to relax your way beyond them and to easily and forever move on.

Your times of embarrassment are truly forever over. You, powerfully, adaptively and forever, have unstoppably moved on; your time for doubt, fear, panic and upset are over. Any and all frustration from the past, any and all blockages from the past, is just easily let go. And leaving you now on each and every breath, and on each and every heartbeat, all old blockages are amazingly just lifting up and off, far, far away from you, both now, always and forever; for in fact, it's time to put the power back into you. You are the powerfully and forever empowered one, drawing upon the energy of every past victory, triumph, breakthrough and success you've ever had, powerfully activating your inner hero right now, to rise to the top, relax past any and all old barriers and unstoppably find newer and better, more powerful ways to thrive and succeed at this, simply just taking your power back from past situations, people and memories that have stood in your way, moving ever onward into a brighter, newer and better day, night and life. You know you have all the time in the world and you are being left alone to accomplish what is a normal and natural function, just like everyone else. You are easily tuning out any and all old distractions, maybe even zoned out, just relaxing all that you are, and relaxing your bladder when comfortable, finding yourself easily comfortable in more and more situations, just feeling better and better about who you are, in a brand new and flourishing chapter of your life. There is nowhere to run, just for you to allow yourself natural relief and relaxation that natural body processes will allow for. You just relax, and feel calm; you relax and allow yourself to go, just like every time you've been calm, peaceful and relaxed. You are powerfully free of over-thinking this; all thoughts, feelings and emotions that once stood in your way, now powerfully and peacefully relaxed beyond, as you are thriving and successfully moving and flowing beyond any and all of this. You have all the time in the world, having forgiven, released and relaxed your way into a better and brighter day in your life, just rising up and moving beyond any and all of this, forgiven, forgiven, forgiven and released. In any and all moments your mind, your body and your emotions are now powerfully being reconditioned to respond any time you need to pee, like you've got all the time in the world. You are alone, easily able to re-tune your powerful and always-working mind to function powerfully like you are alone, just relaxed and tuning out any and all old distractions and just relaxing naturally and peacefully all over and just letting go. This is your peaceful time, your relaxation time, your time to relax and to let go and to relieve yourself, easily able to tune out anything and everything that ever stood in your way, for you now are the mighty one. You are easily able to put yourself into a calm and peaceful place, just like a light state of Hypnotic relaxation, after just a deep breath or two, all of this just getting easier and better as time moves on for you. You relax your bladder when properly situated, and just let go.

And as you relax, you truly realize that from this point forward, starting right now and for the rest of your life-- your relationship with your natural and comfortable urinary process is changing, as your powerful and adaptive, clever mind is now working up, whether you realize it or not, new and better feelings, modes of clearing blockages, whether you know what they are or not, while you are awake, while you are asleep, even while you dream, as you are releasing all old stress patterns, thoughts, feelings and behaviors, as you truly are becoming free and liberated of any and all imbalances, fully restored, fully relaxed, peaceful, able and serene, able to go, able to pee, all old patterns and blockages of any kind are really just draining away, day by day, night by night, moment by moment, in each and every way, until they are gone and gone forever. It's almost as if someone has added a new dimension to you while instilling your ability to go, forgiving, released, letting go and relieved you are and you remain. And all of these old, unneeded, useless, unpleasant imbalances from your past are absolutely leaving you now and they are becoming like a distant yet pleasant past memory, something you've risen above from in your life. Each and every time you have to go, you find your appropriate place, well adjusted, calm, relaxed, peaceful, carefree, leisurely, easy, restful, unconcerned, carefree, undisturbed; you just deep breathe, relax, let go, making your time of peeing a time of stress-free, natural peace, calmness, relief and release. You feel like you can beamingly smile into all areas of your life because you can actually feel the old energies lifting up, off and far away from you, removing themselves from you forever. They are going, going, gone, and gone forever.

You begin to pace yourself, relaxing yourself and finding your proper times and your proper body rhythms and cycles of when to go to and utilize the bathroom, when to go and this just happens automatically, so you sense it, you feel it, and you just know it. Even without realizing this, your mind is just working on this, while you're awake, while you're asleep, even while you dream, successfully handling this, simply just making things right, healthy, proper, just better, just right for you. You now stop and take the appropriate amount of time for yourself and any and all necessary functions. It's just no big deal; you are free of all and any old embarrassments, just as you deserve to be. You have forever moved on.

So as you relax even deeper, you and I both know and realize you have a very powerful mind, a mind capable of great things, both large and small. I wonder if that powerful, unstoppable part of your mind that had once been allowing this to happen and was once working against you, is now willing to work with you, now providing for you in the truest and most powerful of ways, to allow you to re-wire, re-circuit, re-balance, re-harmonize, re-circulate, re-wire the nerves for proper sensitivity, messages, signals and feelings, allowing for more feeling, in just the right amounts and ways that work for you just perfectly, and each and every day and night, you only get better and better at this, forgiving your past, releasing any and all anger, upsetment, rage, doubt and even fear. Free, cleansed, safe and free, liberated you are and truly remain. So in the most powerful, unstoppable and surprisingly successful of ways, which creatively, easily and even unthinkingly allow you to regain your sense of your natural and easy ability to relieve yourself, when it comes to the normal functioning of your body, it's balance, it's harmonies, its needs, its proper and healthy functioning, whether alone or with all people nearby, allows your need to eliminate wastes naturally to flourish and simply flow, just like everyone else's body does. It's reset, rebalanced, recalibrated, even easy, or just maybe, you haven't even yet realized how truly easy it will be for you to do this, as you simply flow into and begin a brand new, healthier, happier, better chapter of your life right now and you feel go good, all of this is so right, so unstoppably powerful, that you just know, it's under way, it's happening, yes it is, both it and you, are completely healthy, reset or simply back to normal. You owe this kind of respect to yourself, you've regained it now and you have and are freely giving it to yourself, you deserve it, you win. Your body is balancing and so is your life, in the most healthy and beneficial ways, that are just perfect for you; almost as if in fact, someone has in fact, reset a switch or a dial or even some type of computer or thermostat within you somewhere, allowing you to comfortably be aware of your new, improved, better, and successful habits and functions, in powerful, successful and amazing ways. You find yourself performing all necessary functions just as you should and just as you need to, as a responsible person, who takes better care of himself. In fact, you are extremely motivated, energetic and unstoppably determined to take better care of yourself, right now, always and forever.

# Overcoming Dental Plaque OCD Response

**Note:** You must be a qualified and certified Clinical Hypnosis professional and have a written note of authorization to perform this or any other complementary hypnosis session from the attending physician, psychiatrist, psychologist, etc., no exceptions.

You are so very deeply and truly relaxed and are allowing damaging, hurtful, repetitive, useless, now unfulfilling and negative patterns to move out of and away from you and your life; in fact, you might be feeling determined to be upbeat, lighthearted and you are unstoppably determined to improve your health and your life, improving and healing all that needs and demands healing within your life, most especially releasing habits and patterns that have ever stood in your way or have hurt, harmed or annoyed you in any way. Your body is your most valuable asset and your mouth and oral hygiene are a vital part of your valuable life assets; your health is most important to you. Only you can take care of your body and your health. You owe yourself and your body the proper respect of good health. Your self-preservation is the first rule of your life.

As an adult, you also know that it is your responsibility to rise above all limitations of the past and to make the most of your life. Beginning right now and for the rest of your life, whenever you are about to take care of your health, most especially your oral health, you shall work in harmony and allow yourself to release your old, unneeded, unwanted, easily removed and now becoming distant fixation and consuming focus on areas of your mouth that had once troubled you, as you now and forever flow ever onward into a newer, brighter, and better unstoppably beginning chapter of your life. You are becoming free of being preoccupied, occupied and overly focused upon your teeth and mouth, becoming free of sucking on your teeth and gums, or running your tongue over any areas of plaque, as this has and does stand in the way of you living and enjoying your life. It's almost like it's becoming less meaningful to you, or at least it's just becoming more and more important to you. What's becoming more and more important to you, is the idea of living your life, leading your life and becoming forever free of feeling, acting, doing, or even thinking anything, whether you are aware of it or not, that will, would or might stand in your way of enjoying your life. You are beginning to focus less and less on your mouth, less and less, while you are awake, asleep and even while you dream, even easily able to create a powerful yet pleasant numbness there whenever, wherever, however, and at anytime whenever you need it or want to do so, your mind is now becoming sharp and focused upon this and you succeed easily, powerfully, dynamically, adaptively and effectively at this with powerfully and beneficial results. It's almost like you've been powerfully washed clean inside, cleansed, healed and everything that once troubled you is now shiny and new.

All of these undeniably powerful and highly effective dynamic improvements are now and forever working with you and for you, in truly powerful and unstoppable beneficial ways. You will relax all that you are, relaxing your body, (relax) you will absolutely relax your emotions (relax) and all of your thoughts (relax) and even your spirit, relaxes powerfully in truly inspired successful oneness. You will relax throughout all that you are and now win over your past, feeling healed, whole and calm, balanced, cleansed, cleaned and relaxed while completely sure of yourself that this is working for you powerfully in the most clever and effectively dynamic of ways.

As you relax, you relax your tongue, really relaxing it, relaxing it calmly effectively and completely, allowing it to go back to more natural and inborn ways of being. As you relax your tongue, you relax from your tongue down, free of old harmful, destructive, disharmonious and repetitive behaviors, allowing only peaceful harmony from your tongue down to relax and to calm and to completely soothe you. You are just becoming less and less interested in the old and less than pleasant ways of going about your life, now effectively calm, balanced, rejuvenated and restored, calm, activating unstoppable happiness and feeling upbeat, easily rising to the top, inspired by every past victory, triumph, breakthrough and victory you've ever had in your life to allow you to unstoppably succeed at this.

And as you are relaxed, you feel like you are cleansed on the inside and even on the outside, because you can feel the old unwanted, and unneeded, useless energies from the past, just lifting up, just lifting up and removing themselves from you forever, allowing them to drift away, just drifting away, far, far away. And as you relax, you feel cleansed, you are cleansing unpleasant past emotions and memories from the past, including all past unpleasant experiences as well. Right now, instead you are relaxed and you shall relax, and allow all old reactions and unpleasant memories to drift away from you, completely and absolutely. For beginning right now and for the rest of your life, you are empowered, and free to relax any and all parts of your body and your muscle system as you decide, including your tongue and all of its reactions, no matter where or when they came from, even reactions to stress of any kind, no matter where or when they came from, because you are the empowered one and you are mightier than old memories, memories and reactions that have now left you, leaving you, now, absolutely, always and forever. All old unwanted reactions you once had, you are now freed from, putting all of them behind yourself, for the reactions you once had as a child or in younger days are now gone. And now you do what's proper for your health as an adult. All memories of unpleasant past dental experiences, are just that, only memories, just like dreams, are right now, drifting away, drifting away, drifting away, until your mind and your emotions are now clear and free; YOU ARE FREE FROM YOUR PAST, YOU ARE UNLIMITED, YOU TRANSCEND, WITH POISE, EASE and GRACE. YOU ARE NOW A PERSON THAT ALLOWS FOR A CALM And BALANCED LIFE, A CALM and BALANCED BODY, A CALM and BALANCED TONGUE, CALM and BALANCED REACTIONS, and AS YOU ALLOW THIS CALMNESS, A PEACEFUL and YET PLEASANTLY NUMBING SENSATION IS YOURS AS YOU DESIRE IT, SHOULD YOU WANT IT.

BEGINNING RIGHT NOW AND FOR THE REST OF YOUR LIFE, you rise above all limiting memories and concepts and labels and responses from the past and this powerful new you emerges, each and every day, getting stronger and stronger. You easily transcend all past experiences of limitation. It might be days, it might be months, it might be hours, it might be moments, or yes, even right now, but before you relax into any and all improvement, you deep breathe, very calm, very slow, very steady, calming, relaxing deep breaths. You relax by breathing slowly through your nose, all that you are and especially the muscles of your tongue, feeling soothing elegant relaxation and almost gentle yet powerful and pleasant numbness spreading throughout all that you are. Relax even deeper now and allow yourself to feel calmness flowing through you like a river of powerful and deeply soothing relaxation energy. As you relax, you notice the pleasant and wonderful feelings that emerge from deep within yourself. You assimilate all of this very enjoyable assistance, better, deeper and more easily, making it your own healing, including new and more powerful and healthy effective ways to succeed at this and all of this becomes a beneficial means to a healthy new you, taking in all and becoming one with the beneficial life-maintaining properties. You realize by breathing through your nose as needed you relax, you heal and you thrive. And beginning right now and for the rest of your life, you move into a happier, calmer, new and better chapter of your life, for the rest of your life, a healthy and new beneficial time of health and healing. Beginning right now and for the rest of your life you are in fact becoming one with your new habits for health, healing, rising above, transcending, into new health in every way and completely happy and balanced vitality. You are free from your past, and you are a new, more alive, healthier you, a person who relaxes and enjoys life and truly is empowered in all that you do.

## Overcoming Insomnia (Worry and Family)

You begin and even better, learn, activate and remember to truly trust in life and extend that trust into each and every moment, readily creating and accepting the true and fine support that life readily gives you. All experiences are now about succeeding or learning, you life now becomes failure-free as you feel so great, so good, so wonderful and so peacefully sleepy, easily able to rest at bedtimes. You easily shelf the day, putting all feeling, thoughts concerns and cares aside, for a time of rest and recharging, about 1 to 2 hours before each and every bedtime, as today has taken care of you, so will tomorrow, just as all yesterdays have and all tomorrows will, on and on, forever and forever. You allow your inner voices to calm down, to rest, to become quiet and drift off. You find newer and better ways to relax, even while there might be, or may be or actually are stressful situations, events or people around, you are feeling fine, willing to relax your way through any and all stress, which is your new and correct and very best and easily activated response to any and all stressful situations, always adapting to finding newer and better ways to take care of yourself, becoming a master at deep breathing and bring stress down to the nothingness it deserves to be, so adaptable, so successful, so right for you at the very best and most powerful of moments, a forever journey into the brighter, better and happier and healthier chapter of your life, creating the kind of peaceful, happy and very well-rested life and body you deserve to have, and now effectively create. You are finding newer and better ways to take care of yourself and loved ones, finding potent, effective, newer and better ways to teach, to lead and guide, to convince, to have them follow your lead effectively, allowing them to accomplish all that needs to be done, as you lead and guide, easily helping all of those you guide to get their jobs done effectively. You are finding a newer and improved rhythm, a new and improved flow, a better and more contented and trusting place of power and harmony for yourself, from within yourself, drawing upon the energy of each and every time, you felt, loved, supported, taken care of, bringing each and all of those moments back here into the right now, re-identified in this newer and brighter chapter of your life, wrapping all of that support and harmony around yourself like a blanket of support, self-support, making it all happen right here and right now, making the foundation of your life, happiness, peace, satisfaction, caring, support, ease, and comfort. You trust in the fact that when you put yourself to bed, you are in bed for the night and free of any fears, feeling calm, comfortable and relaxed, peaceful, and in a state of gentle comfortable ease, nowhere to get to, nowhere to go but to deep soothing and comfortable sleep. You are finding and creating newer and better ways of allowing yourself to fall asleep, putting the day and it's cares upon a shelf. Just deep breathing, relaxing, and just simply and powerfully - **putting your head on the pillow, closing your eyes and falling asleep!** Just like you've done millions of other times in your life. All of your thoughts drift away, you feel so calm, so very comfortable, so able to rest and relax, (Yawn). Just resting down, just like you knew how to do, like when you were a baby, so able to just put your head down and rest. And each and every night, you feel so protected, so taken care of by life, so very peaceful and able to rest and relax, that all of you is easily able to relax, so very deeply and truly, all that You are just putting today up on a shelf, for today has taken care of itself, just as the day before and each and every yesterday before has taken care of you, always and in every way allowing you to either learn or succeed, rising up from past challenges, all of them having made you stronger and more able, better, a survivor, who now chooses to powerfully live and more powerfully to rest and relax, letting all that you are rest and relax, problem and worry-free, correctly responding, by choosing to relax through any and all past struggles, trusting in life and all of the support that life always gives you, easily allowing all that you are to just rest and relax, rest and relax, just rest and relax, at each and every bedtime, just rest and relax, deeply and truly, allowing all that is your powerful mind to, at the appropriate times, each and every bedtime, to comfortably wind down, wind down, wind down, deeply and truly relaxing all and everything that is your body, just to rest and relax, rest and relax, all that are your emotions, to just rest and relax, all that is your mind to know it's just time to slow down, to unwind, to just wind down and to just rest and relax, rest and relax, deeply and profoundly to rest and relax, care free struggle free, at ease, relieved, restfully and powerfully trusting in life, and assured of a great and only getting better and easier night's rest, only getting better and easier each and every night, each and every day, in each and every way, with each and every better self-supportive feeling, feeling so calm, so liberated, so at ease, so relaxed into a brand new and better night's, rest chapter of your life, powerfully, truly, dynamically, correctly and easily choosing to forever and creatively forgive, both others and yourself, of any past pain or trauma, forgiving both any and all blockages, that once or ever stood in your way of having the wonderful night's deep, deep rest you completely deserve, create and relax into, free of any and all dependence on the past, more easily and growing only better and stronger each and every night and each and every day and each and every bedtime, both deeper and easier, free of blockages and sleeping pills, relaxing beyond any and all control issues, truly trusting in life, the life you live, the life your create, the life you now deserve to truly enjoy and do truly enjoy, the life that is now growing ever easier, to rest and relax into, more comfortable, more peaceful, more restful, more at ease in your life, more creatively successful, more supported and embraced by the limitless inspirational energy of each and every past victory, triumph, breakthrough and success you've ever had, allowing your to easily relax, and rest at each and every bedtime, enjoying your sleep more beneficially you are looking forward to getting better, relaxing into this new chapter of your life, you do, easily and powerfully, only getting better and better!

## Overcoming Insomnia and Late Night Eating

Right now remember a time in your past, a time when you were calm, relaxed, hunger free, feeling fulfilled, a time when you were happy, a time when you felt loved, a time when you felt supported and cared for, so comfortable, so calm, so relaxed, so hunger free, so drowsy, so comfortable, almost ready to fall asleep. You easily bring yourself back to that place and to that moment right now. Be there for just a few short moments. With your eyes closed feel that calmness, ease, peace and even the joy and feel its energy embrace you now. And allow that moment's inner peace and calmness to be with you now. Relax and allow your thoughts and emotions to become comfortable and to relax you and let this moment be just like that was. When your eyes are closed, you relax in gentle, soothing calmness and allow yourself to create a relaxing few short moments of inner peace for yourself right now, just allowing all that you are to relax in harmony, relax in oneness, relaxing all over, relaxing body, emotions, mind and even your spirit, to deeply, powerfully and truly relax. And as you relax, you realize and truly recognize, that you have right now made a very true, very powerful, very real decision, to relax and deeply and easily fall asleep each and every night, right through the night, with comfort, ease and deep and profound very restful, drowsy peacefulness. Your stomach, is calm, you've had enough to eat; your body is calm and relaxed. It's almost like a Divinely inspired and guided blanket of sleep energy is floating down upon you right now, floating down from above and with this energy, you just can't help falling into a peaceful, drowsy, comfortable night of powerful rest and it feels so good! So from now on, your sleep is a state to relax into, a place you've easily gotten to each and every night, so very many times in the past and just as easily, just like finding your way home, calm, comfortable and fulfilled and filled up, you relax and find your way into a peaceful sleep each and every night, successfully, calmly, most easily, resting and relaxing all over, sleeping deeply, comfortably, truly, and powerfully, so very comfortably dreaming peaceful, nurturing, supportive and even fun, happy and fulfilling dreams that allow you to awaken each and every morning after a good, soothing, complete and powerful night's rest, energized, invigorated and inspired, in ways that are just so perfect for you.

Beginning right now and for the rest of your life, you are truly beginning to adopt healthier ways of living and being, and you truly start to treat yourself in a more nurturing, more supportive and self loving way, getting better and better each and every day and most especially each and every night, correctly choosing to relax away from and through, any and all tension, any and all stress, any and all emotions that refuse to support you in the most beneficial of ways. You are now empowering all that you are. So each and every night, you allow yourself time to relax, unwind, letting any and all adversity, any and all stress, any and all un-comfort-ability, any and all learning experiences, to just drift away from you, because you deeply and truly recognize that all adversity, just like a boulder being polished in a fast running stream of water, is actually polishing you, in the most truly magnificent ways. You can actually feel all stress and strain, just lifting up, off and very far away from you. Each and every night, you correctly choose to shelf the day you've just been through, just putting it all aside for now, putting it away, almost as if, it were on a shelf somewhere just filed away, just letting today's and tonight's events take their proper place in your life, your experience and your memory, free from all effect on your ability to relax, and you become so sleepy, so drowsy, so relaxed, each and every night getting a wonderful, calm, peaceful, well deserved, and creatively effective nights rest. Each and every yesterday has taken care of you and supported you, this past day has taken care of you and supported you as well, you've even succeeded and sometimes learned and tomorrow will do just the same. And you are truly and deeply, more and more each and every day and night, powerfully trusting in this important fact. The time to react for today is over, the time to react for tomorrow is yet to be, so you are always correctly choosing to relax through any and all stress or old unwanted, unneeded hunger habits, doing better and correctly choosing as well to glide into powerful relaxation, unwinding and making room for your day's and night's activities and concerns to comfortably just drift away, drifting away, lifting up, off and far, far away from you. By unwinding in this way, you have truly begun to learn and acknowledge, new and better ways to care for yourself, to succeed in your life and to trust that your life is unfolding in the most important and beneficial ways possible where you are fulfilled in the most powerful of ways, the very best of ways, for you are always learning or you are succeeding and by learning to relax this way, each and every night or whenever you need to rest, you are allowing yourself to re-energize, to heal, to rest and recharge all that you are and are yet to be. I really wonder if you even realize how truly profound a change this will make in your life, now and in the future, but it doesn't even matter, because each and every day, you'll be enjoying the benefits of a wonderful night's rest. You sleep much better and easier right through the night, calm, comfortable, hunger-free and content, much better without late night eating, than you ever have, doing what you now and forever know is right, as you thrive and succeed unstoppably at this.

There is always something to learn, something to do, some better way of providing for yourself, for your body and a newer, slimmer, healthier, better you, always some better way to love yourself, some better way to give yourself the gift of enrichment, as a new, happier and healthier way of living your life and providing for yourself. You have a powerful and dynamic mind, that's now powerfully working in powerful harmony with you and in your favor and you are better and better each day, becoming an inspiration to yourself, and both women and men alike. You relax and trust in your life and the true fact that you have always been supported by life, you have always been protected, life has always taken care of you, life always takes care of you, even and most especially tomorrow, so each and every night, you relax, sleep and dream peacefully and deeply. You allow yourself to let the day's events go, the day has taken care of itself and now your better nights rest takes wonderful care of you. You trust in the truth of these facts and embrace the support of your life, hunger free, free of old unnecessary habits, supporting yourself even better, as never before. You truly begin to realize that beginning right now it's time to relax into and to develop a better relationship with yourself, and with your ever improving sleeping habits, become balanced and you sleep right through the night, hunger free, calm and comfortable, and it's easy to achieve and you begin to respect and nurture and love yourself treating yourself, as a nurturing supportive parent would a wonderful child, just as a nurturing supportive friend would give to a friend, by allowing better progress, peace, health and sleep in your life, leading your life in peace, comfort, enrichment, reward and empowerment. Already, your mind is making powerful improvements in how you let go and enjoy a rich and peaceful night's rest. I wonder if you even realize how much easier, how much better, how much healthier and how much more powerful and fulfilling, each and every night's rest is going to be for you? In every moment of your life, you trust, you relax, relaxing into proper perspectives and you thrive in most powerful and as yet, un-imagined ways!

## Overcoming Insomnia

Right now remember a time in your past, a time when you were calm, a time when you were happy, a time when you felt love, a time when you felt supported and cared for, so comfortable, so calm, so relaxed, drowsy, almost ready to fall asleep. Bring yourself back to that place and to that moment. Be there for just a few short moments. With your eyes closed feel that calmness, ease, peace and even the joy and feel its energy embrace you now. And allow that moment's inner peace and calmness to be with you now. Relax and allow your thoughts and emotions to become comfortable and to relax you and let this moment be just like that was. When your eyes are closed, you relax in gentle soothing calmness and allow yourself to create a relaxing few short moments of inner peace for yourself right now, just allowing all that You are to relax in harmony, relax in oneness, relaxing all over, relaxing body, emotions, mind and even your spirit, to deeply, powerfully and truly relax. And as you relax, you realize and truly recognize, that you have right now made a very true, very powerful very real decision, to relax and deeply and easily fall asleep each and every night, right through the night, with comfort, ease and deep and profound very restful, drowsy peacefulness. It's almost like a Divinely inspired and guided blanket of sleep energy is floating down upon you right now, floating down from above and with this energy, you can only just allow yourself to fall into a peaceful, drowsy, comfortable night of powerful rest and it feels so good! For from now on, your sleep is a state to relax into, a place you've easily gotten to each and every night so very many times in the past and just as easily, just like finding your way home, you relax and find your way into a peaceful sleep each and every night, successfully, calmly, most easily, resting and relaxing all over, sleeping deeply, comfortably, truly, naturally and powerfully, so very comfortably dreaming peaceful nurturing and supportive and even fun dreams that allow you to awaken each and every morning after a good and powerful nights rest, energized, invigorated and inspired, in ways that are just so perfect for you.

Beginning right now and for the rest of your life, you are truly beginning to adopt and adapt to healthier ways of living and being as you truly start to treat yourself in a more nurturing way, getting better and better each and every day and most especially each and every night, correctly choosing to relax away from and through any and all tension and any and all stress, empowering all that you are. So each and every night, you allow yourself time to relax, unwind, letting any and all adversity, any and all stress, any and all learning experiences, to just drift away from you, because you deeply and truly recognize that all adversity, just like a boulder being polished in a fast running stream of water, is actually polishing you, in the most truly magnificent ways. You can actually feel all stress and strain, draining away, just lifting up, off and very far away from you. Each and every night, you correctly choose to shelf the day you've just been through, just putting it all aside for now, putting it away, almost as if, it were on a shelf somewhere just filed away, just letting today's and tonight's events take their proper place in your life, your experience and your memory, free from all effect on your ability to relax and become so sleepy, so drowsy, so relaxed, each and every night getting a wonderful nights rest. Each and every yesterday has taken care of you and supported you, this past day has taken care of you and supported you as well, you've even succeeded and sometimes learned and tomorrow will do just the same. And you are truly and deeply and more and more each and every day and night powerfully trusting in this important fact. The time to react for today is over, the time to react for tomorrow is yet to be, so you are always correctly choosing to relax through any and all stress and correctly choose as well to relax, unwind and make room for your day's and night's activities and concerns to comfortably just drift away, drifting away, lifting up, off and far, far away from you. By unwinding this way, you have truly begun to learn and acknowledge, new and better ways to care for yourself, to succeed in your life and to trust that your life is unfolding in the most important and beneficial ways possible, for you are always learning or you are succeeding and by learning to relax this way, each and every night or whenever you need to rest, you are allowing yourself to re-energize, to heal, to rest and recharge all that you are and are yet to be. I really wonder if you even realize how truly profound a change this will make in your life, now and in the future, but it doesn't even matter, because each and every day, you'll be enjoying the benefits of a wonderful night's rest. Your powerful mind now and forever improved, even allowing your dreams to become happy, interesting, and pleasant, releasing any and all old harsh patterns now in favor of comfort and ease, relaxing you further and allowing you to peacefully dream, resting and dreaming easily, deeply, naturally, comfortably, supportively and pleasantly, allowing deep and pleasant, beneficial rest.

You are finding and creating newer and better ways of allowing yourself to fall asleep, putting the day and it's cares upon a shelf. Just deep breathing, relaxing, and **just simply and powerfully - putting your head on the pillow, closing your eyes and falling asleep!** Just like you've done millions of other times in your life. You remain, calm, balanced and relaxed, more easily able to sleep most especially when you are or might be contemplating: (name blockage patterns e.g. - worry, fear, upcoming events, etc.). There is always something to learn, something to do, some better way of providing for yourself, some better way to love yourself, some better way to give yourself the gift of enrichment, inner fulfillment and peace, as a new happier and healthier way of living your life and providing for yourself. You have a powerful and dynamic mind, you are better and better each day, becoming an inspiration to yourself and both women and men alike. You relax and trust in your life and the true fact that you have always been supported by life, you have always been protected, life has always taken care of you, life always takes care of you, even and most especially tomorrow, so each and every night, you relax, sleep and dream peacefully and deeply. You allow yourself to let the day's events go, the day has taken care of itself and now your better night's rest takes wonderful care of you. You trust in the truth of these facts and embrace the support of your life as never before. You truly begin to realize that beginning right now its time to relax into and to develop a better relationship with yourself and your sleeping habits become balanced, easy to achieve and you begin to respect and nurture and love yourself, treating yourself as a nurturing supportive parent would a wonderful child, just as a nurturing supportive friend would give to a friend, by allowing better progress and peace and health and sleep in your life, leading your life in peace, comfort, enrichment, reward and empowerment. Already, your mind is making powerful improvements in how you let go and enjoy a rich and peaceful night's rest. I wonder if you even realize how much easier, how much better, how much healthier and how much more powerful and fulfilling, each and every night's rest is going to be for you? In every moment of your life, you trust, you relax, relaxing into proper perspectives and you thrive in most powerful and as yet, un-imagined ways!

## Overcoming Male Sexual Dysfunction

**Note:** You must be a qualified and certified Clinical Hypnosis professional and have a written note of authorization to perform this or any other complementary hypnosis session from the attending physician, psychiatrist, psychologist, etc., no exceptions.

You have decided to relax and to be all that you are you have made an important decision, to enjoy your life, to enjoy yourself and to take pride in yourself and all that you are. The all powerful and dynamic successful part of your mind, is now arranging and rearranging your thoughts and your emotions, to choose to relax into all that is your life, most especially allowing all of your thoughts and fantasies to take the proper place within your emotions, your mind and within all that is your life, forgiving your past truly right now, releasing any and all past judgments, all roadblocks, you forgive your past and move on. You are correctly learning to relax, to live, to love and trust in your life and in each and every moment. You have truly decided that all you have to do to enjoy yourself, is to relax, allow and to trust, taking all proper safe and healthy precautions, to insure your life, your safety and the life and safety of those you care for and about. You now recognize and realize that all thoughts and emotions are just thoughts and emotions, you are the real power in your life and that's really all that matters. There is nowhere to get to, no place for distrust or worry, free of fear, for right now and forever, you are relaxing into all that is your life and that's really just fine with you. You are really just fine, so as you relax deeper and further, I wonder if you even realize yet, how easy it will be for you to succeed in allowing yourself to love, to share, flow, to harmonize with your body, life, emotions, thoughts, just relaxing and flowing, into relaxing into an enjoyable, even pleasurable way of life. All fears, doubts, frustrations, and dysfunctions of the past are becoming like distant memories from your past, almost like a dream you once had, all of their past impact, all of their past effect, even all memory of them are just leaving you now, becoming harder to remember, more difficult to experience, like a dream that has just left you and having gone far, far away from you, forgotten, gone, free, having moved on. Any of those experiences have just polished you anyway, making you a greater person than ever before, but instead now, you realize, you have graduated from them and all of their negativity has left you now, having gone further and further away from you, gone and gone forever. All of you is valid, all of you is eternally worthwhile, all of you relaxes away from and releases the idea of resistance, just going and flowing, you relaxes and embraces and loves all that you are right now and all that you will become, which is what you deserve.

## Overcoming Nail Biting

In this moment you have made an important and powerful life-changing decision, a decision to relax into your life, to trust in your life, a decision in which you will allow yourself to relax through any and all stress, to allow any and all stress, old anxieties, old pressures and even old fears to melt away from you, to just allow yourself to relax and to allow any and all stress, anxieties, pressures and fears, to just melt away from you, because in this moment, you are letting all that has been gnawing at you, to just become smaller and smaller in your world. Its becoming smaller and smaller or I wonder if its because you are becoming bigger and mightier than anything that once affected you in any negative way. In the past, pressures, fears, nervousness and just trying to get it perfectly right used to feel overwhelming, but starting right now, you have realized, as you truly relax into this moment of healing, life-changing empowerment, that you have always learned from and survived each and every moment of your past. Actually and truly, in each and every case, in each and every circumstance, in each and every moment, you've always succeeded, you've always gotten through, maybe even thrived, but somehow, you always had your life improve, in ways that were always meaningful, even though at the time, it might not have been apparent to you. In your past, you might have felt emotionally that you were being overcome, but in actuality, it was you that overcame in each and every moment, even though people, circumstances and events, seemed to be nagging, annoying, or even gnawing at you. You might have even once, picked up the energy of these feelings, thoughts and emotions, and patterned your behavior after them, allowing for self-criticism, self-judgment, fear of life and feeling like you were gnawing away at yourself. But by having made a very important, powerful and forever life-changing decision today, you have correctly chosen, to see, hear, feel and even truly know and live from the real truth. This truth, your truth is that you are empowered, a real life survivor, who has instead, beginning right now and for the rest of your life, really truly chosen to live, to relax, to release all unpleasant aspects of your past, because you have deeply and truly realized that your new, improved correct response to your environment, is to relax, to release and to allow any and all stress and tension to flow around, past and through you, allowing all of it, in whatever its disguise, to flow past and far, far away from you. In life, things are rarely as perfect as we imagine them to be, but by being relaxed, clear, calm, peaceful and centered, we can actually see all people, events and circumstances for the natural perfection of what they really truly are and are supposed to be. The only way life can gnaw at you is by you letting it get to you and by you allowing yourself to gnaw away at you via your own judgments, but you've already moved on and into a better and more healthy place. Already, whether you realize it or not, your powerful, creative, successful and dynamic subconscious mind is reorienting the way you think and feel, to allow for all unneeded, unwanted, unnecessary behaviors from your past to change, to release, to be gone from your life, now always and forever, allowing you to handle most anything, calmly, reasonably, peacefully, in ways that benefit you immeasurably. So in this moment, as you relax even deeper and let go and release, you trust truly in your life, you forgive your past, you correctly choose in the most complete ways, to relax into your brand new future, one in which you trust, heal, forgive, flourish and completely allow yourself to see this new happier you emerging, free of nail biting and picking, free and released from any and all old habits, both conscious and subconscious, that once hurt, upset, embarrassed, humiliated you, because right now, even better and instead, you are beginning, in better and more ideal ways, to support, nurture, care for, sustain, advance and cultivate all that you are. And whether you realize it or not, your old habits are vanishing, vanishing, going, going gone! Your hands heal, your nails and cuticles restore, repair and rejuvenate, just as all that You are restores, repairs, heals and rejuvenates, all of this is something you are quite powerfully sure of, because a brand new chapter of your life, has truly begun right now. Your hands, receive, your hands give, your hands feel, your hands and nails, heal, and express, a balanced calmer you, trusting in all that you touch, and all that you feel. You readily consume and assimilate all of the lessons and energies of all the blessings and inspirations life readily and bountifully bestows upon you, in only the very best and most beneficial ways. Congratulations, the past is over, you are free and healed right now, you absolutely trust in the true fact that your relaxed happier future begins right now and it is bright, happy, relaxed, more and more limitless, brilliant and filled with countless possibilities!

## Overcoming Nail Biting - 2

You always knew your nail biting days wouldn't last forever, so now they are powerfully over. You are and you powerfully and you amazingly remain, calm, balanced and free of old patterns of the past, in a newer and better chapter of your life, most especially if there are or might be times of your being under a lot of stress. You are and you powerfully and amazingly remain, calm, balanced and free of old patterns of your past, in a newer and better chapter of your life, most especially if you are or might be under pressure: studying for a test or while you are taking a test, you choose to treat yourself better than the old ways, and now so you do. You are and you powerfully and amazingly remain, calm, balanced and free of old patterns of the past, in a newer and better chapter of your life, most especially if you are or might be worked up emotionally, instead relaxing, deep breathing steady and calming, life-giving, restorative and balancing breaths, taking better care of yourself. You are and you powerfully and amazingly remain, calm, balanced and free of old patterns of the past, in a newer and better chapter of your life, most especially if you are or might be really upset, angry or frustrated. You are forever free now, free from ever biting your nails without even knowing it, for even if you did, your hands would feel heavy, heavy, heavy, like lead, like cement, they would taste disgusting, totally revolting, and you'd notice all of this instantly and refuse to do it. You are now forever free of old nail biting habits and have moved on. You are just doing so much better and better, I wonder if you even yet realize how easy this is for you as you have truly and unstoppably moved into a newer and brighter, better chapter of your life. You are, you remain, powerfully, cleverly, effectively and even adaptively free of wanting to, or trying to, or actually biting your nails in any way, even or most especially if: at work, if you're working on something that you know needs to be done for a deadline, finding a newer and more supportive relationship and rhythm with your life and the world in general, free of letting anything gnaw at you in any way. It's almost as if you are reborn into a brand new chapter of your life where you are free of this in powerful and substantial ways. Almost as if someone from deep, deep inside of you has completely and substantially reset a switch, a dial, a computer or a thermostat of some kind allowing a new and better day to dawn in your life. You are, you remain, powerfully, cleverly and effectively and even adaptively free of wanting to, or trying to, or actually biting your nails in any way, even or most especially if thinking about a work meeting and you're thinking about what you need to know or say, or you're at your desk trying to figure something out for work. You are, you remain, powerfully, cleverly and effectively and even adaptively free of wanting to, or trying to, or actually biting your nails in any way, even or most especially if thinking of things to write or during any task you must accomplish or perform. Truly your correct response to any and all stress if to relax your way out and beyond it by deep breathing and feeling better, and more supportive. You are and you remain completely free of this, even if you realize you are having a hard-time thinking or with any thinking in general, you are free of ever biting your nails. Whenever you're watching a movie or TV, you are forever free of ever biting your nails. When you're just reading something such as an email, document, newspaper, book, etc., you are finding an appreciation that you are forever free of old patterns and instead are feeling calm, easygoing and doing better, calm and stilled inside, enjoying and absorbing the experience, free of old patterns, calmer and more gentle to yourself. You know, it's almost like you are now and forever freed, just like you've been free from biting your nails all of your life, or for as long as you can remember. You've never done anything self-destructive, just always choosing a better way and you've been finding and adapting to methods where you've taken the very best care of yourself, with happy, healthy hands, a calm and anxiety-free you, just you now, doing better and better, certain, serene and sure you are now, that this is only getting better and better for you each and every day and night as all of you, while you are awake, while you are asleep, even while you are dreaming, is now and forever healing and more and more whole, at least since you can remember. In fact you might just come to realize and even know, you are fine and doing better and better as you now celebrate all of your years of life with happy and healthy hands and a more calm, more comfortable and serene you that now and forever unstoppably emerges.

# Overcoming Neurotic Smoking

Right now remember a time in your past, a time when you were calm, a time when you were, happy, a time when you felt love, a time when you felt supported, and cared for. Bring yourself back to that place. Perhaps it was on a beach, in the mountains, on vacation someplace beautiful. Be there for just a few short moments. With your eyes closed feel that calmness, ease peace and joy, feel its energy embrace you now. And allow that moments inner peace and calmness to be with you now. Relax and allow your thoughts and emotions to relax you, letting this moment be just like that was. When your eyes are closed, you relax in gentle soothing calmness and allow yourself to create a relaxing few short moments of inner peace for yourself right now.

(Optional: Right now you remember a time when you where a little kid, when you got your first bike, be there now for a moment, what color was it, etc. Bring up feelings of building joyous optimism.)

Beginning right now and for the rest of your life, you begin to adopt healthier ways of living, and you start your treat yourself in a more nurturing way, getting better and better each and every day. One new view is that time you spend alone is not a time of loneliness but rather a time to get to know and truly love and appreciate yourself better, a time to create a better relationship with yourself, a time to enrich your life, and to get to know and appreciate yourself better than ever before. And now as an adult, you actually forgive the past mistaken choice you made as a kid to start smoking, forever releasing it from your life forever. You come to truly know, smoking is far from being an old friend, in fact it's a deadly enemy, a predator staking you and meaning you harm, one which you must remove from your life at all costs, so you relax into this and you do.

At the end of each and every meal, after the food is consumed, you relax, you digest, and you deeply breathe in life giving fresh air. You are powerfully free of needing cigarettes, you need your life, you need your health and you need a healthy life, so much more than cigarettes. You focus your attention on your personal health, self-respect and upon your respect for your health and body.

At each and every meal, you eat slowly, comfortably, savoring the food and listening to the signals of your body. When you are full and fulfilled, you stop and push yourself away from the table. Eating now becomes a time of sustenance for you. Slowly eaten, comfortable, calming meals support you and sustain your life energies and fill you with peace, joy, ease, pride and contentment and which allows you to enrich your life.

When alone you relax, and make down time relaxation time or personal enrichment time. You follow your pursuits and actively live your life, no longer just simply reacting to your life. When you have down time, you, read, you learn. You take up pursuits and hobbies and some other activities that support and enrich your life. You learn to support, love and nurture yourself. There is always something new to learn, something to do, some better way of providing for yourself, some better way to love yourself, some better way to give yourself the gift of enrichment, as a new, happier and healthier way of living your life and providing for yourself. You have a powerful and dynamic mind, you are getting better and better each and every day and night, becoming an inspiration to yourself and both women and men alike. You relax and trust in your life and the true fact that you have always been supported by life. You have always been protected, life has always taken care of you. Your life always takes care of you. You trust in the truth of this fact and embrace the support of your life is giving you as never before.

Smoking is always an unhealthy and unpleasant thing to do. Smoking inhibits health and life. Cigarette smoke is a pollutant. Nicotine is an insecticide. Cigarette smoke is destructive, containing only deadly chemicals, disease causing radiation and potentials for deadly illnesses, like cancer, emphysema and heart attacks. As of this moment, getting only better and easier, you have released all desire to smoke, because you are powerfully free of any need for toxicity and trauma in your life. You are absolutely free from smoking in your life, you relax, you've released it, you've just let it go. Instead you remember a time as child when you relaxed and allowed your body to digest food, properly, calmly, naturally, without the need for cigarettes and smoke and you let the child you once were right now to thrive right now in your life. Beginning right now and for the rest of your life, you allow yourself, better moments and better days ahead, smoke-free days, cigarette-free days, because your deserve it. You allow yourself the stress-free comfort of a peaceful nights sleep. Each and every night two hours before bedtime, you shelf the day, and allow yourself to relax deeper and deeper in the true knowledge that each and every day takes care of itself, and each and every day takes care of you. Tomorrow will take care of you, just the same if not better than today did.

You truly begin to realize that beginning right now, its time to start to develop a better relationship with yourself. And you begin to respect and nurture and love yourself treating yourself as a nurturing supportive parent, a nurturing supportive friend, allowing better progress and peace and health in your life, leading and living your life in peace comfort, empowerment, health, self-respect and longevity.

## Overcoming Obsessive Compulsive Behavior – 1

Each and every day night you relax into your life and in each and every moment you begin to feel more and more comfortable, because you can just allow yourself as you once did in your past, to begin to really feel happier, more confident and more successful, because you are and have in fact and in reality, begun a brand new chapter of your life. Beginning right now and for the rest of your life, rising above any and all fears and any and all worries and any and all repetitive behaviors, because you can and because its best for you and for all of those you love, but most especially best for you. You begin to think and react in new and profoundly better ways, feeling better and better each and every day and night. You truly begin right now to relax and trust in your life, in all that you choose to do, all that you think and all that you create for yourself. It really doesn't matter what once happened in your past or how anything might have affected you, for right now in this moment and getting only stronger and stronger each and every day and night, you let go of your past and all of its useless and un-needed habits and fears and you begin to relax and trust in your life right now. You begin right now instead to know that you are finding new and better ways to live your life feeling more and more fulfilled by just being yourself, which is really just fine with you. For in each and every moment, you are forgiving and healing and releasing what doesn't work, including any and all stress, in the most profound and beneficial ways. In this brand new chapter of your life, you are always rising above any and all limits from your past in truly new and powerfully magnificent and truly profound ways, amazing and impressing and amazing everyone, most especially yourself. Each and every day and night, while you are awake, while you are asleep and even while you dream, your relationship with your world, and yourself and all that is your life and your thoughts and your habits and your world is improving and all of it improves dramatically in only the most beneficial ways and becomes more worthwhile and you are becoming more alive, more vital, growing stronger and stronger in every way, more respectful, more lovingly powerful to you and for you, allowing yourself to thrive and rise above any and all past limits and to heal and become whole in ways that are most successful, most perfect and beneficial to you. All old and completely undesirable repetitive behaviors are and have been pockets of resistance to you, resistance to you embracing life, embracing your life. And now by further relaxing, you are allowing all of them to evaporate, dry up and blow away both now and forever, blow away forever from your life. Instead, even better, you allow a more balanced, calmer, happier, easy going, un-resistant way of life to develop, one in which you relax, trust, flow, are in harmony with yourself and with your forgiveness, of all past issues, that had once, in that past chapter of your life, stood in your way of leading the kind of a fulfilling life, you deserve. The force of your forgiveness is powerful, very powerful, completely unstoppable, only growing and getting stronger and more powerful, more adaptive, more healing, allowing for greater wholeness and harmony, each and every day and each and every night. For in this moment only getting stronger and better, a new balanced healthier chapter of your life has begun, whether you realize it or not, allowing you to thrive and heal in truly amazing ways. You are and you remain at ease even while alone or even with other people, even while alone with your thoughts and feelings. You begin to know that all that is your world and your life is wishing you success and abundance and harmony in all that you do, for your life truly supports you in the most beneficial ways, today, tomorrow and forever! You really truly remember and you have always known from deep down inside, that you are always supported by life, a healthy body and highly strong and reactive immune system and as you have begun this brand new more empowered chapter of your life, you begin to relax, succeed and thrive, relaxing through all stress, all tension and all useless and unneeded and unwanted habits and any and all emotional uneasiness from your past, you are and you truly do in fact begin to enjoy life and living. Each and every day and night, you feel and you truly feel and are more supported, more protected and cared for by life, by the Universe and powerfully by Divinity, letting anything and everything that's overwhelming to be handled by a Higher power. As you learn to relax, better and better, you allow yourself to open your dynamic and powerful mind, to like a sponge, absorb and utilize all of the knowledge that you are really going to be OK, you really, really are and each and every day and night, you truly know that you are safe, for you are and you will release all feelings of guilt, panic, fear, doubt and instead each and every day and night, you begin to trust in your life and the support that life readily and most easily gives you, for you have always been supported by life, each and every day of your life, today, tomorrow and all tomorrows, will support you in the most beneficial ways each and every moment. Worry is an empty vessel, it holds nothing, it does nothing and is useless. Instead, each and every day and night, you'd rather, trust in yourself and all of you begins to actually flow with your life. Any and all adversity that you may encounter, has and will actually polish you, like water rushing past a boulder in a fast running stream, you are polished by any and all challenges and adversities in your life, cleansing and healing you in the most profound ways possible, each and every moment free of being compulsive in any of your behaviors: (add topics)- relax, for the world is clean enough, relax, for your immune system is keeping you healthy in the most truly beneficial, powerful and extreme potent ways possible; relax; your world is clean enough, relax; your body is supported by a powerful and magnificent immune system easily and most truly and powerfully keeping you healthy and vital, alive and strong; relax; world is always taking care of you, and your healing becomes amazing, your old habits and fears release right now, you can actually feel them lifting up, lifting up, off and far, far away from you. You are free from being concerned with the word "problem" for a problem is by its nature something that's difficult to change, so better and instead, you become challenge oriented, which means accepting any and all challenges, rising up to meet any and all challenges, because you can, you will and you do, overcome all perceived challenges with poise, power, elegance, grace and ease and limitless success in all moments easily, even when just reacting without thinking. You lean each and everyday and night to let go of struggle as a concept in your life and your correct response to any challenge is to relax right out of struggling in any way, physically, emotionally, mentally and even spiritually, relaxing into a calmer and better way of life and living as you release all old unwanted and unneeded ways from your past. You simply see those old behaviors as past experiences, free from all and any effect upon you right now. You also begin to trust in yourself and in your life, because that's the best choice to make and you are always making the best of all possible choices. All of your new choices for calmness and singular, un-repetitive behavior are correct ones, even while you are feeling awake, energized, while you are preoccupied or even if you are tired in any way, for at any time in your present or future, you will succeed in being happier, healthier, calmer. All of you gains from any and all brand new unlimiting choices and decisions and behaviors that you make, you either learn to do better each and every day and night or succeed, so in every way and the most vital and important ways, you always win, you are a winner, you succeed, congratulations!

You relax and you enjoy your life, and everything for you just always flows, just like a mighty river or ocean, flowing past and around all obstacles, always going where it needs to be and you get to know more and more each day and night, that the flow of your life is eternal. Whenever you feel stress or tension of any kind, you correctly choose, always making the very best correct choice, to breathe deep and steady relaxation breath, you relax all over, relaxing all that You are and all of your tension and stress after just a few short breaths, just melts away, you can actually feel it leaving you, just lifting up off and far, far away from you, and you have limitless confidence in yourself and in your ability to relax and release any and all stress, by just deciding to just relax. Any and all thoughts and ideas are valid, but as you learn to relax yourself, you begin to focus on relaxing and releasing the thoughts and ideas that create limitation in your life in any way, only creating thoughts and habits that truly serve you in the most beneficial ways and you would rather focus upon and do focus upon, the thoughts, sensations, images and feelings that truly support you in the most beneficial ways, you relax and release all that is stressful. And from all of this you begin to view your life in a more loving and supportive way, giving yourself a break, you begin right now to see and to support yourself the way an ideal unconditionally loving and nurturing parent would a wonderful and beautiful child. You correctly, deeply and truly realize, that feelings are just feelings, thoughts are just thoughts, for there are times when you can be hot or cold, tired or energetic, hungry or filled up, because feelings are just feelings and thoughts and they can never really hurt you in any way, but right now, you have really chosen to rise above any and all feelings, any hurts any pain, real or imagined, but you deserve to, you are able to, you can, you will, because you have decided to do so, and you can and you will just because you are unstoppable in achieving this or anything you set your powerful and dynamic and successful mind to, you feel like you've got the whole world in the palm of your hand, easily able to talk to the world, to rise above and succeed in all that you can and will and in fact do accomplish. You feel like you can smile on the inside and even on the outside, because you can and will begin to do all that it takes to succeed, because you really want to, you are able to overcome any and all hurdles. All of your life supports you and you really deeply know this to be the truth, a new and most powerful truth in all that You are you are powerfully supported and succeeding physically, emotionally and mentally and even spiritually. The whole world in its own perfect way is supporting you and you win!

# Overcoming Obsessive Compulsive Behavior - Part 2

**Note:** You must be a qualified and certified Clinical Hypnosis professional and have a written note of authorization to perform this or any other complementary hypnosis session from the attending physician, psychiatrist, psychologist, etc., no exceptions.

Each and every day and night you relax into your life and truly begin to spend time concentrating upon how you can and how you will trust in your life and in your world and how the world and all that is your life supports you. For in each and every moment, you truly allow yourself to begin to feel more and more comfortable and supported, because you can just allow yourself, as you once did in your past, to begin to feel happier, more confident and more successful, because you are and have in fact and in reality, begun a brand new happier, free and calmer chapter of your life. Beginning right now and for the rest of your life, you are always rising above any and all fears and worries and all repetitive behaviors, because you can and because its best for you and all of those you love, but most especially it's what's best for you. Each and every day and night, as well as each and every moment, you allow your powerful and dynamic successful mind to relinquish, alleviate and move beyond any and all limitations in your life, most especially in relation to letting go of old unneeded ideas, thoughts, feelings, symptoms and behaviors that had once stood in your way of having a calm, happy, peaceful, moderate way of life. You really in fact, completely release and relinquish struggle, strain and uncertainty as aspects from your past, you are free from all effect from them right now and forever, in this moment, you have truly gained and have really allowed yourself to trust in your world, your life. And in allowing for things you have organized to remain as they had been and are since you had arranged them, because you trust in all of your past choices and you realize that things are just fine the way they are, which is really truly just fine with you. You correctly choose to relax, relinquish and allow in your life, for the very best way to feel in control of your life, is to relax into the fullness that is your life, each and every day and night, you allow, you trust, you deep breathe, especially in times of challenge and you allow yourself to succeed and to thrive, in all areas of your life. Like a glorious or a beautiful plant, that grows and reaches out to the sky and sun, you truly and deeply realize and recognize, that you are beginning to flow and to harmonize with all that is your life, allowing what's natural around you to happen. Each and every day and night, you are allowing all that is your best to come through, to transcend, to heal, to improve, in all that you wish to accomplish, in all that you will accomplish and in all that you truly do, can and will accomplish, succeeding in all that you do, more successfully in each and every way, more than ever before. You have truly and actually come to understand and react in better and different ways, deeply and profoundly realizing that you have correctly chosen to trust in your life and all that it brings, relinquishing in new and better ways, to overcome worry and shame in new, better, amazing and even surprising ways. If something is cleaned, it will only become less clean at some future time, if something is arranged, it is natural for it to fall into disarrangement at some future time. So as each moment passes, you correctly choose to relax, to trust in your life, and in this world and in Divinity and the very true fact that all of life supports you, so its really, really truly OK with you, to forgive, to release and to even relax through, any and all old thoughts, any and all emotions, any and all old ideas, any and all old experiences, both real or imagined, that may have or in fact have created behaviors that hurt you in anyway, regardless of where they came from, regardless of how they felt, or what your experiences were because all of your past has in fact polished you, taught you and most especially, allowed you to succeed, allowing you to become the caring, loving, thoughtful, sensitive person you are today. Life is always working out for you in the very best Divine order. In this brand new chapter of your life, you have truly in fact chosen to forgive yourself, all of your past unpleasant experiences and disappointments and all of the people involved, because that's what is really best for you and your life right now and that's really all that matters and in your calm relaxed determination, you can only succeed, because you are determined, you are powerful, strong and in your limitless budding and building optimism, you will ultimately and most successfully succeed, because that is the only possible outcome. For in each and every moment, you are forgiving and healing and releasing what limits you, including any and all stress, in the most profound and beneficial ways. In this brand new chapter of your life, you are always rising above any and all limits from your past in truly new and powerfully magnificent and truly profound ways, impressing and amazing everyone, most especially yourself. Each and every day and night, while you are awake, while you are asleep and even while you dream, your relationship with your world and yourself and all that is your life and your thoughts and your habits and your world is improving. And all of it improves in the most beneficial ways and becomes more worthwhile and you are becoming more alive, more vital, growing stronger and stronger in every way, more respectful, more lovingly powerful to you and for you, allowing you to thrive and rise above any and all past limits and to heal and become whole in ways that are most successful, most perfect and beneficial to you. You are and you remain at ease even during situations similar to the past, that allow you to find creative ways to challenge yourself, to rise up, to rise up and above, to transcend old limits, allowing yourself to succeed, to thrive, to remain deeply relaxed and very calm, thriving in all that is your life. You really in fact know, that all of your life truly supports you in the most beneficial ways, today, tomorrow and forever, even enough to powerfully improve your life right now! You really truly remember and you have always known from deep down inside, that you are always supported by life, a healthy body and highly strong and reactive immune system and as you have begun this brand new more empowered chapter of your life, you begin to relax, succeed and thrive, relaxing through all stress, all tension and all useless and unneeded and unwanted habits and any and all emotional uneasiness from your past. You are and you truly do in fact begin to enjoy life the way an ideal unconditionally loving and nurturing parent would a wonderful and beautiful child. And you are living, knowing and acknowledging that you are really going to be OK, yes, you really, really are and each and every day and night, you truly know that you are safe, for you are and you will and are releasing all feelings of guilt, panic, fear, doubt and instead each and every day and night, you begin to trust in your life and the support that life readily and most easily gives you, for you have always been supported by life, each and every day of your life, today, tomorrow and all tomorrows, will support you in the most beneficial ways each and every moment. You really begin, beginning right now and for the rest of your life, to see new and better ways to support yourself. You correctly, deeply and truly realize, that feelings are just feelings, thoughts are just thoughts, for there are times when you can be hot or cold, tired or energetic, hungry or filled up, because feelings are just feelings and thoughts and they can never really hurt you in any way. But right now, you have really chosen to rise above any and all feelings, any hurts, any pain, real or imagined, because you deserve to, you are able to, you can, you will, because you have decided to do so and you can and you will just because you are absolutely determined and truly and absolutely unstoppable in achieving this or in achieving anything you have set your powerful and dynamic and successful mind to, you feel like you can take on the world, talk to the world, rise above, and succeed in all that you can and will and do in fact accomplish. You feel like you can smile on the inside and even on the outside, because you can and will begin to do all that it takes to succeed, because you really want to, you are able to overcome any and all hurdles, you can, you do and you will, in the most creative, impressive astounding and beneficial ways with greatest possible impact in your world and in all that is your creation, your life and in each and everything you do. All of your life supports you and really you deeply know this to be the truth, a new and most powerful truth in all that You are physically, emotionally and mentally and even spiritually. The whole world in its own perfect way is supporting you, and you win!

## Overcoming Past Sexual Abuse (Female) Release, Relaxation and Orgasm

**Note:** You must be a qualified and certified Clinical Hypnosis professional and have a written note of authorization to perform this or any other complementary hypnosis session from the attending physician, psychiatrist, psychologist, etc., no exceptions.

Relax deeper and deeper now and on each and every breath, as you relax, you will decide to allow yourself to expand your horizons by forgiving and releasing all pain and traumas and upsetment and disharmony from your past, all of the old wounds are healing, healing, healed, released and you are moving on. With each and every beat of your heart and with every breath that you take, you allow yourself freedom from your past and its current influence over you, for the only power its ever had is whatever power you've given it and beginning right now, you decide its time to let it go, just letting all of its energy and disharmonies to drift and float, far, far away from you, until they become a distant memory. It becomes unimportant to you and you hardly ever think about it and even if you did, you would feel powerful, very powerful from having risen above it and free, very free from having thrived and prospered in your life, having moved on. You have a powerful and dynamic mind, you are a powerful and dynamic person and you are free from any past connections to any pain and hurt. You have risen above and learned valuable lessons to empower you and now you focus upon memories of good times, happy moments and nurturing life lessons and you are healed, re-identified as a wonderfully powerful person, you have and you will transcend any and all limits, past present or any limits that could possibly arise in the future. So each and every day you are becoming more and more courageous a very powerful inspiration to men, women and children alike.

Beginning right now and for the rest of your life, you breathe, you relax and you allow yourself, peace, calmness and powerful and dynamic inner peace and harmony, for you are alive and living in the right now, living in the present moment, enjoying your life, loving yourself and your loved one, loving being in this present moment, headed into a bright and wonderfully fulfilling future, in every way, spiritually, mentally, emotionally, physically and even sexually. Each and every day, your self-love expands within you, your love for your life, your husband (mate, lover) and the world and all it has to offer you. You are relaxed, you are peaceful, you allow. You live and you thrive in all areas of your life and you embrace all that You are especially your womanhood and femaleness, your love and your sexuality, powerfully, completely and dynamically. You relax, you feel, you allow yourself moments of relaxed intimate pleasures, pleasures that you really deserve, powerfully and absolutely. With each and every day, with each and every sunrise, you allow yourself to deserve and to enjoy as never before. You relax, you release, you enjoy intimacy and feelings of sexual pleasure as never before. Each and every day you get better and better. You relax into the dynamic woman you were born to be, enjoying your body, your sensuality and sexuality, enjoying the moments of pleasure that you are living right now. Life polishes you and you are shining forth as never before in areas of your life. You are releasing more and more, day by day, more of your energies, into your life, becoming more and more alive each and every day, you let go of past pressures and expectations and decide right now and for the rest of your life, you enjoy yourself, your life and your sexuality instead. Just letting all that you are and your innate sexual power, to flourish, ripen, and burst forth into the rest of your life, allowing yourself to relax into orgasmic fulfillment, having made and becoming one with this decision at all times, while you are awake, while you are asleep and even while you dream, only getting better and easier for you successfully. All expectations, controls, pressures, unfairly put on you, regardless of how they got there or where they came from, on all levels right now and for the rest of your life, are now disappearing and are being replaced, by better stronger feelings of relaxation, enjoyment of sensuality, sexuality and deep inner peace and calmness and serenity. So right now, you are allowing all that you are to recognize your powerful and natural inner harmony, spiritually, mentally, emotionally, physically and sexually, to function peacefully and in greatest personal satisfaction and deepest most powerful fulfillment. You deserve, you relax, you allow and you flourish and flow. You are free, spiritually, more free than ever before, you are free mentally, more mentally free than ever before, free, clear, relaxed emotionally, more free than ever before, you are free and relaxed physically, more free and clear physically than ever before, and you allow your sexuality and orgasms to flourish and burst forth free of any effort throughout all that You are into your body, emotions, mind and spirit as never before. No place to get to, just relaxation and pleasure bursting forth. You deserve it, you allow it, it flourishes, bursting forth freely and free of any effort, free from expectations, deeply and naturally and powerfully relaxed.

Take a deep breath and let it out now, allow the breath to make all of this a deep and powerful part of your life and right now you allow yourself to make a decision.

You decide that as you give, so shall you in turn receive and that also very strongly includes, deserving and allowing yourself (to come) and to receive deeply powerful orgasmic pleasure into your life, world and body. You decide to relax and make sex, a time of playfulness and intimacy, a process that all of you relaxes into, sex and sexuality is something that you enjoy and deserve. You are truly allowed by your own powerful permission, to receive pleasure, pure enjoyment, free of judgments, just relaxing and enjoying more and more pleasure each and every time. Sex becomes fun, enjoyable and orgasmic.

You relax and you enjoy, you truly deserve, you allow, you have fun. You might even be surprised at how much more enjoyable this new forever emerging and empowered woman that you forever are, really truly enjoying herself. For you there is no more trying, there is only relaxation and pleasure and all that you deserve, easily and free from effort, this dynamic new sexually fulfilled woman that you have liberated forth into the world and into your life. You don't need to know when your orgasm will come, but it does, free from expectations or any pressure and it will come, you come, powerfully and completely, satisfied as never before, powerfully pleasured, more and better every time and you are liberated into a bright and wonderful right now and future and your (marriage) relationship thrives in the process. You enjoy, you relax, you allow, it just happens and it feels great! All of this happens as a better expression of your love for yourself, your husband (mate, lover), the world, and all that is your life, naturally, easily, freely, effortlessly, as an expression of this new happier you. All of your life supports you, in enhancing your pleasure, even your dreams free up your abilities and energies, allowing you fulfillment, amazing and inspiring even you! You live, you smile inside, you are fulfilled.

## Overcoming Shyness and Anger and Becoming More Tidy

You begin to exude a new energy, almost as if someone from deep, deep inside of you is turning up and tuning up your life force energy, to newer and more powerfully vital levels. As you now feel this and appreciate the profound and life improving change you've made, you're allowing all of those whom behold you to see you glowing with a newer and more pronounced sense of self. You are truly interested in them, and they are truly interested in you and your newer and more abundant, winning ways. You open your heart and allow yourself to share your oneness with them, sharing your very best with them, showing them what defines you, including but far from limited to your personal style, your personal likes and even dislikes. You are easily rising to the top, exuding a new and profound confidence and a new and more lasting foundation of trust and a new belief in yourself and in your life, you become easily outgoing and upbeat, easily taking on any and all challenges. Your ability to communicate your point of view is now and forever enhanced. You are finding newer and better ways of being smoothly able to say, to communicate and to express yourself confidently, comfortably and clearly, sharing what's on your mind, in the most appropriate and direct of ways. You are forever free of holding in thoughts and feelings and forever free of getting angry inside, feeling so emotionally balanced and calm, as you now begin to easily, successfully and dynamically move into a better, brighter, healthier, more powerful and successful chapter of your life. You are finding newer and better ways to dramatically improve yourself, becoming more in tune with your life. You are more easily able to liberate the organized and tidy person you now see, feeling and knowing that you are easily becoming a person, who puts and adjusts everything is into its proper place. You are finding and creating the time and essential action necessary for order in your thoughts, feelings and actions. You are free forever of procrastination. So rather and even better instead, you are becoming active, more and more vital, more and more vibrant and filled with positive feelings and more and more alive, more and more necessary, more and more precise, more and more organized, more and more focused, more and more liberated, more and more cleansed, completely and easily forgiven, released, moving on, healed and forever free. You are working powerfully, precisely and in completely effective ways within the harmony and cycles that allow you to effectively produce results in your favor. Each and every day and each and every night you are easily yet successfully finding newer and better ways, means and methods of feeling, remaining and living, truly and unstoppably redefining yourself and easily becoming an independent, spontaneous, and confident individual, because now you believe in yourself and truly, you know who you are and that you really and truly are one with all of these things. You are liberating those inner qualities out into the world in powerful, limitless and endless supply, in ways that others will not only notice but also truly respect and they now and forever see you as a well ordered person, just as you see yourself this way and it feels wonderful. You are bold, courageous, wonderful, strong, confident, your self-esteem and self confidence are being turned up, and tuned up, almost as if someone from deep, deep inside of you has reset or turned up a switch, a dial, a thermostat or a computer of some kind, unstoppably activating all of your very best, as you even might find newer and more surprising ways of truthfully accomplishing this. All of your life is only getting better and better, with each and every breath that you take and with each and every beat of your heart. As you believe in yourself and truly come to know all of this, all of it getting only, better, easier and more and more dynamic. You come to know you are unstoppable in achieving all of this and even more, as your life expands and lights up the world and lights up the lives of those your life touches, you are doing better and better, more and more fantastically well.

# Overcoming Smoking

There are only good times to remain free of smoking cigarettes, because smoking works against you, and smoking cigarettes is deadly and you are instead living an empowered, healthy, well balanced life. There are only times to become, to be and forever remain smoke-free, cigarette-free; that's where your focus is, and that's where you are and you remain. You are and you remain smoke-free, cigarette-free at all times, every time, most especially on weekends, evenings, mornings, weekdays, workdays and holidays, while you might be stressed, or while you are leisurely relaxing. These are all now and forever, times of health and healing, times of happy empowerment, times of being and forever remaining smoke-free, cigarette-free. Your perception of life and of yourself is improving day by day, night by night, because you are liberated, cleansed, very powerfully determined to be forever smoke-free, cigarette-free, both always and forever remaining smoke-free. All of life works to support you, every sound, every noise, even ringing telephones and sounds from outside, like car horns, sirens and alarms, re-enforce your freedom from smoking in every way every time you hear them. Only your opinions count, so even the negative thoughts, feelings and opinions of others, regardless of who they might be, only bounce off and far, far away from you, because the more they express themselves, the more relaxed and determined you become to remain forever and always smoke-free, cigarette-free, healthy, happy, safe and free.

You have an outstanding and excellent mind. You are becoming an inspiration to men, women and children alike. You feel almost as if you are ready to conquer the world and most especially, you are completely ready to forever successfully conquer the smoking habit, because you are now smoke-free, cigarette-free. You will be hardly ever be thinking about smoking or cigarettes again, but even if you do think of smoking or cigarettes, you will be thinking about it in relation to how much better off you are without them. You are superior to any need for cigarettes because, beginning right now and for the rest of your life, you are smoke-free, cigarette-free, now always and forever, simply uninterested in cigarettes and smoking, having moved on. You are surprised and happily amazed at how truly powerful you really are. You are relaxed, relaxing into a healthier, happier chapter of your life. You are determined so you succeed. You can do better for yourself, you will do better for yourself so, beginning right now and for the rest of your life, you begin to treat yourself as an ideal and nurturing parent would a wonderful child. You will do better, you are better and better, you are smoke-free, cigarette-free. In your past your past, one of your urges may had been to smoke, now your greatest urge, an unstoppable urge that's 178 times greater, growing ever stronger is to remain healthy safe and free, smoke free, cigarette free.

You begin in each and every moment, to empower yourself. You let go of all old excuses for smoking and cigarettes and you begin to really enjoy your life. Your life is your creation and it's getting better and better as you let go of limiting, destructive, unhealthy habits and ideas. You now tap into you tremendous inner strength and limitless inner wisdom, all the energy of your past victories, triumphs, breakthroughs and successes are upon you now, deeply and profoundly inspiring you. You relax, you breathe, you empower yourself and feel the soothing energy of this empowered new you, coming forward into all areas of your life; this strength flowing from your connection to creation and the Universe, flowing through your heart, and your mind, into all areas of your life, creating a better way of life, a new smoke-free, cigarette-free new healthier way of life.

You relax, and you feel the power of all of your past triumphs and breakthroughs and successes. You breathe, and with each and every breath, and with every beat of your heart, you summon up all of this tremendous and limitless inner power and all of the support that life readily and easily gives, as it's always really done. You become and you truly are a powerful, empowered person, this energy is powerful part of all that you are, body, emotions, mind, and spirit are all working in a powerful oneness. Beginning right now and for the rest of your life, you readily and easily allow this boundless energy to allow you to be successful in all areas of your life, especially in terms of you being a liberated smoke-free, cigarette-free person. In fact and in reality, you are truly feeling empowered and inspired as never before. Congratulations, you are now smoke-free, cigarette-free!!!! You feel like you can smile on the inside and outside, you are released, and you have transcended, you are empowered, and now and forever smoke-free, cigarette-free. And now as an adult, you actually forgive the past mistaken choice you may have made as a kid to start smoking. You are releasing it from your life forever. You come to truly know, smoking is far from being an old friend, in fact it's truly a deadly enemy, one that you must remove from your life at all costs. And your tastes change, in your favor. Cigarette smoke begins to taste and smell to you like burning rubber, uggh, how awful! How disgusting, how nauseating that smell! With each and every challenge you create, you achieve better and more long lasting success. And with each and every success, your freedom from cigarettes and smoking gets better and better, stronger and stronger, easier and easier. Each and every moment that you remain smoke-free and cigarette-free, you succeed unstoppably by easily gaining an hour, each hour a day, each day a week, each week, gaining the rest of your life, a smoke-free, cigarette-free life, free, free forever, free at last.

# Overcoming Stress, Life Challenges and Alcohol as a Crutch

You have powerfully and unstoppably decided to take a new tack in your life, to get back on track and to succeed in unstoppably adaptive and effective ways. Your correct response to any and all stress is to first deep-breathe and to rise above it by relaxing your way through it. Just as you've always been able to work well under pressure, you are now finding clever and adaptive ways to rise above the pressures of your life, even if it includes increased case loads at work, finding newer and better ways to deep-breathe, relax and to adaptively and cleverly reduce your stress. Quite often in your past, just some deep-breathing was enough to bring down stress, and you'll just find yourself doing that, while successfully bringing down stress levels most effectively, doing anything and everything that needs doing or has to be done, feeling a new and ever-building sense of empowerment, so committed to success and in the most effective of ways, you are most assuredly succeeding unstoppably, turning once-elevated stress levels around for you to work with in your favor. You make time to flourish in your life, making time, scheduling and adaptively succeeding to make time for romance and intimacy with your spouse (husband / wife) in your life, regardless of change of life cycle or regardless of any event or circumstance, now even better, truly, effectively, cleverly, adaptively and relaxing into the joys of increased intimacy in your life; you make it important, you take and make the time, and it becomes a priority in your life, just doing what needs to be done there. You are becoming upbeat, capable, inspired, flexible and adaptive, easily able to relax and create insights about how to deal with and rise above vindictive and vicious people, allowing yourself time to cleverly succeed and to adapt, allowing your very best insights to come through, while remaining emotionally detached from events and circumstances to provide a clear way and to guide others on your path of clarity, to focus while leading them to better places and better harmonies, often by your own example, always unleashing your very best, wisdom, guidance, thoughts, feelings and perspectives, allowing the most powerful wisdom of your inner therapist to come through, in each and every moment, and this only gets easier, better, faster, more successfully adaptive and effective, in each and every moment and each and every time you are challenged this way, as you succeed skillfully as never before. You rise up and vanquish all hostilities, for you now know and truly remember, you are mightier than any challenge you might encounter; you are and you remain, problem-free, while staying challenge-oriented, shining light, direction and clarity, into the wisdom of the decisions and choices that you make. The light of the love you have for your family, always guides you to the very best decisions, choices and successes, you both now and forever create. You find yourself discussing and creating harmony in all moments and situations that matter the most, most especially when discussing the upbringing of your kids as you are both seeking the very best outcomes; you together, by your design and by your mutual love, always calmly discuss and arrive at the very best of all possible adaptations and decisions, allowing all of the very best choices and decisions that you mutually work out, to transcend any and all disharmonies and challenges. You are talking your life back, rising up and making the very best and most of your life, activating your very best, as if someone from deep, deep inside of you is forever and always turning on a switch of some kind. You are taking your past inner weaknesses and turning them into strengths, polishing up all flaws, remaking yourself shiny and new, powerful and focused, loving yourself in place of destructive self-judgments, forgiving and releasing the past, rising up to become mightier than any and all challenges you have or might be presented with, loving yourself in place of the old habit of beating yourself up, filling yourself up with a new sense of "can do" spirit and now truly, allowing yourself to thrive, doing all that needs doing, and smiling at how cleverly, adaptively you are succeeding, activating new inspirations from the deepest and truest places from your heart, mind and life, with precise and adaptive focus, with calm and balanced emotions, in the very best and most amazing of ways. Skillfully avoiding old and new pitfalls, you are finding new joys and life-supportive experiences, flowing ever onward.

## Relieving Vaginismus

Vaginismus is a condition of involuntary contraction of the PC muscles around the vagina, making sexual penetration impossible or painful. *Note:* You must be a qualified and certified Clinical Hypnosis professional and have a written note of authorization to perform this or any other complementary hypnosis session from the attending physician, psychiatrist, psychologist, etc., no exceptions.

You've always known this condition wouldn't last forever and it's over, and now in the brand new chapter of your life, you have and you unstoppably are moving away from it into the kind of loving and caring, deep desire and joy, martial bliss and harmony you have now relaxed into, and it's now easy. Any and all past conditioning, programming, self-destructive thoughts, ideas, feelings and emotions, actions and reactions, are now and forever forgiven, released and supremely vanquished, in powerfully surprising, clever, fluid and openly adaptive, amazingly effective ways. For you have and are unstoppably developing a new and more powerful, potent and effective, better conditioned reflex during times of intimacy. It continues to happen every time that there is a potential for vaginal penetration, to be open, receptive and ready, emotionally calm and centered, sexually excited, and it's time to assume your rights and potentials as a married woman.

In your mind's eye, in your imagination, picture, imagine or just visualize the opening flower, like a rose. Imagine this to be an opening flower of your love, as you are deeply and truly now creating deep, deep relaxation leading to a new and powerful openness from deep inside of your heart, your mind, your thoughts, your emotions, your actions, your reactions, as you release, forgive, let go of and forgive any and all past energies that have ever blocked you, creating forgiveness of any and all trauma, fear, guilt, forgiveness of any and all mental or emotional pain, just deep breathing and releasing it further and further on each and every breath you are taking and with each and every beat of your heart, almost as if someone right this second, from deep, deep inside of you has powerfully and effectively, truly reset a switch, a dial, a computer or a thermostat of some kind, comfortably and truly allowing yourself to completely open yourself, feeling completely and truly loving, open and trusting, the openness of your love that trust can bring to create vulnerability, for in your oneness and vulnerability of the love you share, lies your greatest loving strength. Any and all old spasms seem to fade away; the ocean is calm and peaceful, strong yet serene. You are feeling calm and fine, open and ready; your flower blossoms and is active. Old uncomfortableness just leaving and going, going, going and gone, like when a kid has the hiccups, which just went away on their own, being replaced by calmness and natural reactions. What was once closed by whatever means, is now open, as it and you and your love for your husband deserve to be. You relax into what is right, normal and proper for your love and love-making, so natural and so very right for you both, as husband and wife. Each and every attempt at intercourse more relaxing, more comfortable, more and more relaxed, all muscles and musculature reactions appropriate; things are calm, muscles yielding and calm, just so ever comfortably melting, warm and heavy, blood-flow working in concert, just relaxing, proper and comfortable, moisture and excitement, allowing your flower to open and expand, blockage-free, open and ready, yielding naturally. You are unstoppably feeling calmness and joy, beautiful unconditional love and healing, relaxation and release, on each and every breath and on each and every heartbeat. Only beneficial, better and better, positive and more unlimited, unrestricted intimacy and intercourse experiences for you from now on. Disappointments now are things from a past chapter of your life, activating your unstoppable inner heroine to rise to the top, as if braced up by every past victory, triumph, breakthrough and success you've ever had, as you are now formidably becoming bigger and mightier than each and anything that ever once stood in your way. Any and all negative sexual messages from your past are now being released, forgiven, healed and released, relinquished and moved away from, surprisingly easily for you now, amazingly effectively and not because I say so, but because you've decided to rise up and move beyond, relaxing like you were meant to, flowering and opening, free of trying or over-analyzing, just in the moment of peace, joy, love and sexual intimacy, your birthright, and simply doing it and flowing ever onward to beautiful vistas and horizons in your life. Sexual intimacy and intercourse, a normal and well deserved part of your married life, are now and forever becoming possible, real and true. Any and all efforts, both large and small, are becoming more and more comfortable, a new day dawning, and a new stress-free chapter of your life now beginning, as your muscle memory is becoming one of openness, calmness, receptivity and ease, free of any effort or control on your part, just allowing it to happen, and so it does. Your nervous system, reset and ready, only now working in your favor, is now open, ready, under your control and receptive to receive your husband, his penis and the loving joy, harmony and bliss you both deserve to share, as you are and you remain re-calibrated, receptive, open, deeply and truly relaxed, in memory and emotion, response and reaction, your muscles now relaxed and well functioning, completely under your responsive control, working supremely in your favor, ready, willing and able, calm and steady functional reactions, sexual excitement, building and building, spasm-free, loose and open, ready. It's time, so it happens, free and released of any and all old pressures, stresses, anxieties or frustrations, relaxed, released, untied, open, practically Divinely-guided and blessed, the nerves controlling your PC muscle group now responding properly, but right now only working now in your favor, reversed from past times, in a brand new and forever chapter of your life, letting go, liberated, freed, reacting positively at the onset of penetration as you now know you can and simply do, all old blockages and hindrances are now and forever just easily and forever bypassed, and you flow easily, cleverly and powerfully beyond any and all of them.

You are and you remain adaptively and cleverly unleashed and ready, open and receptive, free and set free; you let go, and enjoy the pleasurable sex and intimacy with your husband that you deserve, and he deserves, free of pressures, all of this getting only easier and better, deeper and more effective each and every time you repeat this wonderful exercise on your own.

# Weight and Exercise

You are now finding and inventively creating newer and better ways of becoming self-devoted and motivated. You are now powerfully self re-identified as energetic, active and vibrant, truly enjoying your life and doing the things you should be doing to take better care of you. You are now flowing seamlessly into improving your life and extending your well-deserved health, finding supportive and motivating friends, thoughts and actions to support this powerfully and unstoppably. You create new opportunities for self-control, finding times to become more motivated and bringing your exercise goals down to levels of ridiculous ease, because in this new chapter of your life, you truly love and value yourself, creating a new trust in your life and greater and greater self-esteem, self-confidence and self-appreciation, as you are now each and every day and night, learning to better love and heal your body. You are forgiving old and past blockages, that you are now and forever finished with, having unstoppably moved on successfully and victoriously. When it comes to exercise, you just get up and do it, as the superior person you are does, because you are unleashing the superior, very best and most beautiful person that you are, and you are now unstoppable in achieving all that you now deserve to create, so now make this happen. You now find and make the time to take better care of yourself, by packing a good lunch for work, forever free of overpaying for items of lesser nutritional value, finding happiness by taking the time to love yourself better. Each and every evening before a work night, you find, manufacture, create, allow and take the time, the evening before, to prepare a meal to take to work. You enjoy this as you save quite a good bit of money. A new thought, "less is more." So now you allow yourself to leave some of each and every meal behind on the plate as you leave the table, as you now pretty much always feel OKAY, even wonderful about leaving something behind, as your personal sense of victory over past challenges thrives and increases, driving you ever forward. You slow down while eating and know when you are full, forever free of overeating or being overfilled. You find and take the time to prepare veggies and have fruit, in a new process in your life, making the right things available to yourself, taking better care of you. You do love being motivated about shopping and cooking, always lovingly providing for yourself in powerful ways, in a new life-long campaign of self-love and self-appreciation, for the most important person in your world, you. Although convenience items from the freezer are there for a reason, you can and do find newer and better ways to take care of yourself than them. You find your pace, plotting out your day as well as your strategy for success, thinking about dinner in advance, which now becomes easy, finding truer and more powerful gratification by taking care of yourself properly. You find and truly take better care of yourself in all ways, including but not limited to diet, increased yet effective and regular exercise, playing your wonderfully enjoyable hypnosis tape to allow peacefully fulfilling sleep, enough sleep, more of an interest in your getting a better and better appearance, perhaps even becoming a fashion plate, as you smile to yourself inside. You drink more water and skillfully avoid soda and other fattening drinks, even reducing your caffeine intake, you love yourself that much. You create newer and lasting rhythms, finding newer and long-lasting passions, bringing exercise goals down to levels of ridiculous ease, just a few minutes a day, a few days a week, easily exceeding those minutes, making a new routine and bringing new supportive people into the picture masterfully, one step at a time, just like when you do or have done any workout in the past and usually feel good about the fact that you're more active, enjoying the athletic muscle burn, because you know you are doing what's right, loving yourself, as you become lighter, thinner, healthier and better.

## Weight and Life Improvement

Less is more; you fill up sooner and unstoppably take better care of yourself. You eat slowly, correctly, taking better care of yourself, eating like a proper adult, forever free of eating like a child or teenager, forever free of kiddy foods, even just a very small taste is enough for you. You know when to stop and move on, and to relax; you win, lighter, thinner, healthier and better. Slowly consumed foods, properly chewed are better, more natural and just right for you; speed chewing is now a thing of the past; you are moving on, even when things are good, most especially when anything is or might be bothering you. The opinions of others are just that; you are, now and forever, free of taking any limiting criticism or negative actions, reactions or responses; just like those things of the past, they become and are meaningless to you. In fact, what others think of you is none of your business; so you just release it, forgive it, and generally just blow it off. You are bigger, mightier and more powerful than any and all past limitations, judgments or old hindrances; you've grown up and moved on, healthy, whole and healed, stronger, better and more adaptive than anything that had ever once stood in your way in the past. All things that once challenged you or imbalanced you in any way, are, now and forever, learning experiences that you now see and recognize as having polished you. For when you know who you are, when you've forgiven your past judgments upon yourself, when you believe in yourself as you do now, as you have in fact truly moved on, when you now know who you are, as you've released your inner hero, the part of you that is mighty and knows no bounds or limitations from the past, you are re-identified as mighty, powerful, fluid, creative, adaptive, and all things, all elements in your life are now and forever working to adapt themselves to you and to work unstoppably in your favor, to allow you to thrive and succeed as never before, in the most limitless of ways. This mighty you now loves and approves of yourself in dynamic and limitless ways, struggle-free, bother-free, and absolutely thriving in bold and dynamic ways, for your relationship with yourself and your life and in all that you do is now functioning fully in your favor.

What you once expected from others, you now and forever give to yourself, giving yourself limitless amounts of kindness and sincerity. You are becoming a shining light in this world, which now vanquishes and repels negative people. For you are learning to forgive, heal and truly love yourself more so you can attract positive, more unlimited, open and loving people into your life so that you can be in a relationship with good men, good women and greater love. You drop your defensiveness and learn to become mighty in unconditional love, better and better than ever before. You are learning to love and to take care of yourself, bringing your exercise goals down to levels of ridiculous ease, just a few days a week, say 3 days, you will find, create and make the time to exercise for just 2 or 3 minutes, 2 or 3 times a week, just getting up and doing it, easily extending that time because you enjoy it, more motivated to take excellent care of yourself. You burn food, fat, weight and calories, easily melting off 97, 98, or even 101 pounds, allowing yourself to become and remain, healthy and firm.

---

## Weight Management - Reduction

Right now as of this very moment, you have made a very potent and extremely powerful decision, a powerful life changing decision, to change the way you relate to food, eating, releasing all unneeded, unwanted things, including weight from your body, your emotions, your mind and your life in every way. And by relaxing into this decision, you thrive and you win, lighter, better, healthier and thinner. The only reason you eat is to live, for in fact and in reality, you have absolutely become free of living to eat. And whether you realize it yet or not, your powerful and dynamic subconscious mind is working in the most healthy beneficial ways, so right and proper, just for you, to activate powerfully and yet most unstoppably, new and better ways to allow you to become and then remain lighter, thinner, healthier and better, achieving the success you seek, liberating it here into the right now into your life.

This powerful, successful, dynamic and creative mind, your mind, is now forgiving and releasing the past and all of its buffers and blockages against the disharmonies of your past, most especially any and all of the disharmonies of the past, even more especially any point in your past, where you have been or even perhaps felt betrayed, un-empowered, at a loss, full of grief, in need of protection or even empty inside. And as you breathe deeply now, a deep and soothing breath of deeply forgiving, deeply soothing, deep, deep and most powerful relaxation, you just let that breath go, you are powerfully forgiving absolutely anything and everything that has ever stood in the way of this lighter, thinner, healthier and better you from emerging. Just like a mighty river, you flow around, over and through any and all old blockages or challenges from your past now. In fact, you've gotten out of your own way, for your inspired and creative mind is working with you in harmony, powerfully and successfully now and forever, so both now and forever, you win!

You have, whether you yet realize it or in fact will realize it very soon, utilizing the most powerful and determined aspects of all of yourself to begin a brand new happier and lighter, thinner, healthier and better chapter of your life, filled with limitless possibilities. An ever emerging, forgiven, released, better, most powerful you. What fills in the place of those old and useless, unwanted, unnecessary feelings and memories from the past, are very powerful, very true, very real, supportive, inspired, creative, unstoppably wonderful and successful feelings, with the inspirational energy of every past success, victory, breakthrough, triumph, in your life like an unstoppable tidal wave of potent inspirational energy. You experience feelings of limitless support, you feel fantastic and empowered, gaining unstoppable self-esteem, self confidence, full of blessed happiness, so here You are now, right now, completely fulfilled, unshakable, improved and better! As you relax deeper and further, without realizing it, while you are awake, asleep or even while you dream, your powerful and most successful mind, is even inventing more supportive behaviors to lighten and heal you, better ways of living and being that are completely incompatible with any and all old ways of behaving that once caused you to gain or hold unwanted, unhealthy, unnecessary body weight or fat, or overeat in any way. That's right, more supportive behaviors are truly and unstoppably beginning, better ways of being that are completely incompatible with any and all old ways of behaving that once caused you to suffer emotionally, for you are freed and you are feeling even more balanced, adapting and creating more supportive behaviors, better ways of being, living, thinking, reacting and acting that are completely incompatible with any and all old ways of behaving that once caused you to overeat or eat the wrong things in any way, because you right now, are feeling, experiencing or truly even knowing, in the most true and powerful of ways that both your body weight and your life is coming into balance, balancing in the most potent and powerful of ways, in each and every area of your life, balancing in each and every one of your relationships, past, present and future. You truly are balancing and restoring spiritually, mentally throughout each and every thought, harmonizing emotionally in each and every feeling you have, to restructure and support yourself in the most imaginative and truly brilliant, inspired, creative ways and most especially, you are balancing physically, lighter, thinner, healthier and better.

You have properly and correctly and unstoppably chosen, as an adult, to find comfort in your life and in the richness that life readily and most powerfully brings you, each and every day that you now notice. You have chosen to take things one step at a time, relaxing into organizing your personal schedule and absolutely and completely regimenting your eating times, properly and correctly choosing to slowly, peacefully, moderately, free of distractions, eat only at the table in a dining area. You are completely free of all other distractions like TV, so you know what you are eating, moderately, comfortably and slowly, filling up sooner, in the one area of your home where you eat. You enjoy your times of sustenance, sustaining your body, emotions, mind and life by slowly consuming only proper foods, healthy foods and drinks, proper for an adult, just like an adult, in moderation, that allow you to achieve and maintain a proper and healthy weight. Even before you eat, or sit down to eat, even the sight and the smell of the food begins to fill you up, long before you even have your first taste. Your body reacts better, it signals you, so you know when to stop, actually often leaving some of each meal on the plate, which is really just fine with you, as an adult now, you know when to push it away, as you leave the table, your very personal triumph over your past. You feel great.

And as you slow down your eating, your metabolism actually goes up, in the most healthy and beneficial ways, that are just perfect for you, almost as if in fact, someone has in fact, reset a switch or a dial or even some type of computer or thermostat from deep, deep within you somewhere, easily and effectively allowing you to comfortably burn food, weight, fat and calories more efficiently and in the most healthy and beneficial ways; while your speed when eating, actually slows way down, way down, while your metabolism, actually goes way, way up. You become, and you are truly in fact, free from eating food ever again without thinking. I wonder if you even yet realize how easy this is going to be for you or if you'll just notice at some future moment the comfortability of your ease and success. So you just know, you'll succeed in losing (X) amount of pounds, succeeding unstoppably, naturally, comfortably, easily, with limitless truly and creative inspired success.

Take another deep breath and let it go now, relaxing even deeper and feel the soothing embrace of all of the powerful changes going on your limitless wellspring of powerfully inspired, amazingly creative success, from deeply within, your perception of yourself and each and every attitude, is changing, improving, getting better each and every day and night. You feel like you are thriving, in the most powerful and important of ways. Your dream is coming true! Your body image is changing, you can actually see, picture, imagine, or truly even know, this lighter, thinner, healthier and better you, achieving the success you seek, liberating it here into the right now into every facet of your life, for your clothes fit better and more comfortably, you breathe easier, you feel better in fact, YOU ARE BETTER, you see yourself and think of yourself as better in the most truly amazingly creative ways, for this lighter, thinner, healthier and better you is you, right now, emerges unstoppably and all of this is only getting easier each and every time you repeat this enjoyable form of hypnotic relaxation, having found, whether you realize it or not, your key to unstoppable success. You are and you even remain free of and done with forever, after dinner snacks and mid-night snacks, which are uncomfortable to consume and difficult to digest taking better care of yourself than that forever, for in reality and in fact, your meals, your slowly-consumed moderate, proper and healthy adult meals, have completely filled you up and fulfilled you in the most powerful of ways.

## Weight Loss (Neurotic)

In your mind now, picture a calmer, better and more powerful you unstoppably emerging into a brand new and better chapter of your life. You are moving into a place in your life where everything, all thoughts, all feelings, each and every action and reaction is now and forever unstoppably working in your favor to support you in powerful, correct yet amazingly easy and effective ways of helping you to become lighter, thinner, healthier and better in body, emotions, thoughts, mind and life. You have moved on, free from over indulgence, only doing and eating in ways that support this new, healthier and forever you. Right now, your days, nights and each and every moment of you once in the past being a carbohydrate addict, are now and forever over! You love yourself and your newer, lighter, healthier and healing rewardof-a-body better than any bread, better than any pasta, better than any potatoes, better than any chocolate and better than any ice cream. Less is more, you fill up sooner, just a small taste is enough for you, you are so powerfully satisfied, satiated, just moving and flowing comfortably ever onward. You eat only in smaller portions, off smaller plates, in designated eating areas only. Too much as in the past loses its appeal and interest for you, even tasting bad, maybe like dog food if you eat too much. So you stop and you wonder, "What do I need this for? This is silly and lousy." You've truly had enough, so you stop, you dump it, you are forgiven, released and healed, feeling wonderful. You are dynamically free of ever eating anything, even more and most especially, if you are or even might be bored, stressed or most especially whenever hungry. A small taste is enough for you, you fill up sooner and quicker, the smell of the food begins to fill you up long before your first bite. You are calm, you are peaceful, you are relaxed, you are healed, you are enough, you are feeling fine and doing better and better, lighter, thinner, healthier and better than ever before. In this newer and better, self-supporting chapter of your life, feel the love you have in endless and unconditional supply for your family now emerging like energy you can now harness and use to your loving advantage to dynamically assist you in allowing yourself to succeed at this. The love you have for them, the love they have for you, is now working like rocket fuel to help you stick to a better and clever plan, a better and more successful program, a lighter and thinner, healthier and better you, now and forever unstoppably emerging.

It has been said, there is belief – beyond belief, there is faith-- but the strongest, truest and most powerfully effective foundation while requiring the least amount of energy of all of these is your ability to *know* you are fine. You are knowing you are doing well, and you truly know that each and every thought, each and every feeling, each and every thing that ever once stood in your way, is now and forever turned around and is reversed against itself, all of those things, now assets working truly in your favor, you have easily and forever allowed yourself to break through, thrive and succeed at this, as the weight now just seems to melt off and away, far, far away from you.

Relax, and just imagine, or just see and know, that this newer, better, healthier, well-deserved you is now and forever emerging, most especially in spite of any and all things that once ever stood in your way. What once was feared by you, even once thought of to be your fault, is now released, forgiven deeply and sincerely by you, both now and forever, always your greatest strength. Your self-image now just better and better, more easily forgiven, through and through. You love yourself in place of judging yourself; you are amazingly, fluidly, effectively, skillfully and adaptively breaking through here; you are inspired by every past victory, breakthrough and success you've ever had; you are dynamic, unstoppable, winning in the very most profound of ways. Whatever the stress, whatever the discomfort or challenge, you rise up, adaptively and cleverly, clearly and unstoppably inspired, and you powerfully win. Whether it's work, house construction, or anything else, you stop, deep breathe slow and steady breaths, taking all of life in a wonderful flow; calm, peaceful and relaxed you are and you remain. I wonder if you even yet realize how easy it is to lose, melt off or just simply shed, 98, 99 or even 100 lbs.

# Weight Loss – Overcoming Stress and Emotional Eating

You are powerfully free of eating or wanting to eat or craving anything to eat just because you are or might be stressed.

In fact, you've relaxed into a brand new and better, happier and lighter, better chapter of your life, feeling a new sense of being completely in control of your life and your body, in control of your urges, completely freed from the past and in a brighter, better, lighter, thinner, healthier chapter of your life. You are now certain, serene, sure that you are now and forever powerfully free of any and all old urges that once stood in your way, both known and unknown to you, as you are so very easily and successfully moving on, having gained power and control over your life and your body and most especially easily succeeding and triumphing over anything to do with food.

You are powerfully successful and free of being overly hungry, most especially finding better ways of dealing with stress, like detaching yourself from the moment, while deep breathing, calming down, feeling better, free forever of ever using food as a crutch to deal with stress. In fact, you've relaxed your way into a brand new and better, happier and lighter, better chapter of your life, feeling a new sense of seizing the moment while being completely in control of your life, and your urges have gained power and control over your life, and most especially easily overwhelming in your favor anything to do with food. Free forever you are and you remain of ever eating simply because food is there. You are taking so much better care of yourself now, in this lighter, thinner, healthier, and better chapter of your life, than ever before. Just a small taste is enough for you; less is more, you are filling up sooner, one bite, one fork-full, one spoon-full, one taste, that you savor in your mouth to taste, finding complete fulfillment, you find not only calming, but now you know better, you've had enough, and right then and there, you're done.

Your clever, always-working-in-your-favor, adaptive mind, is now creating a moment of pause and realization within you that allows you to break free forever from patterns of the past, right now you are forever freed from old and finished past chapters of your life, as you are now and powerfully remain instead where you wanted to be, should be and are now steadily and firmly, adaptively and cleverly even creatively are. You now focused on savoring a small taste, rather than eating without tasting, just a small taste, even one bite, is enough for you. This makes you feel wonderful, and you are wonderful, as your mighty inner hero is now activated working only in your favor to powerfully break you free here. You are powerfully successful and free of being overly hungry, overeating, or craving anything, simply feeling content and comfortable, even un-hungry, even when sad.

You are now creating, manifesting, and replacing the old ways to better deal with your emotions in a more balanced and harmonized way, determined to rise above and finding better ways to live your life more enjoyably and upbeat. In a previous chapter of your life, you may have eaten just for no reason, in this new, better, improved more success-oriented chapter of your life, you are finding every reason along with adaptively creative better reasons to become and forever remain lighter, healthier, thinner, better, while creating reasons, reactions, thoughts, feelings and adaptations and even more especially better ways, to feel fulfilled, calm and centered, inside. You are now like a sea of tranquility, with a healthier and higher metabolism, as the unneeded, forgiven, released, and seemingly melting away excess weight, that you now seem to be releasing, in easily effective ways, seems to be thriving and releasing even on its own. I wonder if you even yet realize how truly easy it's going to be for you, as now melting away week, and calories, to seems to be just melting off, relinquishing and releasing, just effectively melting away, 28, 32 even 34 lbs. as all of this just seems to be happening powerfully and effectively without even a second thought.

---

## Weight Loss 2006

Less is more, you fill up sooner; it's really OK now as an adult to leave some of each and every meal on the plate as you leave the table. Smaller plates are better, just fine for you. You are doing fine, feeling wonderful, filled, fulfilled and fantastic. In this newer and better chapter of your life, you can leave some food behind; less is more; you fill up sooner and feel fine. You begin to enjoy the luxurious and flowingly refreshing taste of water; it tastes as good as your favorite beverage, rapidly now it becomes your favorite beverage, because it's time and you say so, and so it is.

You find comfort in your life, in your world, in the love you have for yourself and for the love you have for your family and loved ones, and in all that you are, seek and do. You are powerfully free of eating or wanting to eat or craving anything like starchy fast foods and you're powerfully successful and free of kiddy foods, now that you are an adult, free of craving or wanting snack foods, fast foods, taking and making the proper time to eat, relax and enjoy, filling up sooner. You find and truly take better care of yourself in all ways, including but not just limited to diet, increased yet effective and regular exercise, playing your wonderfully enjoyable hypnosis tape to allow peacefully fulfilling sleep, enough sleep, more of an interest in your getting-better- and-better appearance, as you smile to yourself inside. You drink more water and skillfully avoid soda and other fattening drinks; you love yourself that much. You create newer and lasting rhythms, finding newer and long-lasting passions, bringing exercise goals down to levels of ridiculous ease, just a few minutes a day, a few days a week, easily exceeding those minutes, making a new routine and bringing new supportive people into the picture masterfully, one step at a time, just like when you do or have done any workout in the past and usually feel good about the fact that you're more active, enjoying the athletic muscle burn, because you know you are doing what's right, loving yourself, as you become lighter, thinner, healthier and better. You are dynamically moving into a better time in your life, easily succeeding at becoming lighter, thinner, healthier and better. You are powerfully free of eating or wanting to eat or craving anything like starchy fast foods and you're powerfully successful and free of kiddy foods, now that you are an adult, free of craving or wanting snack foods, fast foods, taking and making the proper time to eat, relax and enjoy, filling up sooner, because you are powerfully becoming lighter, thinner, healthier and better, powerfully filled up with the correct foods at proper mealtimes, which is really just enough for you. You now move into a newer and better chapter of your life and you tend to eat less, filling up sooner, fuller and more completely, easily able to leave food on your plate. You are hunger-free, snack-free, eating properly, more important and most especially free of snacking between lunch and dinner, or even after dinner, most especially free of old cravings and old un-needed urges; you eat less; less is more, enjoying smaller portions and filling up sooner, tasting and savoring flavors and sensations, enjoying your life, lighter, healthier, thinner and better, more now than you ever did when you used to overeat. You easily stick to the less-is-more point of view in your life, easily able to stick to a proper regimen of eating that's healthier for an adult and lighter for your health and longevity. You bring your exercise goals down to a level of ridiculous ease, just three days a week, for just a few minutes a day, enjoying yourself so much, easily meeting and quite often exceeding those goals, just getting up and doing it, lasting long enough to enjoy the results you deserve, creating a newer, better, lighter and thinner, healthier you, who now and forever unstoppably emerges. You now move into a newer and better chapter of your life and you tend to eat less, filling up sooner, fuller and more completely, easily able to leave food on your plate. You are powerfully free of eating or wanting to eat or craving anything like fast foods, junk foods and you're powerfully successful and free of kiddy foods, now that you are an adult, because you are powerfully becoming lighter, thinner, healthier and better, powerfully filled up with the correct foods at proper mealtimes, which is really just enough for you. You are hunger-free, snack-free, eating properly, more important and most especially free of snacking between meals, most especially free of cravings and urges. You feel so calm, so inspired, so super upbeat and bright; you feel ambitious, easily raising activity level, even deep breathing or walking when you feel up to it, in spite of all challenges, and even if you are inactive, you are hunger-free, craving-free, free of eating anything without first thinking and stopping and deciding in your favor to do better and better. Just as soon as you are full, noticing it sooner, you've had enough, you have unstoppably moved on, free of wanting or needing a treat; you've had enough and enjoy truly the benefits of a lighter, thinner and better you, feeling so fine and wonderful. You are on top of the world, having limitless willpower and adaptability to succeed at this easily and dynamically, energetically, vigorously and enthusiastically succeeding at this. In fact, you've relaxed into a brand new and better, happier and lighter, better chapter of your life, feeling a new sense of being completely in control of your life, your urges, free of any and all old urges that once stood in your way, easily and successfully moving on, having gained power and control over your life and most especially easily over anything to do with food. Your correct, proper and right response to any and all stress is to relax your way through it, and you easily succeed at doing this, finding your healing process more powerful, more fulfilling, more adaptive, more healing in the most amazing and profound of ways, just flowing beyond any and all personal challenges, problem-free, challenge-oriented and most successfully learn to live one day at a time.

## Weight and Life Motivation

Your relationship with food is now improving in your favor; each and every thought, habit and action in this brand new and better chapter of your life, now sees and reacts to food as a source of nourishment. Less is more, less is more; you fill up sooner and know when you've had enough. You are now learning and completely determined to take the very best care of yourself, as the weight just seems to melt off and you are enthusiastic about the power and effectiveness, the ease and grace you now discover from deep, deep within yourself. You are problem-free, challenge-oriented, rising up to meet all challenges wherever they come from with the courage and drive of a mighty, mighty hero, just like you've always actually done. You are forgiven, healing, healed and released from the ways and patterns of the past; not because I say so, but because you have once and for all, once and forever put your foot down and taken charge of your life here.

You are motivated to move beyond the ways of old and move into a newer, better, more motivated way of life and living, being true to yourself, maybe even energetic and re-enthused about your life and your world. It's almost like someone from deep, deep inside of you has reset a switch, a dial, a powerful and-or effective computer of some kind, allowing you to get motivated, lively and re-excited about your life. You find joy in little things, newer things, things of enjoyment, even things involving work, because you realize now that life is about living and living is something you are determined to do; upbeat, happy and clear, you are moving forward unstoppably. You begin to believe in yourself, trust in your life and a new thought dawns upon you: your life is now supporting you in better and truer ways, just as it always has, only in this brand new chapter of your life, even better and better than ever before. You are willing to feel good, even great about yourself, in this brand new, dawning chapter of your life. You find things to enjoy, laugh about, be upbeat and clear about, focused, working toward new goals that are not only interesting, but also thrivingly support and excite you. You heal, you forgive, you take better care, you trust in your life and knowing who you are and how you are there to take the very best care of yourself, just relaxing beyond any and all old barriers from your past into the very best days and nights, opportunities you now create and embrace, making all of this your very own, feeling directed, healed, forgiven, released and taken care of in your life and in your world and in each and everything you are thinking, doing, feeling and acting and reacting to, moment by moment, with each life-giving and life-supporting breath you are taking. With every move you are making and with each and every beat of your heart, you are doing better and better, just fine, learning to not only just live your life, but to thrive and to savor the joys of each and every moment, making the whole experience a Masterpiece. You know who you are; you are excited about your life and your world, and you know who you are and what you are interested in and excited by, and do all that it takes to accomplish your life goals, which are surprisingly more and more apparent to you. You take on new things with ambition, pacing yourself, taking care, loving yourself and those around you, but most especially yourself, as if the floodgates of love and healing within you from, deep, deep inside of you are now opened to provide limitless support, forgiveness, healing, heroic courage, wisdom, energy, vitality, passion, joy and the ability to rise above the old ways, creating a passionate paradise for you right now, as things are seemingly falling into place, easily and precisely accomplishing all that you now set out to do, and that you do, and all that you will do, unstoppably, rising to the top, doing all that it honestly takes, because you now know you can.

# Extras – Health and Well-being

NOTE: This is a section of additional suggestions I've written for various sessions. As with the rest of this text, please read and select or adapt the suggestions that apply to your client (patient) to fit their specific needs. By using this section, you are agreeing to pre-reading, rewriting, adjusting and adapting these suggestions to individual and specific needs.

Beating Insomnia and Insecurity – *Extras* - You become and are willing to rethink, reformat, remold, redefine and reformulate yourself, in the best and most potent ways possible, as a more relaxed, lighthearted, happy go lucky and joyous and even carefree person, so easily able to find better and even heavier, deeper and deeper and better ways to sleep. You are finding better ways, more true fulfillment in your life and in your days and nights, taking better care of yourself and enjoying your life. You are willing, ready and able to find newer and better ways of being more and more, even forever free of denial and negativity, easily able to become and remaining able to see what's real, forgiving the past, forgiving yourself, and moving ever onward into a brighter and happier life and future, one that you create with inspiration, positivity, unlimited-ness, moving ever forward enjoyably to reach your life goals and dreams, trusting in your life and those people and experiences you magnetize or repel with the power of your thoughts and presence. You are moving out into the world, seeking from within your fulfillment and joy, redefining yourself and your methods of living your life, easily allowing yourself more and more each and every day and night to enjoy life and have fun, forever free of and moving beyond and above physical problems, beyond disease, pain and discomfort, into a place of ease, joy, harmony and peace, which are now and forever remaining your constant companions. You are now enjoying both readily and easily the bounty and prosperity that life readily brings that you now enjoy, readily willing to be and forever remain fulfilled, sharing the wealth of who you are with others and making the world a better and brighter and happier, more upbeat place, sharing all that you are. You are finding more and more inspired and truer ways to supplant and override both any and all old negative and uncomfortable and destructive guidelines, so easily and successfully replacing them with positive messages, encouraging yourself to lead a more fulfilling, outgoing and pleasurable life, and in this, you are truly unstoppable, creative and passionately successful, empowered by all of the energy of any and all past victories, breakthroughs, triumphs and successes from your past, completely resting and relaxing your way into to this, you win and you are more willing to succeed in all that you set out to do, you thrive in new and profound ways.

**Smoking – *Extras* -** Imagine or just think about moving back to a past time in your life when you were and are smoke-free, cigarette-free. Feel the energy of who you were then connecting to the energy of who you are now, it's almost like you are connecting back to a past time in your life when you had a choice to make, except this time, you are now merging with this past you and you are now making a better choice, to become and forever remain, smoke-free, cigarette-free, now and for the rest of your life. You now enjoy a healthier life, a better life, a more fulfilling life, loving yourself and your health, always living your dreams and fulfilling yourself each and every moment, extending your life and your health, doing better for yourself, doing all that you know you should do, and just relaxing into this and doing it, because you have truly moved on. You are and you both now and forever remain smokefree, cigarette-free, most especially whenever you wake up. You are and you both now and forever remain smoke-free, cigarette-free, most especially before you go to bed. You are and you both now and forever remain smoke-free, cigarette-free, most especially before you get on the bus. You are and you both now and forever remain smoke-free, cigarette-free, most especially after you got off the bus or train, You are and you both now and forever remain smoke-free, cigarette-free, most especially before you go in to work, You are and you both now and forever remain, smoke-free, cigarette-free, most especially before you go into a building or when you come out of a building. You are and you both now and forever remain, smoke- free, cigarette-free, most especially during (name activity- e.g.- house cleaning). You are and you both now and forever remaining smoke-free, cigarette-free, most especially whenever you watch TV. You are and you both now and forever remain smoke-free, cigarette-free, most especially whenever you're on the computer, staying safe and feeling contented and fine. You are unstoppably successful at this, moving on and quitting smoking forever, extending your life and maintaining great health for yourself, extending longevity, sleeping easily, comfortably and powerfully and right through the night, always remaining remain smoke-free, cigarette-free, always extending your life, your health and longevity. You are and you both now and forever remain, smoke-free, cigarette-free, most especially whenever you wake up. You are and you both now and forever remain smoke-free, cigarette-free, most especially after meals, in fact, you are beginning to despise smoking and seeing, smelling or sensing in any way, cigarettes or cigarette smoke. You begin to loathe, despise and intensely hate, cigarettes or cigarette smoke, because you've moved on, feeling healthy and fine. * You are and you forever remain, smoke-free, cigarette-free, most especially right after eating a meal, feeling fulfilled, peaceful, contented and happy, far more satiated and better smoke-free, cigarette-free. You are and you forever remain, smoke-free, cigarette-free, most especially during times at night with a movie, remaining smoke-free, cigarette-free, during any and all movie watching. You are and you forever, remain smoke-free, cigarette-free, most especially while on the phone with friends, listening better and being more of a friend to both them and yourself by forever remaining free of smoking and cigarettes, being proud and happy about that, keeping yourself alive, healthy and safe. You are and you forever remain, smoke-free, cigarette-free, most especially at work, finding newer and better ways of remaining clear, happy, healthy safe and free, extending your life and your health, seeing your kids grow up and your grandchildren born. You are and you forever remain smoke-free, cigarette-free, most especially after a night's sleep, after sleeping deeply peacefully, easily and restfully, after becoming and forever remaining, smoke-free, cigarette-free. Upon awakening, you are unstoppably determined to remain, smoke-free, cigarette-free, extending your life and your health, easily throughout the day and for the rest of our life.

You are and you forever remain smoke-free, cigarette-free most especially right after eating a meal, feeling fulfilled, peaceful, contented and happy, far more satiated and better smoke-free, cigarette-free. You are and you forever remain smoke-free, cigarette-free, most especially after a cup of coffee, tasting and enjoying the aroma and sensations far better than in the past. You are and you forever remain smokefree, cigarette-free, most especially during commercials on TV, remaining smokefree, cigarette-free, during any and all TV watching. You are and you forever remain smoke-free, cigarette-free, most especially when getting into a car or while driving, driving better and more safely free of smoking and cigarettes, being proud and happy about that. You are and you forever remain smoke-free, cigarette-free, most especially when leaving a store, finding newer and better ways of remaining clear, happy, healthy safe and free, extending your life and your health, seeing your kids grow up and your grandchildren born.

You are and you both now and forever remain smoke-free, cigarette-free, most especially whenever you get into your car. You are and you both now and forever remain smoke-free, cigarette-free, most especially while at work and most especially after both breaks. You are and you both now and forever remain smoke-free, cigarette-free, most especially whenever you wake up. You are and you both now and forever remain smoke-free, cigarette-free, most especially whenever you have a cup of coffee. You are and you both now and forever remain smoke-free, cigarette-free, most especially while at home and when watching TV. You are and you both now and forever remain smoke-free, cigarette-free, most especially after each and every meal, feeling contented and fine.

You are and you both now and forever remain smoke-free, cigarette-free, most especially whenever you are hanging out with your friends at meetings. You are and you forever remain smoke-free, cigarette-free, most especially during the first moments of the morning with your coffee. You are and you forever remain smoke-free, cigarette-free, most especially after each and every meal. You are and you forever remain smoke-free, cigarette-free, most especially after with any kind of drink or any sort of alcoholic beverage. You are and you forever remain smoke-free, cigarette-free, most especially in the middle of the night or when waking up to go to the bathroom. You are and you forever remain smoke-free, cigarettefree, most especially WHEN you may be or might get NERVOUS or UPSET or even while you're calm. You are and you forever remain smoke-free, cigarette-free, most especially after sex, enjoying the afterglow so much better smoke-free, cigarettefree, feeling more love, peace and happiness, as you remain healthy, safe and strong.* You are unstoppably successful at this, moving on and quitting smoking forever, extending your life and maintaining great health for yourself, your husband, your kids, sustaining your life so you can see your kids get married and become a grandparent, guiding the generations to greatness, smoke-free, cigarette-free, now always and forever.* You are and you forever remain smoke-free, cigarette-free, most especially when you are with people that are smoking, you feel so much better, happier, healthier and free, becoming and forever remaining, some free, cigarettefree. * You are and you forever remain smoke-free, cigarette-free, most especially when you are on the phone at home, feeling fine. You are and you forever remain smoke-free, cigarette-free, most especially when you are in the car, driving carefully, defensively, safely, sanely and remaining calm, comfortable, focused and relaxed. You are and you forever remain smoke-free, cigarette-free, most especially when you are out drinking. You remain a shining example to those who see you've quit, which encourages them to follow your lead and it feels great to be a leader. You are and you forever remain smoke-free, cigarette-free, most especially when you are bored, finding newer and better ways to find activities to occupy yourself and to truly enrich your life, your world and your mind.

You are and you forever remain smoke-free, cigarette-free, most especially at work, finding newer and better ways of remaining clear, happy, healthy safe and free, extending your life and your health, more and more easily releasing any and all stress in newer and more profound and dynamic ways, easily releasing and all stress after just a few short and deep, slow and steady breaths, easily finding balance and inner peace. You expand your methods of reducing and eliminating stress, most especially like when you run and lift weights to counteract stress levels, except even better right now, you succeed always and forever remaining, smoke-free, cigarette-free at all times, every time, easily succeeding at this, doing better for yourself, easily extending and improving your life, your longevity and your health. * You come to truly know, smoking is far from being an old friend, it's a deadly enemy, one which you must remove from your life at all costs, so you move on, free of any and all past mistakes and moving on into a brighter, better, healthier future, the kind you truly deserve. You now always take the time to remember that smoking cigarettes is a very deadly and a disease-bringing agent. You are moving on and so you steadfastly refuse to enjoy smoking, as it is a health hazard and you deserve better. You must consider quitting, so you remain concerned about your health, happiness and life. You look forward to the positive health effects quitting will provide, smoke-free, cigarette-free,

free of ever missing smoking cigarettes. You are absolutely determined to remain healthy, safe, strong, free and with a long life and abundant health, taking care of yourself and finding inner peace with all of this. You've truly and forever re-identified yourself, moving into a newer and a safer and healthier chapter of your life, an habitual non-smoker, ex-smoker, most especially forever remaining smoke-free, cigarette-free, most especially in the morning when awakening. You are most especially forever remaining smoke-free, cigarette-free, after every meal, most especially forever remaining smoke-free, cigarette-free, before bed and even while in the car. * You now unleash the power of your unstoppable, strong mind, to work with you unstoppably and effectively to accommodate you. In this you know yourself well, taking better care of yourself, always pushing for more, smoke-free, cigarette-free, happy with only the very best, absolutely determined to move on free of smoking cigarettes, happy, healthy, safe, free and strong, and it feels so great. * You are and you forever remain smoke-free, cigarette-free, most especially when bored or even when upset or excited. You are and you forever remain smoke-free, cigarette-free, most especially after a night's sleep, after sleeping deeply, peacefully, easily and restfully, after becoming and forever remaining, smoke-free, cigarette-free, the sleep even allows you to be more determined and successful, as your dreams support your health and longevity and ability to become and forever remain, smoke-free, cigarette-free, in a new and forever better chapter of your life. You are and you forever remain smoke-free, cigarette-free, most especially after you eat. You are and you forever remain smoke-free, cigarette-free, most especially when stressed whether at home or work, in fact, you succeed, anywhere at any time and it's easy. You are and you forever remain smoke-free, cigarette-free, most especially when you are on the phone, relaxing into a brand new and healthier chapter of your life. In fact, and in reality, you are always finding the very best reasons to remain healthy and extending your health and your life. * You are calm, smoke-free, cigarette-free, nicotine free every time, anytime, all times, most especially when you are anxious. * You are you forever become and you forever remain, smoke-free, cigarette-free, nicotine free when you are tired and / or hungry, and excited or even happy. A new day dawns right now, in a brand new chapter of your life. * You find yourself becoming interested in new things, new thoughts, new ideas, new ways of enjoying and living your life, completely enthusiastic about your world and your life. But even if you get bored, you are forever determined to become and remain, smoke-free, cigarette-free, nicotine free. *You find yourself finding deep breathing, slow calming soothing breath, a powerful new ally, a friend, a powerful replacement for overcoming monotonous time. * And your tastes change, in your favor. Cigarette smoke begins to taste and smell to you like burning rubber, uggh, how awful! How disgusting, how nauseating that smell! You are and you remain smoke-free, completely free of cigarettes, even if you are driving, even if stressed, driving a long distance, light traffic, heavy traffic, you remain determined and you are smoke-free, completely free of cigarettes. You are and you remain smoke-free, cigarette-free, choosing health and life, most especially in uncomfortable situations, easily healthy and free during arguments, via phone or in person, or while unfamiliar with surroundings, most especially on job interviews. You've moved on with your life, releasing any and all disharmony and negative past influence, powerfully and truly forgiving any and all past mistakes, which you now forgive and call consider past learning experiences, polishing experiences. You are doing better, feeling better, living healthier and better, in powerful and real ways. Most especially you shine into your life, feeling great, being and remaining, smoke-free, cigarette-free, in social settings, feeling more at ease and quite often at ease in social settings, feeling appreciated by yourself and the world, perhaps in a bar or a restaurant, completely free of any and all desire to chain smoke in powerful and successful, dynamic, creative and imaginative ways. You find better and more healthy ways to relax and escape, better and more effective diversions: from work, from school, from your parents' house- even anyplace where smokers are segregated from the general population or populous. Most especially you feel surely and truly proud and free, effective and motivated to become and forever remain smoke-free, cigarette-free, when you write- either grading papers, working on the computer, while writing in your journal, etc. Even more powerfully and effectively and amazingly, yet easily and successfully, even if you might feel depression or anger, you are now willing to express yourself, freeing yourself up in the healthiest and very best of ways, liberating all emotional and mental energies in constructive, dynamic and corrective ways, healing and whole, expressing and emoting, constructively, in harmony and balance, being and remaining, smoke-free, cigarette-free. You are and you remain smoke-free, cigarette-free, most especially in the morning with coffee, both before, during and after a cup of coffee, tasting and enjoying the aroma and sensations far better than in the past. * You are calm, smoke-free, cigarette-free, nicotine free every time, anytime, all times, most especially when you are anxious, stressed out or even when you might be aggravated, powerfully free of the adrenaline trigger, having moved on, smoke-free, cigarette-free. You are calm, smoke-free, cigarette-free, nicotine free every time, anytime, all times, most especially when you see or might notice someone else lighting up a cigarette, and most powerfully smoke-free, cigarette-free or when you smell smoke, because you have moved powerfully onward into the next chapter of your life. You are powerfully and forever determined to remain free of smoking and cigarette and their deadly and devastating influence, each and every morning when you just as soon as you wake up. You are as well as unstoppably determined to remain smoke-free, cigarette-free each and every time before you go to sleep. A new day dawns in a brand new chapter of your life. You are and you remain smoke-free, cigarette-free, choosing health and life, most especially at times when you are about to enjoy each cup of coffee, most especially when you first wake up and about an hour after dinner, free, free at last, smoke-free, cigarette-free, living in healthy ways to extend your health and your life. You are and you remain excuse free, activating the action of success, you thrive and succeed at this. You are you are so super motivated to move cigarettes and smoking out of your life forever, and for good, for your self and for all of those you love, most especially for yourself. You might even feel amazingly powerful, because your old unwanted and un-needed urges have melted away. You are released, you are and you forever remain smoke-free, cigarette-free, urge free, nicotine free, most especially after eating anything, reinforcing this freedom in better ways basically every hour, even while you are drinking alcohol, a shining example of your triumph over the past, having moved onward, forgiving and releasing the past, making an better choice now as an adult, happy, calm, balanced and relaxed, you are a smoke-free winner. Smoking distasteful and disgusting to you. You love fresh breath and breathing and a healthier life, healthier body.

SMOKING (**Extras 2005**) - You are just saying no to smoking, and yes to a healthier and happier life. You are and you both now and forever remain, smoke-free, cigarette-free, most especially whenever you wake up, starting the day, finishing the day, all throughout the day, fresh, healthy, happy and relaxed, smoke-free, cigarette-free.

You are now and powerfully are forever free of ever relying on cigarettes to ease your stress or to gain any kind of comfort. You instead, find that your are taking better care of yourself and find yourself easily breaking through and are now and forever unstoppably succeeding in your life, but most especially succeeding at this, smoke free, cigarette free, nicotine free. You are and you forever remain substance free starting with cigarettes and it's easy. You bring your best drives, determinations and inspired successes to this while easily succeeding, free of any and all old urges. Your greatest new urge, is to be and forever remain, smoke free, cigarette free. You are back in control of your life and your health right now. You know, it's amazing, it's almost like you've been free of smoking and cigarettes forever, like reconnecting to a past smoke free you say at the age of X, making the decision to never start, so you haven't and you completely moved on. You are powerfully reinforcing all of this limitless success, bringing up the energy of all of your very best, while being and forever remaining smoke free and cigarette free.

**Smoking Couple's** (**Extras 2005**) - You work with your spouse, watching each other's backs, smoke free, cigarette-free and are forever succeeding easily. This is your newer and better way with dealing with things. You remain smoke-free, cigarette-free, you deep breathe calming, clearing, cleansing breaths, and more easily relax, calm down, feeling powerful, well adjusted, happy and relaxed. You are, and you both now and forever, remain smoke-free, cigarette-free, most especially during any vacation, because you've taken a permanent vacation from smoking and cigarettes, liberating your life and allowing yourself a happy and healthy, well-deserved extended life. You begin to loathe, despise and intensely hate cigarettes or cigarette smoke, because you've moved on, feeling healthy and fine. You are, and you both now and forever, remain smoke-free, cigarette-free, most especially after each and every meal; cigarettes are a thing of the past, you've moved on. A cigarette feels completely uncomfortable and is really more and more disgusting; you've moved on, and you are feeling fine. You are, and you both now and forever, remain smoke-free, cigarette- free, most especially whenever you are, or might be, drinking coffee and most especially whenever you are having any kind of alcoholic beverage, or around people who are drinking coffee or are drinking alcoholic beverages, and most especially whenever you are around anyone who is smoking, you are and you become, forever remaining free of smoking and cigarettes, moving on into a brighter and better chapter of your life. You are, and you both now and forever, remain smoke-free, cigarette-free, most especially whenever you are, or might be, talking on the telephone. You are, and you both now and forever, remain smoke-free, cigarette-free, most especially whenever you are, or might be, playing the slot machines, even finding others around you nearby who are smoking offensive, or even finding a smoke-free section to play in, you are rising up and feeling fine, in a brand new chapter of your life, smoke-free, cigarette-free.

Smoking (*Extras 2004*) - * You know, it's almost like you are jumping over the years back to a time when you were 12 years old, and making a powerful and forever commitment to yourself; so even when you were 13, you were, remained and forever were, smoke-free, cigarette-free, for then, for now, forever and for always. * It's almost like you are jumping over the years back to a time when you were younger, and making a powerful and forever commitment to yourself; to even when you were younger, jumping over the past 60 years to now and forever make a better more fulfilling life-long decision, where you were, remained forever, smoke- free, cigarette-free, for then, for now, forever and for always.

* You are, and you both now and forever, remain smoke-free, cigarette-free, and are truly finding newer and more clever ways to stay safe and free, most especially whenever you are or might be walking from the train to go to the work, or most especially when you are (name situations) walking from work back to the train. You are now and forever liberated, safe and free of finding any and all old excuses or places to smoke. You are so much happier, healthier and more peaceful, forever remaining smoke-free, cigarette-free, thriving in your life. * Regardless of weather, whether it's warm or not so warm, hot or cold, you are and you forever remain, smoke-free, cigarette- free. You are and you remain, smoke-free, cigarette-free, most especially at parties, a shining example to all who behold you, showing your friends and fellow party-goers, a path to a healthier and happier life, more determined than ever before. In the face of any and all challenges, you are and you forever remain

smoke-free, cigarette-free, most especially when stressed, or upset, just more happy and balanced, smoke-free, cigarette-free. Your body, whether changing or remaining the same, keeps you in better balance, smoke-free, cigarette-free. You are and you remain forever, smoke-free, cigarette-free, most especially whenever you are with your boyfriend, a shining example to him, showing him a path to a healthier, happier life, extended life, more determined than ever before, most especially when he comes back in September or whenever he's around. You will eat "healthy" meals, forever free of snacking or eating to replace cigarettes, living your healthier life to the fullest. Free of snacking, reducing snacking, only healthy snacks, all things in moderation with food. * You are, and you both now and forever remain, smoke-free, cigarette-free, most especially whenever you get up in the morning. You are now and forever free, liberated and moving on from reaching for anything to smoke; most especially smoke-free, cigarette-free, urge-free, craving-free, even before your coffee. You are, and you both now and forever, remain smoke-free, cigarette-free, most especially always after you eat. You are, and you both now and forever remain, smoke-free, cigarette-free, most especially whenever you are talking on the telephone, truly living and enjoying your life and your conversation and friendships better, smoke-free, cigarette-free. You are, and you both now and forever remain, smoke-free, cigarette-free, most especially during stressful situations, forever liberated and moving on, staying more calm, balanced and relaxed, smoke-free cigarette- free; feeling a newer and more profound sense of calm and peacefulness, free from smoking and cigarettes, than you ever did with them. You are, and you both now and forever remain smoke-free, cigarette-free, most especially whenever you are bored; always finding better things to enjoy and support yourself with, now that you are smoke-free, cigarette-free, now, always and forever. You are, and you both now and forever remain, smoke-free, cigarette-free; in fact, completely free of ever needing a cigarette, most especially whenever you are or might get nervous. You are an unstoppable winner, forgiving any and all past blockages or harsh and negative self-judgments, learning new and better ways of loving yourself better and better than that; and now you are truly liberating your best feelings of victory, triumph and success, easily able to quit and just say no. You are redefining concepts in your life; anything you once considered a failure or a mistake is now and forever a learning experience, as you are moving on, liberated, cleansed, healed and free. It feels like the first day of Spring, a breath of fresh air, now that you are free of smoking cigarettes. You are, and you both now and forever remain, smoke-free, cigarette-free, most especially each and every morning when you get up, and most especially free of cigarettes and smoking before you go to bed at night. You are bound and determined, more than ever before in your life, to demand to live a healthier life; and you just do that. You are so very motivated, so unstoppable at this and anything you've set your powerful and unstoppable mind to, more now than anything before. You are, and you both now and forever remain, smoke-free, cigarette-free, most especially of looking for a cigarette whenever you're on the phone.

You are and you both now and forever remain, smoke-free, cigarette-free, most especially each and every morning. You are, and you both now and forever remain, smoke-free, cigarette-free, most especially whenever you wake up during the night. You are, and you both now and forever remain, smoke-free, cigarette-free, most especially whenever you wake up; you are and you remain smoke-free, cigarette-free, ready and powerfully determined to remain healthy, safe, strong, happy and extend your life. You are, and you both now and forever remain, smoke-free, cigarette-free, most especially whenever you may encounter or think about encountering stressful situations. You are, and you both now and forever remain, smoke-free, cigarette-free, most especially whenever you are bored or even if you might be lonely; at all times, each and every time, you are and you remain smoke-free, cigarette- free. You are, and you both now and forever remain, smoke-free, cigarette-free, most especially if you anticipate not being able to smoke, like before going into a movie theater, or anything to do with the movies, being and remaining smoke-free, cigarette-free, happy, healthy, safe, comfortable and strong.

You are and you remain forever smoke-free, cigarette-free, most especially when drinking coffee, truly enjoying your mornings and coffee by remaining smoke-free, cigarette-free, while extending your life. You are and you remain forever smoke-free, cigarette-free, most especially while driving your car, driving more safely, sanely and securely, insuring a safe trip for yourself and for those you love. You are and you remain a shining example to everyone you know, most especially to your co-workers during break times at work; your example might even get you to help them to extend their lives as well. You are and you remain forever smoke-free, cigarette-free, most especially when you're bored and most especially when you are under stress. You are and you remain forever smoke-free, cigarette-free most especially just after sex, truly enjoying the intimacy and afterglow much better and loving much better free of cigarettes than you ever did with them, happy to love and be together forever, healthy, safe and free.

You are and you remain forever smoke-free, cigarette-free, most especially when you first wake-up, truly creating a happier and better day, smoke-free, cigarette-free, safe, strong, and living healthier and longer, doing all the right things to stay healthy and remain alive. You are, and you remain forever, smoke-free, cigarette- free, most especially when under stress, becoming problem-free, challenge-oriented, resolving any and all challenges with effectiveness and clever, confident ease. You are, and you remain forever, smoke-free, cigarette-free, most especially after eating, taking care of yourself, for yourself and those you love in the very best of ways. You are, and you remain forever, smoke- free, cigarette-free, most especially if you are bored and most especially when you are under stress. You are, and you remain forever smoke-free, cigarette-free, most especially when you might be having a drink or two with the guys (gals); your example might even get you to help them to extend their lives as well. * You are, and you both now and forever remain, smoke-free, cigarette- free, most especially whenever and most especially and in spite of continuous stress; you stay unstoppably on the wagon and win. You are, and you both now and forever remain, smoke-free, cigarette-free, most especially whenever and most especially in spite of being surrounded in your house by three smokers, showing them the way to succeed, as you stay healthy, safe and free, happily improving your health and improving your life. You are, and you both now and forever remain, smoke-free, cigarette-free, most especially free of smoking cigars and you want to stop smoking everything; so now you do. Just like when you are in the office, you powerfully, cleverly and faithfully remain free of smoking, being true to yourself. You are, and you both now and forever remain, smoke-free, cigarette-free, most especially of smoking anything in the AM before you go in and are powerfully and cleverly smoke-free, free of smoking anything when you get home. You are, and you both now and forever remain, smoke-free, cigarette-free, most especially whenever and most especially and in spite of sneaking anything or ever again using the cigar smoke to mask the odor, living better, doing all that it takes and doing all the right things for yourself, smoke-free, cigar-free, cigarette-free. You stop for health reasons, doing all that it takes to easily, successfully and cleverly win; so you do, you've now and forever moved on, smoke- free, cigar-free, cigarette-free, now and unstoppably always and forever. *You both now and forever remain smoke-free, cigarette-free, most especially whenever you are stressed. You both now and forever remain smoke-free, cigarette-free, most especially whenever you are bored. You both now and forever remain smoke- free, cigarette-free, most especially after you eat; whether it's lunch or any meal at all, you are feeling fine. You both now and forever remain smoke-free, cigarette-free, most especially whenever you are with your friends. You both now and forever remain smoke-free, cigarette-free, most especially whenever you want to take a break from work, even at 10:30 with a friend; being your own best friend, you are and you remain smoke-free, cigarette-free. You both now and forever remain smoke-free, cigarette-free, most especially whenever you are outside, even in the hallway of your building. Your wife's assistance is now appreciated by you as she is loving you and helping you, just as the whole world is now working in your favor to help you to remain smoke-free, cigarette-free. You are now having and powerfully developing a strong aversion to cigarettes, as you now know that they will otherwise kill you; so they are gone and you feel fine.

**Smoking Cessation: Teenage –** *Extras* - Being and forever remaining smoke-free, cigarette-free, both now and always and forever an ex-smoker, a survivor that has unstoppably and undeniably moved on, is both now, always and forever the cherry on top of everything you do, you are absolutely determined to remain, healthy, safe, happy, strong and extending your life, and becoming a leader in quitting the self destructive smoking habit, a model for others to follow. You are forever free of craving a cigarette after you eat, feeling so much better, happy, balanced, and whole, free of cigarettes than you ever did with them. You are forever free of craving a cigarette after you drink coffee, feeling so much better, happy, balanced, and whole free of cigarettes than you ever did with them. You are forever free of craving a cigarette, while you are having a talk socially, feeling so much better, happy, balanced, and whole free of cigarettes than you ever did with them. You love being free forever of the death and miserable illness and stink that smoking cigarettes brings. You are so much more powerfully successful and deeply relaxed and relieved of stress after just a few short and deep, powerful soothing breaths, so easily and deeply naturally calm, so wonderfully and enjoyably stress-free. You are a winner in life. Smoking is for losers, you are now and forever re-identified as a winner, an ex-smoker, non-smoker, moving on, doing better than that for yourself, not because I say so, but because you know what you are doing here is right, natural and the very best and right choice for you. So you very enjoyably relax into this and you succeed and win, an inspiration and leader to all of those you know.

**Smoking Extras 2006 -** Your last Cigarette may have been last week, a few hours ago or just a few minutes ago, but your days of smoking are done; they are over. For truly and undeniably, you are in a new chapter of your life, a better place and feeling fine, smoke free, cigarette free, breathing better, really feeling healthier, improved, enhanced, upbeat, can-do and fine, contented, satiated, satisfied, fine and free, regaining health and harmony, vitality and energy, extending your life, doing the right thing here.

This time, you are sure, you are serene, you are certain, you are both now and forever done with smoking and cigarettes, you are done, you've moved on and you are feeling and forever remaining fine, wonderful, fantastic and relaxed, smoke-free, cigarette-free. You are forever releasing any and all emotions and feelings that ever tied you to smoking and cigarettes, free, free at long last, feeling wonderful.

You are and you forever remain smoke-free, cigarette-free, most especially when you are with people that are smoking, most especially your husband; you feel so much better, happier, healthier and free, becoming and forever remaining, smoke-free, cigarette-free, free of any and all monkey see-monkey do behavior.

You are, and you both now and forever remain, smoke-free, cigarette-free, most especially whenever you are alone in your apartment, sitting and thinking, just doing better things to enrich yourself and your life and to extend your health, smoke-free, cigarette-free, happy, healthy and doing just better and better.

You are far more rejuvenated, taking a break, smoke-free, cigarette-free, really enjoying a few peaceful moments taking those breaks from your housework throughout the day to sit and relax without a cigarette. You feel extra rejuvenated going on after that, healthy, safe and free, always remaining smoke-free, cigarette-free, always extending your life, your health and longevity. Relaxing quiet-time is now better smoke-free, just doing what's right for your health, your life, your longevity while enjoying a quiet, relaxing moment by yourself.

You are, and you both now and forever remain, smoke-free, cigarette-free, most especially whenever you are with your mother or in her house, while showing her the way to a better and healthier, smoke-free life. She's proud of you as well as all you are doing in taking back your health, making better choices while now and forever taking charge in your cigarette free and healthier longer, well deserved life. The more you see her smoking, the more you are easily and forever, smoke-free, cigarette-free, happy, healthy and doing just better and better, just setting and example and balance, as it becomes easier and easier. Regardless of event or circumstance, you are and you are forever, smoke-free, cigarette-free, happy, healthy and doing just better and better, as it becomes easier and easier, most especially whenever you might be drinking, whether outside in bars or even at parties. It's all becoming a permanent part of your life; you are so very powerfully and easily becoming and remaining smoke-free, cigarette-free, happy, healthy and doing just better and better as you walk to work and even better and more profoundly free you are during your lunch break, but most especially the minute you walk out of work.

You are and you forever remain smoke-free, cigarette-free, most especially right after eating a meal, feeling fulfilled, peaceful, contented and happy, far more satiated and better, smoke-free, cigarette-free. You are and you both now and forever remain smoke-free, cigarette-free, most especially after you get off the train when you walk.

You begin to loathe, despise and intensely hate, cigarettes or cigarette smoke, because you've moved on, feeling healthy and fine. You are and you forever remain smoke-free, cigarette-free, most especially when stressed, handling and adapting yourself better, smoke-free, cigarette-free.

Smoking has restricted you, your health, your money and the way you live your life. You, now and forever, have put your foot down and have forever restricted yourself from smoking, and thereby free up yourself and your life, and now you feel upbeat, happy and great. With budding and building anticipation, you are on top of the world here and winning, unbeatable, unstoppable and sure of yourself and your smoke-free-forever life.

You are, and you both now and forever remain, smoke-free, cigarette-free, most especially whenever you are or might be in-between-clients at work, focusing on relaxation and success better, smoke-free, cigarette-free.

You are, and you both now and forever remain, smoke-free, cigarette-free, most especially upon awakening and using the bathroom. You are, and you both now and forever remain, smoke-free, cigarette-free, most especially in the morning while at the computer, checking E-Mail, reading your various message boards, news, and web surfing. You are, and you forever remain, smoke-free, cigarette-free, most especially after a great night's sleep, after sleeping deeply, peacefully, easily and restfully, after becoming and forever remaining, smoke-free, cigarette-free. Upon awakening, you are unstoppably determined to remain smoke-free, cigarette-free, extending your life and your health, easily throughout the day and for the rest of your life. You are, and you forever remain, smoke-free, cigarette-free, most especially when getting into a car or while driving, driving better and more safely, free of smoking and cigarettes, being proud and happy about that. You are, and you remain forever free of ever smoking, upon starting the car and driving to work in the morning. You are also forever free of smoking while driving the company truck during your work day, around town, to and from your various jobs throughout the day. You are, and you forever remain, smoke-free, cigarette-free, most especially when you are in the car, driving carefully, defensively, safely, sanely and remaining calm, comfortable, focused and relaxed. You enjoy your vacation trips so much more, smoke-free, cigarette-free, doing what is right for your health and your life, extending your life and your health. You are, and you forever remain, smoke-free, cigarette-free, most especially while at the computer, editing photos. You are, and you forever remain, smoke-free, cigarette-free, most especially when you work around the house, doing home improvements, automotive repair, home maintenance, etc. You are relaxing, smoke-free, cigarette-free, after a job well done, as you sit back, and relax, breathing cleanly and clearly and admire your work. You are, and you forever remain, smoke-free, cigarette-free, most especially right after eating a meal, feeling fulfilled, peaceful, contented and happy, far more satiated and better, smoke-free, cigarette-free. Whether it be a quick sandwich at lunch, at dinner at home, or a prepared meal at a restaurant, you solidly are and remain smoke-free, cigarette-free. You've truly and forever re-identified yourself, moving into a newer and a safer and healthier chapter of your life, both now and forever a habitual non-smoker, ex-smoker, most especially forever remaining smoke-free, cigarette-free, most especially in the morning when awaking, most especially forever remaining smoke-free, cigarette-free, after every meal, most especially forever remaining smoke-free, cigarette-free, before bed and even while in the car. You now unleash the power of your unstoppable strong mind, to work with you unstoppably, to accommodate you in this knowing yourself well, taking better care of yourself, always pushing for more, smoke-free, cigarette-free, never just content, absolutely determined to move on free of smoking cigarettes, happy, healthy, safe, free and strong, and it feels so great. You are forever free of lighting up or having a last smoke of the day after waking up on the couch or while watching T.V. before heading upstairs to your bedroom for the night.

Smoking Extras 2007: You always knew that someday you would have smoked your last cigarette, and that day has passed once and for all; in fact, forever and ahh, it feels so wonderful to be so free, smoke-free and forever cigarette-free. You are and you remain free of ever wanting to smoke anything, most especially after a meal, for in this moment, as well as in all future moments, you enjoy the meal you ate and have just eaten, feeling so much better, feeling fulfilled, calm, centered, happy, satisfied, while remaining smoke-free and cigarette-free; things are just right and better, free from smoking anything, as you are remaining true to yourself, and your future, and your children, so much better, smoke-free, cigarette-free, your greater craving and urge, to become and ever remain smoke-free, cigarette-free. All things that ever stood in your way, now reversed back upon themselves; you are and remain forever liberated, safe and strong, your mighty inner hero now active, allowing and ever emerging stronger, mighty smoke-free you to rise to the surface and to break through here.

You are forever free of smoking; you love being and remaining, smoke-free, cigarette-free. Gone now and forever with great relief are the times when you felt sick after smoking a lot. You've moved on, you are free, smoke-free, cigarette-free, safe, serene and secure. You are bound and determined to feel better and better, being true to a smoke-free, cigarette-free you, absolutely bound and determined to be and remain, smoke-free, cigarette-free, feeling fine and wonderful. Taking better care of yourself and being true to your health, most especially in regard to the Stints, you're creating clever and dynamic ways of becoming and remaining forever smoke-free, cigarette-free, extending your health and your life for yourself and for those whom you love unstoppably and unbeatably. You are and you remain forever smoke-free, cigarette-free, most especially when peaceful, calm, and most especially remaining true and steadfast, smoke-free, cigarette-free most especially in any time of panic. All things that ever worked against you, are now reversed and working against themselves in your favor to achieve a lasting power and inner strength as if you've put your foot down once and for all truly against smoking cigarettes, now feeling free forever, truly and unbelievably effective, most especially during any and all of what might have been your weak moments, now your greatest strengths, all things seemingly falling into place in your favor. You are and you forever remain smoke-free, cigarette-free, most especially when someone else lights up, you having risen above and feeling fine and doing better and better, feeling better about yourself and your life, living a newer and better truth. When you get up in the morning the first thing you do is to relax, thrive and to absolutely refuse to light up a cigarette, finding it easier and easier, choosing powerfully and achieving results easily and cleverly, dynamically and easily to extend your health, your wealth and your life, smoke-free, cigarette-free. You are calm, smoke-free, cigarette-free, nicotine-free every time, anytime, all times, most especially when you go to the bathroom, so much more fulfilled and relaxed, happy, contented and calm, smoke-free, cigarette-free. You are and you both now and forever remain smoke-free, cigarette-free, and truly finding newer and more clever ways to stay safe and free, most especially whenever you are or might be nagged by your friend about smoking, she now a supporter and ally in this powerful yet easily won fight, helping and assisting you in your powerful and thriving success, you learn to welcome her help.

You are and you both now and forever remain smoke-free, cigarette-free, most especially whenever you wake up, better and more effectively enjoying each and every morning, smoke-free, cigarette-free, free of any and all old cravings, while truly enjoying a few moments of morning relaxation and focus at the kitchen table while drinking tea and reading the paper, being true to your health, life and longevity, smoke-free, cigarette-free. You're feeling better about yourself and your life, while remaining healthy and focused on your longevity, smoke-free, cigarette-free, your greatest urge to remain and stay that way, creating a healthier life and a better you, while extending longevity, most especially while expressing and sharing, even feeling any emotion, especially when you are or even might be in any way stressed, angry, hurt, sad, upset and even when you are happy, you cleverly and adaptively forever remain smoke-free, cigarette-free, feeling calm and powerful, focused and driven, forever determined and unbeatable, you are, you remain smoke-free, cigarette-free, just doing better and better all of this becoming easier and easier. You are inspired to unstoppably succeed. You are and you forever remain smoke-free, cigarette-free, most especially when you are on the phone, while enjoying your conversation and friendships better, while relaxing into a brand new and healthier chapter of your life; in fact, and in reality, you are always finding the very best reasons to remain healthy and extending your health, longevity and your life. In fact it may cleverly seem to you, that all of this is especially easy to powerfully and forever remain smoke-free, cigarette-free.

**Smoking Cessation and Golf** -- You are and you remain smoke-free, cigarette-free, most especially while playing golf, whether stressed or relaxed, you are doing better for yourself, for what the pros know, what the pros do, with the pros move like, you now know, you now move like, you now do, you now confidently enhanced and more able, generating a more relaxed and focused you, playing a better game, with smoking and cigarettes now just a distant memory far, far away from you. Actually, you're enjoying the entire experience better while playing better smoke-free, cigarette-free now and forever, re-Identified foundationally now that you are and forever remain a nonsmoker who plays better golf and liberates from themselves from places deep, deep inside, a masterful and better golfing experience through your fine tuned actions and retuned body and mind, feeling only better and better about yourself, not because I say so, but because it is a true fact that in this smoke-free and cigarette-free chapter of your life you are in a new and better chapter, as you radiate from heart and mind, harmony and balance, liberating a brighter and better more skillful you who lives a better day and a better night unstoppably seizing the moment and readily and successfully living your dreams of feeling content and comfortable while remaining smoke-free, cigarette-free, feeling wonderful.. All of this just getting easier and better on every breath and on each and every beat of your heart and, in fact, you may even feel that you have never been so sure of anything before and sure in your life as you are surely smoke-free and cigarette-free forever and always.

**WEIGHT - *Extras (2005)*** You are powerfully free of eating, or wanting to eat or craving anything to eat, just because you are or might be stressed. Less is more as you fill up sooner, and have had enough, feeling fine. You make sure your refrigerator is well stocked and supportive of you, filled with proper foods for an adult, like fruits and vegetables, that support a better, lighter, healthier you. You set up times and proper-only places to eat; less is more; one plateful is enough for you; you actually take pride in leaving some of each and every meal on the plate as you leave the table. You are dynamically moving into a better time in your life, easily succeeding at becoming lighter, thinner, healthier and better. You are powerfully free of eating or wanting to eat, or craving anything like hamburgers, pizza, etc. - choosing to eat meals that better support your health and longevity. You're choosing to eat an apple or orange for a snack, powerfully remaining free of and moving beyond kiddy foods, foods intended for children, finding comfort in yourself and in the richness that is your life, free of old ways and foods like cake or sweets, actually surprised at how easy it is for you to thrive and succeed at this. You just find yourself relaxing into a better and more powerfully supportive way of life and living; you want to exercise; you have the machines, but this time when the time comes, you just get up and do it, this time, each and every time, feeling better and resting better right through the night after exercising, feeling better and better, more and more upbeat about yourself and your life. Just like getting up for golf, you are harnessing the energy of your very best and most optimistic, upbeat motivational aspects, and moving into a better and better chapter of your life. You remain powerfully free of overeating, holding weight, gaining weight, in any way, even if you've had a stressful day, seeing your home base as a stress-free sanctuary. You remain powerfully free of overeating, holding weight, gaining weight, in any way, even if you've challenged by blockages from your past. Because in fact, you have dynamically moved into a brand- new and better chapter of your life, feeling better and better about yourself and cutting yourself a break, easily leaving the challenges of work at work, and learning and creatively putting your day's cares up on a shelf at work, and once out of work, moving into a brighter and happier moment of your life. The occasional proper snack in moderation, like an orange or an apple, during a football game is just fine with you, urge-free, craving-free, you are doing just fine. - You know when you've had enough, so you stop, you fill up sooner, you realize that less is more, you are released, rejuvenated and re-identified as a newer, healthier, lighter and doing-better-for-yourself person. You are free of overeating, holding onto weight, gaining weight or eating anything without thinking, even if you are bored. You chose to eat the proper foods for yourself, realizing that you are improving your health, your future, your life with each and every slowly consumed, well- balanced, meal that you eat to sustain yourself. It's almost as if someone from deep, deep inside you has reset a switch, a dial, some type of computer or a thermostat from deep, deep within you, easily allowing you to burn food, fat, calories, weight more efficiently. * You are powerfully free of eating or wanting to eat or craving anything to eat just because food is around. You are powerfully free of eating or wanting to eat or craving anything to eat just because you are or might be stressed. You are powerfully free of eating or wanting to eat or craving anything to eat just because you are or might be angry. You are powerfully free of eating or wanting to eat or craving anything to eat just because you are or might be bored. You are powerfully free of eating or wanting to eat or craving anything to eat just because you are or might be depressed. * You are dynamically moving into a better time in your life, easily succeeding at becoming lighter, thinner, healthier and better. You are powerfully free of eating or wanting to eat or craving anything like breads and carbohydrates. You're powerfully successful and free of kiddy foods, now that you are an adult, free of craving or wanting cake, chocolate, ice cream, because you are powerfully becoming lighter thinner, healthier and better, powerfully filled up with the correct foods at proper mealtimes, which is really just enough for you. You are hunger free, snack free, eating properly, more important and most especially free of snacking between lunch and dinner, or even after dinner, most especially free of cravings and urges at approximately (name time – e.g.- 5:30 in the afternoon) always craving free, filled up, un-hungry, free of salty deserts including chips or anything like them, because you have dynamically moved into a brand new and better chapter of your life, even free of having cake and coffee most especially around (name time – e.g.- 9:30-10:00 p.m.). Instead, if you decide to snack, should you even ever think of it, you become a big fruit and vegetable eater, eating wholesome and properly for yourself, joyously extending your life and your abundant health, because you'd like to be, so you do and so you are and so you remain.

You feel so calm, so inspired, so super upbeat and bright, you feel ambitious, easily raising activity levels, even deep breathing or walking when you feel up to it, in spite of all challenges and even if you are inactive, you are hunger free, craving free, free of eating anything without first thinking and stopping and deciding in your favor to do better and better. Just as soon as your are full and noticing it sooner, you've had enough, you have unstoppably moved on free of wanting or needing a treat, you've had enough and enjoy truly the benefits of a lighter thinner and better you, feeling so fine and wonderful, you arc on top of the world, having limitless willpower, easily and dynamically energetically, vigorously and enthusiastically succeeding at this. * In fact, you've relaxed into a brand new and better happier and lighter better chapter of your life, feeling a new sense of being completely in control of your life, your urges, free of any and all old urges that once stood in your way, easily and successfully moving on, having gained power and control over your life and most especially easily over anything to do with food. You're powerfully successful and free of being overly hungry, most especially free of picking all day, regardless of the time of day even around dinnertime while you are cooking. You're powerfully successful and free of being overly hungry overeating, or craving anything, you are most especially free of picking all day, even if you and your spouse (husband / wife) are fighting. You're powerfully successful and free of being overly hungry overeating or craving anything, feeling content and comfortable, even if you skip lunch, finding newer and better ways of providing three proper and healthy for an adult of your age, meals for yourself. You are powerfully remaining free of indulging in cookies or cake before dinner, steering clear of kiddy foods, because now that as an adult, you are hunger free, providing yourself comfortably and with more complete nutrition, like fruits and vegetables. You are extending your life, most especially when stressed, at home or out of the home. Your new and healthier way of correctly and powerfully dealing with stress is to relax your way through any and all stressful situations, so you are easily able to relax more, in any and all situations. You are powerfully free of craving or wanting of kiddy foods, junk foods, now that you are an adult, having healthier grown up tastes. You are easily and effectively avoiding them, you've moved on. You're powerfully successful and free of being overly hungry overeating or craving anything, you feel content and comfortable, even un-hungry, even when your in-laws and stepchildren are brought up into a conversation or when they are over. You're finding newer and better, more complete ways of feeling fine. You are finding newer and better, more remarkable ways to feel better, even while you might be stressed or depressed or even if you feel alone. You are absolutely determined to do better for yourself, as you become thinner, lighter, healthier and better. You remain powerfully free of overeating, holding weight, gaining weight, in any way, even if you've gone food shopping of if you've bought everything - most especially when your closets and refrigerator are full! * In fact, you've relaxed into a brand new, better, happier and lighter chapter of your life, feeling a new sense of being completely in control of your life and your urges. You have gained power and control over your life and most especially easily over anything to do with food. *You're powerfully successful and free of being overly hungry, most especially free of picking all day, regardless of the time of day even if you get up at (name time - e.g.- 3:30 am) and when you arrive at your office at (name time e.g.-5:15 am. or 6 am). You are and you just remain hunger free, even un-hungry and content. You correctly choose to eat only at mealtimes, feeling full, you know when to stop. Less is more, smaller portions are enough, seeing yourself anew and you're feeling fine. Enough is enough, so you've moved on powerfully, which is enough for you. You are hunger free, most especially when stressed, at home or most especially even at work. This is your highly effective, newer and healthier way of correctly and powerfully dealing with stress. Your correct response, both now and forever is to relax your way through any and all stressful situations, so you are easily able to relax more, so adaptable in any and all stress situations. You are powerfully free of craving or wanting of kiddy foods, now that you are an adult, with healthier grown up tastes, easily avoiding cake, candy and chips, as a healthier better way to treat yourself and to increase your longevity. So you find yourself enjoying more and more improved choices in your diet and in your life, like eating more fish, turkey burgers and low fat items that taste better and are more appropriate for you, that help you promote and to maintain greater health, energy and longevity.

Most especially after dinner, you know you've had enough, so you move on and feel fine, moving beyond picking, rather and instead, picking a healthier and better, more fulfilling way to live and to enjoy your newer lighter, better and more energetic body, easily able to rest with a luxurious state of slumber, balancing you, healing you, restoring you, right through the night. Even your dreams work in your favor to rest you and to inspire you to succeed, lighter, thinner, healthier and better. You're powerfully successful and free of kiddy foods, now that you are an adult, most especially free of eating candy (chocolate), cupcakes, pies, pastries and cookies, which are too sweet for your tastes, so overly sweet. All of that begins to make you feel physically sick, so you move on and easily and forever, away from them, so much better off in your life without them. You choose to eat and actually eating only healthy foods, proper for an adult, proper for longevity and health, so appropriate, so tasty, so right, foods you are now and forever enjoy for health and well being on all levels, just for you. You easily achieve your goal and desire of becoming lean, slim and trim, as you easily find newer and more powerful and creatively successful methods of staying that way. You relax into this and you win. Your correct, proper and right response to any and all stress is to relax your way through it, and you easily succeed at doing this, finding your healing process more powerful, more fulfilling, more adaptive, more healing in the most amazing and profound of ways. You just seem to be flowing beyond any and all personal challenges, problem-free, challenge oriented and most successfully learning to live one day at a time. *You're powerfully successful and free of kiddy foods, now that you are an adult, most especially free of chocolate chip cookies, cheese, pasta and breads, forever free with all of this just getting easier for you to remain free of greasy foods, childish foods from the past, such as chicken fingers, French fries and pizza. You've grown up now, and you truly know and easily live the ideas and ideals that it's time to behave and to properly and healthily eat as an adult. But even if you do taste a small sample, you'll have enough, you'll fill up sooner, having satisfied the craving. You'll feel and be satisfied after just a few short bites or a quick and tiny taste. You are powerfully free and moving beyond eating for no reason while at work, most especially when you have nothing to do, you find newer and better ways to pass the time, learning and improving yourself, enriching yourself, making the very best and most of your time. You make and take the time to eat right. Your very best place is your home, you find your one place there, perhaps it's in your kitchen or your dining area, ONLY THERE. You only eat there, at your designated eating areas, at regular meal times, smaller portions, less is more as you fill up sooner. You eat to live only and you are forever free of living to eat. You find time to enjoy your life make the time to love, to live and to laugh, finding numerous times each and every day to laugh and to enjoy yourself as this newer, brighter, lighter, better and healthier you emerges. * You begin to lose fat, your weight comes down, a newer, lighter, happier and better you emerges unstoppably. You begin to eat properly, right, and correctly. As an adult, you find yourself relaxing into better choices, better ways of being, thinking and reacting, choosing only the very best for you to eat. And you easily and successfully and victoriously, thrive and win at this, so powerful, so easily able do this for the rest of my life so I can see your son / daughter grow up. You choose health, you change, you improve your life for the better, even surprising yourself, at how easy this is and becomes for you. For you've begun a new and better, healthier and happier chapter of your life and this feels great. * You find yourself filling up sooner, faster, easier, with smaller portions, finding newer and better ultimate pleasures with your loved ones, yourself and your life. You get up, you move on and out into the world with clear and determined optimism, ready to live, ready to share or yourself, with a zest for life, just like you did years ago. You are determined to live and have a good time, making the most of each and every day and night, the very most of every moment. You begin to treat yourself like a good and loving friend, always taking better care of yourself and following your very best advice. And you enjoy taking better care of yourself, you enjoy creating a masterpiece of a body and a life, clear, sharp and determined, you win. This time, you break through. You find yourself giving and gaining love from others and yourself in better ways. Having grown up, having survived, you now start to live and a newer and better, brighter, more optimistic, lighthearted you begins to emerge, not because I say so, but because it's the nature of your own powerful and determined unstoppable powerful mind to do so and you do. For you have forever moved on by enjoyably relaxing into a newer, brighter, lighter, happier and better chapter of your life. You remain free of overeating even if you are or become emotional. You are doing better for yourself, doing better and better, in the very best and most powerful of ways. * You are dynamically moving into a better time in your life, easily succeeding at becoming lighter, thinner, healthier and better. You are powerfully free of eating or wanting to eat or craving anything like starchy foods and you're powerfully successful and free of kiddy foods. Now that you are an adult, you are and easily remain free of craving or wanting cake and cookies. You are powerfully becoming lighter thinner, healthier and better, powerfully filled up with the correct foods at proper mealtimes, which is really just enough for you. You now move into a newer and better chapter of your life and you tend to eat less, filling up sooner, fuller and more completely, easily able to leave food on your plate. You are hunger free, snack free, eating properly, more importantly and most especially free of snacking between lunch and dinner, or even after dinner, most especially free of old cravings and old un-needed urges. You eat less, less is more, enjoying smaller portions and fill up sooner, tasting and savoring flavors and sensations, enjoying your life, lighter, healthier, thinner and better, more now than you ever did when you used to overeat. You are easily stick to the less-is-more point of view in your life, easily able to stick to a proper regimen of healthier and lighter eating for an adult, for your health and longevity.

You bring your exercise goals down to a level of ridiculous ease, just three days a week, for just a few minutes each day, enjoying yourself so much, easily meeting and quite often exceeding those goals, just getting up and doing it, lasting long enough to enjoy the results you deserve, creating a newer, better, lighter and thinner healthier you, who now and forever unstoppably emerges. * You now move into a newer and better chapter of your life and you tend to eat less, filling up sooner, fuller and more completely, easily able to leave food on your plate (or on the tray, table). You move into a better and brighter place of proper adult nutrition, free of any old and childish addictions to carbohydrates, especially, sweets. You are frustration free, choosing to feel satisfied and fulfilled. Less is more, enough is enough; in fact, you now find it easy to lose weight, moving on into a better and brighter life. And you are unstoppably free of eating, overeating or wanting to eat, even if you are or might be bored, anxious, nervous, or simply to avoid doing something else. You enjoy eating, stopping sooner, feeling lighter, thinner, better and happier, easily avoiding overeating and the resulting past guilt it brought. Becoming and remaining lighter, thinner, better and healthier, more active, allows you to fully enjoy the good things in life. In fact, in this newer and better chapter of your life, you would rather exercise than indulge yourself as you now fully and firmly and forever know exercising would be significantly better for your health. So you just get up and do it, bringing your exercise goals down to a level of comfortable ease. * You find better things to do with your thoughts and your life, free of hunger, free of picking at food, even if you are bored, upset, happy or looking for something to do at home or out in the world. You remain interested in better things and find newer and better interests, even if you find yourself bored or upset, happy or unhappy or are looking for something to do at home. Your tastes are changing and improving in your favor, allowing you to become and forever remain, lighter, thinner, more active, healthier, better with a brighter outlook. You are taking better care of yourself, moving on and away from junk food, because you deserve better than that. And your tastes change and improve in your favor. You're just sick of junk foods, their flavors are changing, becoming boring, silly and way too sweet or way too salty, so happily, you are moving on, into greater looks, greater health, greater success, greater energy and a longer and healthier life. And all of your life works to support you in this, as you are easily able to sleep right though the night. Every thought, feeling, idea and action works to support you in this, while you are awake, while you are asleep, even while you dream, even your happy and peaceful dreams work to support you in this. You are peaceful, you are calm, you are serene, fearless, bold, courageous, looking at your life as a bold new adventure, each and every day and most especially every night. * You are absolutely free of going through phases, moving beyond the ups and downs, finding steadiness and comfortable ease, because as you've relaxed, you've relaxed your way into a newer and brighter and happier and healthier way of life and living. In reality and truly forever, you are amazingly relaxing your way into a lifetime of smoothly flowing times. You are now bringing up unstoppable feelings from moments in your life when you went through phases coming to an end. You are easily and successfully remaining binge free, truly and forever finding foundational peace and stability, calmness and ease, doing ever better for yourself, as you become lighter, thinner, healthier and better, and more active, more upbeat and better, truly doing better than ever before. You are eating only to live, free forever of living to eat. You make and are fundamentally committed to keeping a regular and healthy regimen of scheduled meals. You are eating only what's correct for an adult your age, to extend your health and your life. Smaller is better, you fill up sooner, less is more, less is enough. You know when to get up, when to leave the table, choosing to eat off smaller plates, very often leaving some of each and every meal on the plate as you leave the table, which is really just fine with you. You choose to take better care of yourself as an adult, eating what's proper, choosing to eat a diet free of kiddy foods, which is really just fine with you now that you've moved on, even while at home, free of noshing, finding better ways to enrich yourself and to enlighten yourself, perhaps reading or anything productive. * You find better things to do with your thoughts and your life, free of hunger, free of picking at food, even if you are bored, at home, at work or out in the world. You remain interested in better things and find newer and better interests, even if you find yourself bored. You find that active is better. You enjoy moving around, even walking. You feel so motivated to move around, to walk, to enjoy the physicality of walking, moving into a newer and better chapter of your life, free forever of just sitting around. You move on and as a adult, you are taking better care of yourself to become lighter, thinner, more active, healthier and better, eating more fruits and vegetables, to extend your life and your health, forever moving beyond eating too much bread or starchy products. Your self-confidence is growing, and improving, changing and growing in your favor. You take better care of yourself and you even feel super motivated, having a building and budding sense of motivation to take the very best care of yourself. * You find yourself hunger free and choose to better enjoy your life. You're active, when appropriate, physically, emotionally and mentally and achieving your goals and hopes, living your very best dreams even if you are BORED, ANXIOUS OR EMOTIONALY DOWN, even if you are or might be NERVOUS or even if you are feeling like you might want to PULL OUT your HAIR. You are hunger free even if you are tired. You find new and better ways to pace yourself, finding new rhythms and times, a powerful and better structure of eating and success for becoming lighter, thinner, healthier and better. You are finding your correct places to eat, the only places where you'll eat. You are and forever become free of eating without thinking again, correctly choosing to eat in your designated eating places at a slow and comfortable pace, filling up sooner, living and feeling better. And you remain craving free, slowing down while powerfully activating a higher metabolism, filling up sooner and more powerfully, feeling more comfortable and truly craving free. As a powerful part of your adult life, you find leaving some food on the plate is just fine with you. You choose to eat in smaller portions, just enough for you. You find yourself leaving some portion of each meal behind on the plate, a powerful victory over the past, a win, you are moving forward. You are easily able to successfully leave some of the food in front of you behind, and it feels great. I wonder if you yet realize how easy it will be for you to lose (name the amount of pounds, never a round number - e.g.-152 lbs.), as you relax into this and thrive and succeed. * You find it not only possible, but easy to lose 32, 48, even 52 lbs. as you relax into this, succeed and win, lighter, thinner healthier and better. You know when to stop, when enough is enough; you are easily able to stop, put the food aside and move on, becoming more and more active. You've chosen to do better and better for yourself, choosing to eat only the right foods in moderation, to fulfill your need to be alive. You eat to live only. Overwhelming food cravings are easily becoming a thing of the past for you, as you've moved on and you've relaxed into a newer and better chapter of your life, and it feels great. It's almost as if someone from deep, deep inside you has reset a switch, a dial, a thermostat or some type of computer, from deep, deep within you, easily allowing you to burn food, calories, weight more efficiently, free of carbohydrates. Your desire is more and more easily, just not there for carbohydrates. You've moved on and it feels great. This time, you are easily succeeding at keeping off the weight, sticking to what you know works. You relax into this, you succeed, you thrive you win, lighter, thinner, healthier and better. * Your correct, proper and right response to any and all stress is to relax your way through it, and you easily succeed at doing this, finding your healing process more powerful, more fulfilling, more adaptive, more healing in the most amazing and profound of ways, just flowing beyond any and all personal challenges, problem-free, challenge oriented and most successfully learning to live one day at a time You find yourself easily motivated to use your exercise machine (name type), realizing that a superior person just gets up and does it. So you do it, just two or three minutes, two or three times each week, often just enjoying yourself so much and running substantially longer. You find yourself employing new and better methods, motivations and strategies to exercise, easily fulfilling a newer and burning passion to become and remaining activate and losing weight, keeping the unwanted weight off forever and choosing to be healthy. You are easily succeeding at this. For truly, you now even more powerfully have this resolve in your powerful and unstoppable mind. You think, you now and live from the idea that you need to eat less, slowly and properly, filling up completely and sooner, in correct, proper and healthy amounts for yourself now. As a healthy and long living adult you are feeling better and you know that means you are feeling emotionally as well as physically better. You now need and want to eat only healthier foods. You are your own person, in charge of your life. You guide, you glide and you protect yourself even while you become and you remain thin in worthwhile ways, free of being annoyed or bothered by anyone, even or most especially when you are thin. You are so determined to have a happy and long-lasting and comfortable life (marriage), problem-free, struggle free, happy and long lasting, always in your best comfort zone while being and remaining thinner, lighter, happier and better, the rest of your life. You are feeling so very deeply, truly and profoundly motivated when it comes to healthier ways of living and your life. You are so motivated, upbeat, light hearted and excited. You are energetic when it comes to weight loss as a well deserved improved you, more energetic and successful, always being and remaining more positive in general, forever and successfully emerges.

You find it fun and pleasurable to remain forever free of overeating at mealtimes. You are taking better care of yourself and finding newer and more clever ways of becoming and forever remaining lighter, thinner, healthier and better. Less is more; you fill up sooner and know when you've had enough and take optimum care of yourself, most especially at dinner time, eating less and enjoying it more, forever free of ever feeling stuffed. You front-load your meals, eating more nutritious breakfasts and lunches, so that when dinnertime comes, you eat light and feel fantastic.

You sleep right through the night, hunger-free, un-hungry, establishing newer and more supportive patterns while remaining surprisingly hunger-free, feeling better and sleeping better, free of consuming any late night or mid-night snacks, most especially free of sweets and cakes, taking care of yourself like an adult, free of eating or reacting like a teenager.

You are excited to attend social gatherings, finding the camaraderie fun and showing them and feeling a glowing fun, as a newer, lighter, brighter and better you unstoppably emerges.

Your powerful and highly effective, adaptive and subconscious mind is, now and forever, powerfully working in your favor to effectively allow you, in the most potent and powerful of ways, to keep you and your diet free from: sweets, fats, salty snacks (such as chips and nuts), and most of all chocolate; less is more, even just a small taste is enough for you. You find yourself, now and forever, easily making and sticking to sensible and healthy food choices. You are making the time to drink at least six glasses of water or appropriate other liquid, each and every day. You are easily able to get up, get moving, and exercise! Your mind wanders to making a schedule and flexible yet structured plan, then following through with it! You find yourself now working more effectively, following a regimen that includes an objective measure of results -- such as joining and attending your weight group, enjoying the camaraderie and support. Less is more; you fill up sooner, controlling portions, most especially for starches and proteins. Even a fatty food or sweet might be all right to eat, just remember proper proportions; less is more, you fill up sooner, you've had enough, it's Ok to leave some of each and every meal on the plate as you leave the table, which is really just fine with you, both now and forever. Most especially during Holiday times, you are feeling fine; less is more, you fill up sooner, you've had enough and easily find yourself filling up sooner, even if there is food in front of you. You trust in all of this and in yourself, and trust in your life. And you clear things up and clean out the clutter in all areas of your life, succeeding as never before.

**Weight Extras 2006 -** Less is more, you fill up sooner, it's really OK now as an adult to leave some of each and every meal on the plate as you leave the table. Smaller plates are better, just fine for you. You are doing fine, feeling wonderful, filled, fulfilled and fantastic. In this newer and better chapter of your life, you can leave some food behind, on the plate, on the table as you leave the table, that's just OK with you! Less is more; you fill up sooner and feel fine. You begin to enjoy the luxurious and flowingly refreshing taste of water; it tastes as good as your favorite beverage, rapidly now it becomes your favorite beverage, because it's time and you say so, and so it is. You find comfort in your life, in your world, in the love you have for yourself and for the love you have for your family and loved ones, and in all that you are, seek and do. You are powerfully free of eating or wanting to eat or craving anything like starchy fast foods and you're powerfully successful and free of kiddy foods, now that you are an adult, free of craving or wanting snack foods, fast foods, taking and making the proper time to eat, relax and enjoy, filling up sooner. The energy of what once was your weakness has now turned around to become your greatest strength. You are powerfully free of eating or wanting to eat or craving anything to eat just because you are or might be at a social event – less is more, you fill up sooner and you've had enough; you know when to stop, you are filled up, you are fulfilled. You only eat at proper mealtimes, only when hungry, easily and actively becoming lighter, thinner, healthier and better. You are powerfully and forever free of overindulging, taking better care of yourself, free from wanting or eating kiddy foods, like Breads & Cheeses together, or overdoing Complex Carbohydrates: Bread, French Fries, Potatoes, Cake, Cookies, Pastas, or even Overindulging in Whole Wheat Carbs, just relaxing into a newer and better way, so super motivated and free, feeling wonderful, taking much better care of yourself and your health, vigor and vitality, lighter, thinner, healthier and better, more active and enjoying the way your body moves, as you move, as the weight just seems to melt off.

You are, and you absolutely remain, easily and completely free of binge eating, especially at night; you are calm and full, un-hungry, satisfied and comfortable. You eat only at designated eating areas, only at mealtimes. Less is more; you fill up sooner, eating only one plateful, off a smaller plate, easily leaving some of each and every meal on the plate, which is really just fine with you. You know you're doing better and better. You are finding newer and better ways of controlling yourself. Less is more; you fill up sooner; you are easily only doing better and better. You are moving well beyond any and all binge eating, and remaining free of kiddy foods, like sweets and other nutritionally unsupportive foods, beyond any and all foods intended for children, feeling so good, so sure of yourself, so good inside and out, so selfsupported, taking only the very best care of yourself. Just a small taste is enough for you; you've had enough and you are easily moving on, more and more active, feeling a newer and more loving, self-fulfilled and self-supporting sense of yourself. Your heart is warm and happy; you feel love, you love yourself enough to move on and take better care of yourself, lighter, thinner, healthier and better. Your life is sweet, you are doing wonderfully; you are moving on from overdoing it with sugar to maintain optimal health; you enjoy looking forward to eating and consuming the wonderful nutrition that fruits and veggies provide. You easily succeed at dropping, losing and becoming lighter, 33, 34, 36 lbs. lighter, thinner, healthier and better; in fact, the weight just seems to easily and forever melt off, and you feel free, free at long last, lighter, thinner, healthier, better, and more and more wonderful, happy, healthy, safe, while extending your life, completely content.

Just imagine deep breathing, being and feeling calm, happy, relaxed, being at your very best, rising to the very top and succeeding, thriving and breaking through. Just imagine seeing yourself getting ever closer to your goal of being and remaining forever, 67, 69, or even 71 lbs. lighter, as your energy is up, you are more motivated, moving, with greater activity, a size 34 waist rapidly becoming yours. Right now and only better and easier, you are becoming free of eating late at night, after dinner, most especially whenever you are alone, forever free of old ways and childish habits, like going down to the basement and eating while in front of the TV. You eat only in designated eating areas only; you eat to live, free forever of ever living to eat. Wow, it really feels great to be forever free of old ways; enough is enough, even a small taste is just enough for you, eating only in designated eating areas. You see and come to know it's time to grow up, and live and be a healthy adult; cookies are for children, adults do better, and so you do. Your tastes change in your favor, eating (brand name – product here) cookies and/or peanut butter and chocolate cookies, now a thing of the past; they are too sweet, too much kid-stuff, uggh! Less is more, you fill up sooner, even a small bit is enough for you, moving on and keeping carbs lower and lower, lesser and lesser in your diet, protein and vitamins better and better, more satisfying for you.

As easy as it once was to fall off, in this newer and better chapter of your life, you stay on with this, ever onward you stay and you go. It's easy, not because I say so but because you've decided to do so and it just really is, most especially clever at this, staying with it, keeping culprit foods out of the house or just away from you, most especially on weekends, powerfully and substantially on weekends. You bring your exercise goals down to levels of ridiculous ease, just a few minutes or even seconds a day, a few days a week, just fine for you, easily exceeding those moments and enjoying yourself, breaking through, exercising at the gym or even at home or just walking or life-cycling; you enjoy it, you make the time, you are wonderful and successful, you just make it happen. Just like in years gone by, but only easier and better now, moment by moment, breath by breath, you are both now and forever maintaining a good weight, regularly exercising, free of pizza and sugar. In your powerful and adaptive, clever mind, now working in your favor, you imagine and truly know you are dynamically back on track, back to the gym, free of silly and insignificant kiddy foods like pizza or any sugar products, and low on the carbs. Your need and desire to get back into your (34) inch waist pants is now being realized and lived; it's yours now, you are doing all that it takes, seizing the moment, taking the opportunity, feeling great, doing better. You break through this time, you win.

**Weight – Stress Eating (2005) -** You are finding yourself filling up sooner and easily stopping when you are done. You've moved into a new chapter of your life and have moved into a brighter, better more comfortable place, easily succeeding at all of this. Your powerful mind is more relaxed, yet effectively working on all of this to absolutely and unconditionally insure your ultimate success at this in easy yet surprisingly effective ways. You are powerfully determined to just know when to stop eating. You are forever free of overeating, most especially stress eating. You now know when to stop, when to relax and when to move away from your plate and food and so you do. Only right, healthier and better foods, that serve you best, foods in smaller amounts and in moderation, fill you up sooner and relax you, making you feel fine, you know when to stop and so you do, feeling relaxed, stress free and happy. You are mightier than any stress you might encounter. Your correct and absolute response is to relax your way thorough stress, trust in life and rise above any and all challenges. Stress just seems to melt off on each and every deep and slow steady breath that you take. Weight just seems to melt off on each and every deep and slow steady breath that you take You almost feel like you have a new lease on life, resting peacefully throughout the night, resting deeply and comfortably yet easily able to start the day as scheduled as your body clock now begins to work in your favor to get you up on time and to tune into your morning wake up time and enjoyably start the day, like any normal person. You have made up your unstoppable mind to forever remain free of ever again eating until feel like you might explode. You are doing better and taking better care of yourself, relaxing through any and all things that once ever stood in your way. You find newer and more effective ways of explaining, and teaching those around you to get their jobs done on time, even when under pressure, like an ideal teacher or parent. You complete all tasks quickly as all unnecessary weight melts off easily and quickly. You are easily finding newer and better ways to melt off all unneeded, unwanted and unnecessary weight.

**Weight**- You begin to take better care of yourself, just like taking care of children, you begin to moderate and think of the nutritional content of what you are eating and what you are desiring to eat, and you are learning and evolving into taking better and better care of yourself. Free from the past, you are moving into a brighter and better way of feeding yourself and taking care of yourself, eating to live, free forever of living to eat. You find healthy, healthful and balanced meals in smaller portions, better, more desirous and more appropriate for yourself. Even if you have to prepare your meals a day or so in advance, you are easily taking better care of yourself and free forever of eating kiddy foods, like at times after work in the past when you devoured 6 ounces of Cool Whip and two bowls of cereal, because you are moving on, into a brighter and better day and way of living your life. And when you've finished your dinner, proper for an adult, proper for you, you've had enough and you've moved on, free forever of old, unpleasant and self-destructive habits, like binging on M&M's or a bag of microwave popcorn every night, because you are learning to take better and better care of yourself both day and night. As a special gift to yourself, so very well deserved, you have quit smoking in June 1992, and now most especially, it's gift time once again for you, so you are easily and adaptively and in surprisingly effective ways, finding newer, improved and easier ways to shed and rid yourself of 33, 34 or even 36 pounds. Regardless of event or circumstance, in your life or in the world, you are powerfully and effectively determined to become and forever remain excusefree, super-motivated and moving on with your life, as you are skillfully and easily becoming in so very well deserved ways, lighter, better, healthier and thinner.

Relax deeper and further, further and deeper, and allow yourself to remember or to just feel a time in the past in your mind when you were doing well, feeling fine and upbeat, so relaxed, so on top of the world, completely unbeatable, inspired and empowered, above and beyond any and all things that might have ever stood in your way. In fact, truly, you are allowing yourself right now, in this moment, to be inspired to rise to the very top, braced, strengthened, fortified, yet flexible by the energy of every past feeling and knowing experience of every past victory, triumph, breakthrough and success you've ever had. You are easily and effectively learning to take better and more proper care of yourself, tending towards moderation, healing, balance, harmony and forgiveness. Harshness from the past now giving way to gentleness, mildness, comfortability and ease. You are learning to relax your way through any and all stress; your now- and forever correct response to stress is to relax your way through it and rise above it, with calm and gentle breath, and a balanced and peaceful centeredness; you are, on each and every breath and each and every heartbeat, learning and succeeding at doing better and better, feeling fine and just simply flowing with life. Not because I say so, but because it's the nature of your own powerful and dynamic mind, spirit and personal sense of empowerment to do so. Your body, emotions, thoughts, feelings, and inspirations, now working powerfully, effectively and dynamically in your favor to improve your body, habits, feelings, thoughts, actions, reactions, to inspire only your very best and personal greatness, to allow you to thrive unbeatably, so much more sure of yourself; you are powerfully unstoppable, easily able to sleep, rest, relax deeply, peacefully and profoundly, whenever you need to, after just a few deep and calming, steady and powerful breaths, taking the very best care of yourself, free of old destructive and self-destructive habits that ever once stood in your way; you are the mighty one now, right now and forever, having not only survived, but rather having been polished by life. You are so easily able to actively and unstoppably achieve a better life, and more easily and powerfully reach your goals, most especially free and doing ultimately better, at night as well as in the day, but most especially at night. Your body, comfortable and pleasantly numb whenever you need it to be so, after just a few deep and steady breaths. Patient, calm, pleasantly numb or detached when you need it most, beginning a newer and better chapter of your life right now, treating yourself with respect and kindness, harmony and balance, and newer and better focus develops, and this is just something you relax into and thrive at, so amazingly and surprisingly well, a newer and budding sense of forgiveness from the past, a budding and ever-building sense of focus and optimism, now building, building, building - so unstoppably; you are now-and-forever reconditioned, rejuvenated, only your very best flowing up and rising to the top, just doing better and better, as you learn and activate treating yourself like a loving parent would a beautiful child, loving yourself and treating yourself with kindness, caring and respect.

**Weight-** Less is more; you fill up sooner and begin to eat like a proper adult, taking the very best care of yourself, forever free of eating like a teenager. Smaller portions, in moderation, slowly consumed as you fill up sooner and feel fine; you've had enough and you move on easily and forever into a newer, lighter, thinner, better you. Even a small taste is enough for you; one bite or mouthful and you've had enough junk; you are too important to ever over-indulge in any foods, whether nutritious or, most importantly, ever over-indulge in overeating junk food again. Most easily, you are moving on from and are free from foods intended for children and teenagers like candy, chocolate, ice cream, cake, cookies, a variety of chips, and soda; you are far too important, and your health and longevity are more important than the childish ways of the past. You only eat in designated eating areas of your home or any place you eat, choosing forever to be free of distractions like TV while eating; less is more; you fill up sooner, often choosing to leave some of each and every meal on the plate as you leave the table, which is really just fine with you, as you build a budding and thriving sense of fulfillment and sense of personal victory over your past, into your lighter, thinner, better and brighter future, now that you are an adult and are making better choices. You only eat when you are hungry; you fill up sooner; you know when you've had enough, and you easily and powerfully move on. You make the time; you take the time to take better care of yourself.

Weight *(Extras 2004)* – You have correctly now and truly realized it is time for you to take better care of yourself, to extend your health and your life and to grow up, in terms of how you are treating yourself. As a powerful part of this new and improved you, you are taking powerful and better care of yourself. Less is more, just a taste is enough; you are moving on and you are feeling fulfilled. You are easily able to be happy, safe, fulfilled and free by cutting out: diet coke, enjoying more healthy beverages like water, or easily just limiting wine to one glass when out to dinner, but really, most always, you just otherwise only drinking cool and completely refreshing water. You are flowing into a new and better chapter of your life, free of binge eating, choosing to eat healthy foods, proper for an adult, using the power of your dynamic and powerfully effective, working in your favor, subconscious mind, which is now always working in your favor, powerfully functioning and supporting you in the most dynamic of ways, easily allowing you to achieve this, allowing you to truly and unstoppably be the master of your own fate, easily, effectively and powerfully, in even surprising ways, allowing you to control old patterns like past binges of fattening junk foods. You are so much better off, free of kiddy foods, foods intended for children, like: ice cream, pizza, bagels, muffins, breads, chocolate, sugary things, etc., than you ever were without them. Less is more, even in extreme times, just a taste of anything for you is enough; you've grown up, moved on and had enough. Your portions are smaller, you now as an adult are allowed to leave some of each and every meal on the plate, which is just fine with you, just as I have learned to and is now imparted to you, into your mind, actions and life, becoming one with you and new, easily taken and adapted to part of your life. Your portions become smaller, less is more. You fill up sooner. You are free of overeating any portion that might be too large, leaving the unwanted and undesired rest behind. You become more interested in moving around, creating more joyous body movement, while bringing your exercise time down to levels of ridiculous ease. You take the time you need to exercise a minimum of 30 minutes a day, by bringing your goals down to a level of ridiculous ease, just 2 or 3 minutes a day, two or 3 times a week, finding personal fulfillment time, becoming surprisingly more diligent making time for feeling good, (name favorite exercises) with yoga, pilates and running. You are taking care of yourself properly, better, and easier, in a more consistent and paced way, everything becoming in your favor, you are more and more health conscious, learning to truly and unconditionally love and take care of yourself better and better, caring for yourself magnificently, even surprised at how easy this is for you.

You are powerfully free of eating, or wanting to eat, or craving anything to eat just because you are or might be under stress, or most especially when you are or might be trying to make a deadline, you are and you remain calm and relaxing into a better way. You are powerfully free of eating, or wanting to eat, or craving anything to eat, just because or even if your family life is very stressful. You are finding newer and better ways of dealing with your wife, and clever and inventively effective ways of dealing with your teenage son's problems. You are powerfully free of eating, or wanting to eat, or craving anything to eat, just because you need to escape. You powerfully, effectively and beneficially relax into a better way and better day.

Taking care of yourself, you eat in ways to powerfully and adaptively improve your health; so you still eat properly and choose only the very best of foods. You are improving every thought, feeling, action and reaction in every moment, easily and effectively succeeding with shining and glorious success.

You are powerfully free of eating, or wanting to eat, or craving anything to eat, just because you are or might be disappointed in any way, shape or form: be it business, friends, any sort of betrayal, or about your sex life in any way. You easily stop eating when satisfied, knowing when to stop; enough is enough; you've had enough; you are fulfilled, easily improving your physique, feeling satisfied. You are doing better, doing best when minimizing your intake of simple carbohydrates. You are easily eating less and enjoying it more; you're also consciously and subconsciously making the better and better, only the best of all possible choices.

You begin to eat less, filling up sooner, the sight and smell of any and all food filling you up long before your first bite, taking better care of yourself, whether you are encountering stress or even if you are calm. You begin to eat less, taking better care of yourself, whether you are around other people or alone. The point of view that matters to you is your own; in the long run, the opinions of others are just that, just points of view, to be learned from or to be put aside. You put aside everything and anything that interferes with you becoming lighter, thinner, healthier and better, whether it's opinions of others, stress, emotional feelings, or mental patterns, most especially any and all of the things that once caused you discomfort or distress, becoming clearer, sharper, better, more fluid, more flexible. Less is more, you fill up sooner and thrive, lighter, thinner, better and healthier, in even surprising, adaptive and fluid ways. Less is more, healthier foods like fruits and veggies taste better and appeal to you now, so much more than ever before.

Now that you are learning to appreciate yourself, you can do anything! You have now made up your powerful, adaptive, highly effective mind, which is only getting stronger, better and more effective at reducing and eliminating all behaviors, thought and feelings that once caused you to Stress eat, choosing to deep-breathe and calm down and thrive and succeed in their place. You are finding newer and better, more completely adaptive, fluid, skillful and eminently successful ways of reducing and even eliminating any and all cravings for breads. You are finding newer and better, more completely adaptive, fluid, skillful and eminently successful ways of reducing and even eliminating any and all cravings for pastas. You are finding newer and better, more completely adaptive, fluid, skillful and eminently successful ways of reducing and even eliminating any and all cravings for butter, as you truly and unstoppably learn to appreciate yourself, even if others don't.

You know from deep, deep inside of you, that you want this to work for you. So you just want and make it happen all around you. You unstoppably want and easily achieve eating in more healthy and beneficial ways. You want to and so you stick to your exercise routine, bringing your exercise goals down to levels of ridiculous ease. You want to and so you become and easily remain a size 5, and stay that size. You are easily free of anyone to throw you off track by saying any words that might stand in your way; you are, in fact, feeling mighty and are easily rising above and transcending any and all old limits, now in this brand new chapter of your life. Proud and sure of yourself, you are amazingly unstoppable at this, feeling proud of yourself, taking your life back, truly getting amazing results from this highly effective and enjoyable experience.

You are powerfully free of eating or wanting to eat or craving anything to eat just because you are or might be bored or even aggravated. You are finding new and better balance from deep, deep within yourself, eating only to live, free of just picking, your relationship with food is now improving in your favor, so you are finding just the proper and right balances in things for yourself, lowing the carbs and balancing them with proteins and other nutrients. You make, create the you-time, to sit and eat in the daytime, making time, taking time, properly, just for you. You frontload your meals, eating more earlier, less and later in the day, more and more less unhungry later in the day, especially at night about 7 or 8. You are feeling less hungry and more filled up and fulfilled later in the day. You find that through this new form of deep, profound and powerfully effective relaxation, you are so very, very easily able to achieve your goal of becoming more effectively active, passionately driven and so easily able to take all of the necessary steps to lose weight. You are finding newer and better, more completely adaptive, fluid, skillful and eminently successful ways of reducing and even eliminating any and all cravings. You find that through this new form of deep, profound and powerfully effective relaxation, you are so very, very easily able to achieve your goal of becoming more effectively active, passionately driven and so easily able to take all of the necessary steps to lose weight, easily succeeding at your goal of losing (name pounds in numbers, avoiding 5's and zeros) 97, 98 or even 102 or 103 pounds, while being and becoming lighter, thinner, healthier and better.

You find that through this new form of deep, profound and powerfully effective relaxation, you are so very, very easily able to achieve your goal of becoming more effectively active, passionately driven and so easily able to take all of the necessary steps to lose weight for your wedding. You are bound and more unstoppably determined than ever before in your life to just get up and do it exercise-wise, effectively guided by the inspiration of every past victory, triumph, breakthrough and success. You have a powerful determination to get up and exercise, as a superior person just gets up and does it, so you do. You just have all the necessary and needed energy to get off the couch and exercise. You are in a new and brighter chapter of your life, moving beyond and forgiving the past. In your last chapter of your life, you might have been a yo-yo dieter or had once in the past long ago depended on diet pills; but now you are unstoppably beyond that, becoming lighter, thinner, better, and healthier, just getting up and doing it, now only eating in smaller proportions and filling up sooner, only the proper foods consumed in moderation and in smaller and healthier proportions, free of kiddy foods, proper for you, proper for an adult, extending your health and your life. You are just doing fine and now it's easy, for any and all blockages from your past are melting away and your powerful and determined mind is now forgiving and releasing any and all patterns, fears, anxieties, doubts, judgments and feelings that ever caused you to become or remain overweight. Your powerful mind is now working in your favor, to allow you to achieve all that you must and will achieve. You now have a taste for veggies and healthy foods; you are moving beyond old cravings like cravings for carbs and craving healthy foods, in moderation at mealtimes only, choosing to eat in designated eating areas only. You are so easily able to change the past and move into a brighter and better way of life and living. In this newer and better chapter of your life, you are now re-identified. Where you once might have been an out-of-control binge eater, you are now in control and taking better care of yourself, eating to live only, so easily able to take control of how you eat. And from all of this inspiration and unstoppable success, you are so easily able to finally achieve your real goal -- to finally be happy with yourself.

You are feeling fulfilled and full, after each and every regular and normally proportioned meal that you eat as a healthy adult. You begin to know, less is more; so you are willing to use smaller plates, put less on your plate, almost like your brain and stomach are communicating faster. You also realize that you can now stop whenever you want to and now as an adult, it's OKAY to leave some of each meal on the plate, as you develop a new and more healthier you.

You slow down when you eat, filling up sooner, knowing and acting upon when enough is enough. You are eating only at designated mealtimes and in designated eating areas only, at a table, free of watching TV, following your very best guidance, following the actions and advice you'd give your best friend to follow, even if that best friend is you.

You bring your exercise goals down to a level of ridiculous ease, exercising just 2 or 3 minutes each time, 2 or 3 times a week, easily and regularly exceeding those goals, finding within yourself, the superior person who just gets up and does it; so you do, enjoying your treadmill time, a time to unwind, relax and get thinner, lighter, better and healthier, and gradually increase your speed and duration. You find a new pace for yourself, finding a consistency in your eating time, pacing yourself, spreading out your smaller yet more fulfilling and healthier-for-an-adult, healthier-for-you meals, regardless of event or schedule. Even if it's fast food, which you will always leave some leftovers to throw out, you eat less and will order a healthier meal, like a scrumptious salad. You have a powerful determination and unstoppable motivation to get up and exercise. As a superior person just gets up and does it, so you do. You just have all the necessary and needed energy to get off the couch and exercise. You are easily able to see, to notice and to remember, that you have and continue to improve your life through a better diet, proper for an adult, healthy for an adult, better for yourself, easily able to bring walking as a form of exercise into your life, a few times each week, bringing the goal down to a level of ridiculous ease, just 2 or 3 minutes, 2 or 3 times a week, easily exceeding these goals, going beyond that 2 or 3 minutes, letting it become a half-hour or hour most often. Each and every time that you make and create time to exercise, you recognize that a superior person just gets up and does it, exercise-wise; so you do, you like it, you love it, it feels great, so very enjoyable, a special gift of longevity that you give yourself. You find yourself easily motivated to exercise, enjoying the relaxation, release, benefits, longevity and enjoyment that exercise can and will bring you. You are letting go of the past and all past blockages and blockage patterns; you know that a superior person, you, just gets up and does it, so you do. Instead, even better right now, you are feeling upbeat, motivated and energetic when it comes to exercise, most especially at the end of the day, DOING THE CARDIO EXERCISE THAT you not only NEED, but now look forward to and find new ways to look forward to and now and forever and ever, only getting easier and better, truly enjoying yourself as you do it so happily and enjoyably. You even find the time to Use Your STEP WHILE WATCHING TV, getting the most out of your life and your experiences, maximizing your time to succeed, even. You are supplementing Your CURRENT 1 MILE WALKS with Your DOG AND Your STANDARD WEIGHT MACHINE WORKOUT TO INCLUDE 2 OR MORE Miles, as you bring your goals down to a level of ridiculous ease and comfort, relaxing into this and cleverly thriving and succeeding. You are making and taking the time to WALK IN THE EVENINGS, maybe just going for a 2 or 3 minute walk, easily exceeding those goals by using more time while the pressure is now off and draining far, far away. And just to break things up, you find you are USING Your STRETCHING AND AB WORKOUT VIDEO about ONCE A WEEK. You are absolutely determined to be free of any and all excuses, taking better care of yourself than that, to better take care of yourself and to lovingly provide for yourself, you PREPARE BREAKFAST IN THE MORNINGS so you are un-HUNGRY, in fact, powerfully hunger-free and calm, balanced, filled up and fulfilled BY THE TIME you GET TO WORK, even stocking your home with fruit that you now make and take the time to eat in healthy ways. As you love your veggies, you now are making and taking the time to be comfortable, whole and EXCUSE-free, HASSLE-free, now Preparing VEGGIES, because you LOVE THEM AND moving beyond all former excuses, taking better care of yourself than that, to better take care of yourself and to lovingly provide for yourself, rather than Substituting A CARB, because it's easier and more pleasant to thrive and succeed. And as you have been getting better about it, you now continue and strengthen the trend you've been following of PREPARING MEALS AT HOME, calm, comfortable, relaxed, thriving and succeeding.

You are powerfully free of eating, or wanting to eat, or craving anything to eat, holding weight or gaining weight in any way, just because you are or might be stressed. Even if and most especially if the stress is, may be or might be coming from your parents. Even if and most especially if the stress is, may be or might be coming from your children, even if and most especially if the stress is, may be or might be coming from your husband. You are powerfully free of eating, or wanting to eat, or craving anything to eat, holding weight or gaining weight in any way, just because you are or might be bored or even if lonely. You find yourself taking comfort in a new and thriving love you are building for yourself, more comfortable; free of snacking, eating the wrong foods, or overeating, now and forever doing better for yourself, in the most clever, most effective and powerful of ways, in this new and improved better, brighter and more powerful chapter of your life. You feel like you are just flowing with life, moving on, and even better, more easily able to deal with aging and the change of life, all things now just taking a natural flow and rhythm for you. You are adaptive, now finding and utilizing the very best, most focused and highly effective ways of coping, managing, dealing with your mother's illness; in fact, truly, you are unstoppably succeeding at all that you have put your mind to and now effectively accomplish all that needs to be done.

You are powerfully hunger-free, calm, balanced and relaxed, finding newer and better ways to occupy your time, following your interests and living your dreams, whether you are excited or even if you are bored. You are powerfully free of eating or wanting to eat or craving anything to eat just because food is around, always remaining free of eating all day long, hunger-free, like someone from deep, deep inside of you has turned off a switch. Less is more, you enjoy eating less. You live better and feel lighter, better and more whole. You are powerfully moving beyond eating kiddy foods, now that you are an adult, doing better for yourself, giving yourself love in place of kiddy foods, feeling fulfilled. You are powerfully free and doing, better free of desert, than you ever did with dessert as a way of ending the day. You are doing better for yourself, your weight loss; you're feeling better and lighter; in fact, your success is its own reward.

You easily and correctly choose to relax, calm down and eat less; less is more, less is fine, less fills you up sooner, better and faster than ever before, at each and every mealtime. You stop, you slow down, you fill up sooner, you take your time and you know when to stop eating; so you easily do, whatever the food, wherever you are, eating slowly and filling up sooner; you win, easily satisfied, even small meals, each and every small meal, all smaller meals, always fill you up; you are powerfully stuffed sooner and powerfully satisfied. You find newer and better ways to relax, free of fattening foods and drinks, moving beyond anything and everything that can stand in the way of a newer, better and slimmer you. Anything that stands in your way, you are forever moving beyond, even if it's beer, because you are taking better care of yourself. If you must have a beer, it's one light beer, and you've had enough, and you've moved on feeling forever healthy and fine. You choose to do better and eat enough to sustain your life, and smaller portions are just right for you to accomplish all that you need to and feel fine. You are more determined than any other time in your life to be and forever remain lighter, thinner, healthier and better.

You are taking better care of yourself, at all times, each and every time, treating and living and reacting in ways that are most effective and respectful for yourself. You are and you remain free of snacking, because you are already full, already fulfilled and are most especially free of snacking at night, because in reality and in fact, you've moved on. You are and you remain powerfully free of eating or overeating even if you are bored or even if you are depressed in any way, finding newer and better ways of being excited and upbeat about living your life as the masterpiece it deserves to be; you are so determined to feel great! You are moving into a newer and better realm of your life, free of destructive behaviors, taking wonderful care of yourself, even in newer and better ways, most especially after drinking alcohol in moderation, having had enough of it, moving on. You are learning better ways to love and to truly take care of yourself and are unstoppably, cleverly and very effectively determined to feel better about yourself when you haven't overeaten, so you eat just enough, at designated eating places only, and only at mealtimes. You stop, you move on, you've had enough and you are fine and un-hungry, or just maybe hunger-free. You move beyond foods intended for children, most especially any carb cravings, moving beyond kiddy foods and any desires for them, most especially cereals, pretzels, breads, feeling fine as it's now easy for you to become and remain, lighter, thinner, healthier and better.

You are easily finding newer, more clever, easily and successfully activated and highly effective ways to be motivated to find, make and create all the time necessary to eat right, easily planning and developing strategies for any and all necessary planning, shopping, chopping, cutting, cooking, doing all that it honestly and effectively takes to take well deserved and better care of yourself. You are powerfully free of eating or wanting to eat or craving anything to eat just because it's sweet, especially just after a meal because you have moved unstoppably on and now as an adult, you are finding newer and better ways to love yourself, free of kiddy foods, foods you've grown up past and moved beyond now that you are an adult, treating yourself in a more loving and a better way. This even becomes easier as you easily and surprisingly and most effectively move beyond late night snacking, taking better care of yourself; less is more, you win and are victorious over past moments of blockage, for now you are insured success. You eat less, less is more and you easily and effectively leave some of each and every meal on the table, on the plate and in the larger plates, bowls and containers they were served in or stored in, finding a newer and better, happier and more carefree you emerging, even if you have to throw leftovers out, that's Okay, as a newer and more powerful, slimmer, trimmer and healthier you emerges, most especially your kids'. You enjoy drinking more water, giving your body what it needs to succeed here, taking better care of yourself, washing you clean inside and restoring abundant health from deep, deep within.

You are powerfully free of eating, or wanting to eat, or craving anything to eat, just because you are or might be trying to console yourself. You are powerfully free of eating, or wanting to eat, or craving anything to eat, just because you are or might be worrying, lack physical companionship or anything at all, because as you move into this new and ever improving chapter of your life, you are trusting in life more and more, providing only the very best for yourself; all alone time now time for you to love and take better care of yourself.

You will find newer, more clever and more adaptive ways for remaining now and forever free of gaining weight again, as you love and take care of yourself in the most profound and powerful of ways.

You are easily able and creatively ready to follow the Weight Watchers Program, relaxing into this and winning, just 3 meals a day, 3 snacks with portion control, so easily able to eat slower and drinking a sufficient amount of water. You are feeling fine, doing better, always doing what's right for yourself even if you have periods of anxiety, as you are learning newer and better ways of now and forever remaining free of ever turning to food for comfort; and it's easy, and your mind, emotions and body now are reconditioned in your favor. Your mind is upbeat, calm, powerful and strong, always working in your favor; less is more, you eat less and fill up sooner, sustaining yourself throughout the day.

Feeling upbeat, flowing ever onward, beyond periods during the day when you got tired, because you are now retuned and energetic, most especially between the hours of 3 and 6 PM. You are and you remain problem-free, stress-free, even struggle-free, most especially AFTER DINNER, because you've had enough, because you are feeling and truly are fulfilled. Right through until you RETIRE FOR THE NIGHT, AS LATE AS 1AM, you've conquered, squashed and forever vanquished BINGE TIME. You've grown up and into a newer and better chapter of your life, moving beyond kiddy foods, moving beyond carbs, cake, cookies, chips, pretzels and ice cream, flowing forever onward beyond any and all needs for comfort food. You are comforted; you are enough; you forgive any and all past issues; you are moving on, truly living your dream of forever and ever losing weight, feeling better and achieving the very most out of life.

Weight and Exercise – (*Extras*) - You've lost X lbs. this past year. That's great, now you owe it to yourself to keep up the good work. So as you relax into this newer and better way of being and into a brand new chapter of your life, you find that you can easily succeed at this. You are easily able to see, to notice and to remember, that you have and continue to improve your life, through, a better diet, proper for an adult, healthy for an adult, better for yourself, easily able to bring walking as a form of exercise into your life, a few times each week, bringing your goal down to a level of ridiculous ease. Each and every time that it's time to exercise, you recognize that a superior person, you just gets up and does it, exercise wise, so you do, you like it, you love it, it feels great, so very enjoyable, a special gift of longevity that you give yourself. You now think of and see snack foods as kiddy foods, such as candy, ice cream, cake, as foods for children, far healthier foods for adults sustaining adult health are better for you. Adult foods, so right for you and better tasting, are all a part of the newer and improved things you doing for yourself. As an adult, you are easily able to do better for yourself than you did in the previous chapter of your life. You are more and more motivated to succeed at this, in fact and in reality, you feel and truly are super motivated, to do what you know works, to keep the weight down, keep the weight off, to keep on exercising, creating the healthy, strong, vigorous body and vibrant health you deserve to have to create the kind of a healthy, happy, balanced and harmonious future you deserve to be true to yourself.

Weight and Emotions –(**Extras)** - Each and every day and night you are finding new and better, easier and more effective ways of becoming and remaining free of carbohydrate cravings. In fact, you are so much more free of carbohydrate cravings as your newer and more proper diet is balancing ways of your eating, that you are finding it easy to remain aligned with a balanced diet, feeling fine. **You find comfort in your life, moving a little bit each and every day to a powerful new place of better, more effective and successful internal communication and self-support, each and every day finding newer and better ways of re-identifying yourself in a self-supportive way and actually acting on those newer and more inspired feelings of self-support, in the truest and most amazing of ways, feeling greatly satisfied in amazing newer and better ways. And even after just a few short and deep breaths, you find yourself realigned, proud to be alive and happy and content, moving past any and all blockages, releasing any and all blockages, both known from your past or even yet unknown to you. And you are more willing to feel great in amazing and wonderful ways, or just pleasantly numb from any and all old pain, really trouble free, moving on, living and enjoying your life, taking better care of yourself, making and taking the time for yourself, time you need and you deserve, taking care of yourself in endless supply and finding newer and more efficient ways of achieving this. You are forever becoming an endless reservoir of self-support creating the kind of support and feelings of self-love, as a way of loving yourself better. Just being there in better ways for the people you love, including yourself but most especially for others as you are there now for yourself. You give yourself the support and attention you deserve and as you do, you find more and more each and every day and night, you are relaxing into a newer and more improved, better relationship with yourself, with your world and with the people you attract into your world. You've now realized in your past, from within your vulnerability comes your greatest strengths. But even better now, you are feeling so on top of the world and full of life, you are now feeling so supported and taken care of, so very and definitely upbeat, so willing and completely able to re-identify and un-limit yourself, that you are unstoppably moving into a brand new chapter of your life. A place where you succeed, a place where you forever are whole and healed, a place of more and more love and support, more and more success and inspiration. A place where you allow yourself, self-support and attention, where you allow yourself to be thinner, happier, brighter and better, in the most profound of ways, relaxing into this, you deserve this and you win.**

**Even More Weight** – (***Extras*** ) - You find the time to take better and better care of yourself, providing the time to eat slowly, properly, in the healthiest ways, regardless of event of circumstance, including times while you may be stressed. You remain hunger free and craving free, even free of binging or overeating most especially free of being sick. You are allowing yourself to remain healthy, calm, peaceful and relaxed. You are calm comfortable and relaxed, feeling a new zest for life, remaining free of overeating or snacking, most especially when you are tired, especially after school (3:00-6:00). You've grown up now, you've accepted that, with a practical child like innocence and clarity. And your adult tastes, have forever improved in your favor, as you become and forever remain lighter, better, healthier and thinner with a higher metabolism. You have improved in the most healthy and proper ways for yourself. You remain free of eating foods and snacks intended for children, kiddy foods, like doughnuts and cakes. You are excessively hunger and craving free, maintaining health, balance and well being, to sustaining yourself properly as an adult, even free of carbohydrate cravings, drinking water in their place, which powerfully fills you up. You feel contented, your correct response now as an adult. You choose to eat dinner earlier, better and a lighter dinner, choosing to eat a larger breakfast and or lunch in place of a former and now released unhealthy habit. You even find you burn food, fat, weight and calories while resting or even while sleeping, remaining hunger free as your new metabolism is activated, it's just going up and up and up. You are feeling so upbeat, so positive, cheerful and optimistic, so unshakable and unstoppable in all of this, finding better times, cycles, rhythms for yourself, just getting up and going, so re-excited about your new outlook on your life, practically re-invented, bringing your exercise goals down to a level of ridiculous ease, just getting up and doing it, just for 2 or 3 minutes, 2 or 3 times each week, quite often exceeding this because you feel so good, so motivated, so ready, so willing, so able to improve your body, emotions, mind and life, so you do, and it feels great. * You are and you both now and forever remain **succeeding, as you win, lighter, thinner, healthier and better, most especially remaining free of** excessive carbohydrate eating You find moderation, inner peace, calmness and truly you are and you remain hunger free, peaceful and content, correctly choosing to **eat less and less carbohydrates and sweets, free eating of kiddy foods, foods you've grown up past and moved beyond now that you are an adult. You are treating yourself in a more loving and better ways. A personal sense of victory and inner pride allows you to go beyond your past desert urges, doing better for yourself. Less is more, you** have improved in the most healthy and proper ways for yourself. You remain free of eating foods and snacks intended for children, kiddy foods, like doughnuts and cakes, you are excessively hunger and craving free, maintaining health, balance and well being, sustaining yourself properly as an adult, even free of carbohydrate cravings, drinking water in their place, which powerfully fills you up, feeling contented, the correct response for you now as an adult, always and forever. You choose to eat smaller portions, because you are actually feeling fine, truly, very powerfully and in fact, filling up sooner, choosing health over unhealthy over eating, sustaining your health and body for well deserved longevity, taking better care of yourself. Just as you would advise a good friend, you eat proper, healthy, balanced meals, so right for you. You are committed and determined to maintain health, relaxing into all of this so you win. You are feeling so upbeat, so positive, cheerful and optimistic, so unshakable and unstoppable in all of this, finding better times, cycles, rhythms for yourself, just getting up and going forward. You are so re-excited about your new outlook on your life, you feel practically re-invented, giving this gift to yourself, something you deserve to have, something you give to yourself, using the buddy system with your spouse, quite often exceeding expectations, because you feel so good, so motivated, so ready, so willing so able to improve your body, emotions, mind and life, so you do, and this feels great. * **You have limitless will power and determination. Your will power and determination are building, building, building, day by day, night by night. You are easily able to stick with a diet and stay away from foods when you are not hungry. You are absolutely free of eating out of boredom, you've easily moved beyond being habitual, all emotions work in your favor now and forever with you easily and effectively allowing you to thrive and succeed. You have moved into a better place in your life, you take better care of yourself, your tastes have changed and improved, having moved beyond any and all old useless tasteless needs and urges, eating less and less carbohydrates and sweets, treating yourself in a more loving and a better way. You now move into an area of your life where you are slowly adjusting your natural diet, where you fill up sooner, eat less and feel great. And it's so easy to do, you succeed, you win, lighter, thinner healthier and better.**

The powerful part of your subconscious mind that once stood in your way, now and forever works with you to attain a lighter healthier better you. And you are easily able to become X lbs., in amazingly wonderful ways. You are lighter as you relax into this and succeed, doing just fine. You are now doing the opposite of your past, relaxing into this and succeeding. You eat only when you are hungry and it feels great to be alive, healthier, lighter, thinner, better, feeling great in every way, you easily succeed.

You find yourself easily able to lose 61, or 62 pounds, becoming lighter, thinner, healthier and better. You are full in the evening, hunger free, calm, balanced, relaxed, completely at ease, comfortable and fulfilled, completely satisfied from all you've eaten earlier in the day, fulfilled, enough is enough.

You easily move on and away from junk food. You now see what is called junk food as just that, junk, something to be thrown out and moved away from in your life. You only put healthy things into your body, to sustain your health and to beneficially extend your longevity. You are forever free of eating, wanting, even thinking about wanting or having kiddy foods like cake, candy and ice cream. Now as an adult, doing better and better, you've moved on, only eating what is necessary to sustain and maintain your health and your life. You know you need to eat healthier foods, so you do, all things in moderation. You take the time you need to exercise a minimum of 30 minutes a day, by bringing your goals down to a level of ridiculous ease, just 2 or 3 minutes a day, two or 3 times a week, easily exceeding those limits. Less is more, you fill up sooner, and you move on into your life, always eating smaller portions at each and every meal.

**Weight - Mental and Emotional** (Extras 2004)- You are finding newer and better ways to trust in your life, remembering times of feeling upbeat and re-excited about life and living, more active, more vital, activating times of action and activity, becoming and remaining upbeat, mentally, emotionally, and in very powerful and positive ways, truly feeling like the world is yours; you are living each moment on top of the world, unstoppably becoming lighter, thinner, healthier and better. You are powerfully learning to forgive yourself, releasing old and harmful past judgments you had once accepted from others or placed upon yourself, embracing life and living, finding newer, more fluid and more adaptive ways of releasing any and all old useless patterns, that once ever stood in your way, loving yourself in place of old ideas and punishment patterns, becoming delighted about yourself and your life, in each and every moment, guilt-free, punishment-free, learning newer and better ways to love yourself more and more, powerfully free of overeating, taking only the very best care of yourself, free of any and all old repetitive behavior patterns that in the past you had once used or thought of using to hurt yourself or stand in your way. You are free, liberated, cleansed and feeling better, doing better, doing all that it takes to do better, taking better care of yourself. Your ever growing self-love and self-respect, now allows you to forever become and forever remain, lighter, thinner, healthier and better, more active and more vitally alive, trusting in yourself and in your life, in your world, only taking the very best care of yourself, in even surprising and more powerful ways. Your newer and ever growing sense of self-love, tuned up, turned up, is now allowing you to move beyond the past and to flourish anew, re-identified as becoming and easily remaining lighter, thinner, healthier and better, easily avoiding the hurtful pitfalls and patterns of the past, easily, skillfully and dynamically. You truly are embracing the newer, lighter, thinner, more loved and self-appreciated you, unstoppably and in clear and clever, powerfully successful ways, newer and better ways in each and every moment. You are finding newer and more productive ways of taking the very best care of yourself, finding better things to do than old patterns that once caused you to overeat, entertained by life and living, taking a greater interest in your life, in your world and in things you find fascinating. You already are sincerely finding comfort in your life, in your world, in yourself, free forever, free at last. Free of ever taking comfort in foods of any kind, you take comfort in loving yourself and appreciating yourself better and better; you love yourself way too much to backslide, so you are and you remain flowing ever forward, in endless supply, embraced by every past victory, triumph and breakthrough you've ever had in your life; all of the beneficial energy urging you on successfully, into a newer, better, brighter, more elegant, self-loving, self-supporting moment, a better taken-care-of you is now emerging at all times, each and every time, most especially you are easily free forever of any out-of-control eating, most especially during the day or at night, playing your tape, calming down, reducing stress, sleeping right throughout the night, un-hungry, filled up and fulfilled, having had enough, resting better, living better, loving yourself better, as you are, becoming and are easily, successfully and skillfully remaining, lighter, thinner, healthier and better, fulfilled, filled up and doing all that honestly needs doing to make this work for you in the truly most potent, profound, and powerful of ways, skillfully and truly succeeding, giving yourself a break and thriving, easily and powerfully amazing yourself with powerful and fantastic results, truly and fantastically lighter, thinner, healthier and better, doing all that it takes in healthy and proper ways to get this done, in healthy and most powerfully proper ways, you are thriving and succeeding, feeling fantastic, you are fantastic.

**Weight Extras 2007:** You are and you remain safe, comfortable, centered, hunger-free, so in your success-zone of empowerment, while becoming and while easily remaining lighter, thinner, healthier, and better, mostly especially whenever challenged in any way, even if challenged mentally or emotionally by life situations, even more so, while easily and cleverly achieving any and all of your goals. In fact, you are delighted are feeling healthier and better, rising up to be in fact your very best, easily rising to the very top, most especially while you are or might be challenged by any stress.

You profoundly think to yourself and know: less is more, I fill-up sooner, I know when to stop, easily relaxing beyond any and all old areas of challenge from previous chapters of your life. You are easily, cleverly, and dynamically, succeeding, as the lighter, thinner, healthier, more energetic, more dynamic, more unstoppably empowered you, forever rises up dynamically, to achieve all that you've put your mind to here, amazingly and adaptively breaking through here, while relaxing beyond any and all old barriers, simply thriving, having grown up just a little, into the next chapter of your life, free and better, healthier and whole. Your new philosophy cleverly becomes and remains, less is more, I fill up sooner, just a small taste quenches any and all hunger, I know when to quit, I know when to stop. I win! Even just a small taste of carbs or cake, is enough for me, my former biggest weaknesses, now my greatest moments to shine; now my greatest strengths.

You remain calm, comfortable, happy, peaceful, centered, serene, un-hungry, satiated, while drinking plenty of like the water washing you clean inside, all times, and every time, most especially you know you are unstoppably succeeding in breaking through here easily, without over-thinking, most especially in between 9:30-

10PM, hardly ever thinking about that time, barrier free all evening, if you do think about the times you once felt challenged, you are unbeatably recognizing how truly easy this is for you.

You know it's truly amazing, I wonder if you even you realize how truly easy this is becoming as you simply just seem to be melting excess away, carefree and with very little effort, 49, 51 or even 59 lbs. Surely you're begun a brand new chapter of your life, and all things are getting better and better, I wonder if you yet realize how truly easy this is going to be for you unstoppably achieve any and all goals, that winningly break you through, while losing, 39, 40 or maybe even 58 lbs, relaxing beyond all barriers and challenges from the past. You now unstoppably flow into the best things in your life, steadily and unstoppably moving ahead, doing even better from all you've gone through, and you now, the mighty one.

You find yourself easily able, recalling, remembering, and performing, all that it takes not only to learn but to carefully and thoughtfully find the time to remember, and to correctly take the very best care of yourself, while eating healthier and taking better care of yourself as you know you should and now are. All of you is now taking power, inspired, effective and empowered. You are and you remain, focused on unstoppably improving your life, and most especially your body, thoughts, habits, and feelings, all things now are cleverly working in your favor as you break through here.

In this brand new and better chapter of your life, you have and are, foundationally reinterpreting, effectively in your favor, each and every thought, each and every feeling, each and every habit, each and every action, every reaction, in order to improve your life while easily, skillfully, and even surprisingly, you are substantially correcting what was or might have been bad snacking habits, truly taking better care of yourself, as all things just seem to be falling into place, most especially, after dinner and even more so during any and all T.V. watching.

Feeling rejuvenated and foundationally reinvented, it takes little to no effort on your part for you to effectively concentrate on eating healthier at work, And so it is, and so you do, so effectively and easily.

It has been said that little steps mean a lot. Each step effectively leading to the next. So easily you are starting and sticking with an exercise program, perhaps just two to three minutes a day, two or three days a week, during downtime, perhaps even before bed, afterwards easily able to sleep and rest peacefully through the night.

Your mind, now fine tuned, reset, recalibrated, your concentration now so very clear, so very sharp, so laser-beam-like precise You are now interested in your life, in newer, improved and more amazing ways, confident you are and you remain cleverly effective and knowing that your concentration has truly improved and is only getting better and better.

You find it not only possible, but truly easy to lose 41-44, 46, lbs. as you relax into this, succeed and win, lighter, thinner, healthier and better, as the weight just seems to be melting off, shedding pounds, fat, and calories, so easily raising your metabolism, almost as if someone from deep, deep inside of you, has reset a switch, a thermostat, a dial, a computer of some kind, easily, effectively and comfortably raising your metabolism, as the weight just seems to be going away on its own. You more active, and in the very healthiest and best ways possible, you breaking through here, as all can see, a lighter, thinner, healthier you now unstoppably emerging.

You are finding yourself filling up sooner and easily stopping when you are done. You've moved into a new chapter of your life and have moved into a brighter, better, more comfortable place, easily succeeding at all of this. Your powerfully effective mind is more relaxed, yet effectively working on all of this to absolutely and unconditionally ensure your ultimate success at this in easily yet surprisingly effective ways. You are powerfully determined to just know when to stop eating. You are forever free of overeating, most especially stress eating. You now know when to stop, when to relax and when to move away from your plate and food, and so you do. Only right, healthier and better foods, that serve you best, foods in smaller amounts, properly shooed and slowly consumed while in moderation, fill you up sooner and relax you, making you feel fine. You know when to stop and so you do, feeling relaxed, stress-free and happy. You are mightier than any stress you might encounter; your correct and absolute response is to relax your way thorough stress, trust in life and rise above any and all challenges. Stress just seems to melt off on each and every deep and slow, steady breath that you take, dynamically reconditioning you into a better chapter of your life. You almost feel like you have a new lease on life, resting peacefully throughout the night, resting deeply and comfortably yet easily able to start the day as scheduled as your body clock now begins to work in your favor to get you up on time and to tune into your morning wakeup time and enjoyably start the day, when one alarm clock rings after the first three rings like any other person. You have made up your unstoppable mind to forever remain free of ever again eating until you feel like you might explode; you are doing better and taking better care of yourself, relaxing through any and all things that once ever stood in your way. You find newer and more effective ways of explaining and teaching those around you how to get their jobs done on time, even when under pressure, like an ideal teacher or parent. You complete all tasks quickly as all unnecessary weight melts off easily and quickly. You are easily finding newer and better ways to melt off all weight.

You are enough, you have enough, and just as you always have done, you are doing just fine, except now, you are doing even better; trusting in the support life gives you. Your new and correct response to any and all stress is to relax your way through it via deep breathing while instead, thriving, rising above any and all challenges and feeling wonderful and peaceful, stress-free, balanced, relaxed in body, emotions, mind, and even spirit.

From the top of your head, to the tips of your fingers, even to the soles of your feet and tips of your toes, with each and every slow and steady and centering breath and with each and every heartbeat, you're allowing all thoughts, feelings, experiences from the past, actions, reactions, to anything that has ever, does ever or will ever, create an experience of anxiety or stress, to just melt away from you, like some sort of sticky steam moving up and out or just like light, fluffy clouds just vaporously drifting away.

Like a mighty river flowing down the side of the mountain in the spring, you flow over around any and all old barriers from past chapters of your life, flowing through, over, around and beyond any and all things that ever once, in the past chapter of your life, stood in your way. Free you are now of any and all old barriers, as you are just simply moving on and into the very best days of your life, rising to the top, living your life, deep breathing your way into a more serene, more empowered, wholly inspired, mightier, better you. And like a boulder in the center of that fast running stream of water rushing down the side of a mountain in the spring, all old, unneeded, unwanted and now forever vanquished patterns of anxiety and all stress all just seem to be and truly are in fact, just simply flowing around you and beyond you, polishing you up and driving you ever forward, into the shiniest, brightest, best, existence, the masterpiece of a better brighter and lighter life, as a lighter, thinner, healthier, better you, that you deserve and now unstoppably create forever emerges. You are making all of this your very own, as your mighty inner hero is now activated; the part of you that is doubtless and dynamic, capable of saving children from great danger, is both now and forever liberated -- dynamically, actively and precisely, working only in your favor, to allow you to unstoppably create, while succeeding each evening, afternoon and morning, in even surprisingly wonderful and dynamically precise ways, effective methods and strategies to achieve any and all goals you set your mind to, as you're in a brand new chapter of your life, lighter, thinner, healthier, better. Less is more, you fill up sooner, your metabolism going up and up, in just the very best ways, so right for you, almost as if someone, from deep, deep inside of you, has reset a switch, a dial, a computer or thermostat of some kind, allowing your metabolism to go up and up, easily allowing you to effortlessly burn food, fat, weight and calories, just melting all of that off easily, both achievably and in dynamically powerful effective ways, which will last the rest of your lifetime, as you have unstoppably and unbeatably begun a brand new chapter of your life, lighter, thinner, healthier, better, with a higher metabolism, a less-is-more mentality in terms of how you eat, choosing to eat in designated eating areas only, far from distractions of the media, like television, while maintaining healthy body awareness, eating from smaller plates.

Less is more, you feel fine and wonderful, all of this just getting easier and better every day, every night, on every breath, and on every heartbeat, sure of yourself, both now and forever, that you are just breaking through here, you win, undefeatable and unbeatable, doing just fine. Free from eating ever again without thinking, you now are and you now remain. You're now creating clever strategies with thoughts, feelings, and ideas, whether you realize what they are or not, to melt away stress and anxiety, all body fat just healed, released, forgiven and healing, as your body is feeling wonderful and free, lighter, thinner, healthier and better, all of this just getting easier and better each and every day and night, all things working to improve your life with deeper, higher impact and greater results. Free of kiddy foods, you are and you both now and forever remain. Just a small taste is enough for you, of the things you love, like pasta or bread, chocolate or soda, even hot dogs or pizza, as you are more easily able to leave some of each and every meal on the plate, at the table which is just fine with you. Now that you are an adult, you are and you remain with the active ability to take the very best care of yourself. This time truly it seems like everything is just working in your favor, as your weight comes down and your blood pressure drops to a healthier place, as your knees begin to knit together and feel better.

When it's bedtime, you put the day upon a shelf, for yesterday has taken care of you, today has taken care of you, tomorrow will be just the same, trusting powerfully in your life you are and you remain powerfully able to trust in the world around you, just as life has always done. You are and you remain certain of yourself and your life, your empowerment and your new unlimited potentials. Your life, your creation, shall do just the same, taking the very best care of you. Your mind is now powerfully made up to sleep right through the night or to fall back to sleep, whenever you need to; even if hungry in the middle of the night, your first choice is a glass of water which sweeps away completely, all feelings of hunger, and allowing you to feel drowsy to fall back to sleep right away.

You are unstoppably entering a brand new chapter of your life, lighter, thinner, healthier, better, as the unneeded and now released weight seems to be melting off, as your metabolism is comfortably and safely going up, and up, almost as if someone from deep, deep, inside of you, has reset a switch or a dial, thermostat or computer of some kind, as you are easily and dynamically able to manifest, and even create, new habits of insured longevity, and better health. Less is more; you are filling up sooner; you are unstoppably becoming, lighter and, thinner, adopting and adapting yourself powerfully, skillfully, and dynamically, to better thoughts, and experiences, habits, and desires, even if you don't realize that as yet, you trust in this very important fact for it is all happening around you.

Less is more; a small taste is enough for you; perhaps one forkful, or one spoonful, is just enough to satisfy you and you find yourself drinking more and more water, and other liquids, which also seem to be satisfying and satiating your hunger, in unbelievably effective ways, keeping you lighter and thinner, and hunger-free, most especially before, and during, and after, 10:00 PM.

You are now reinvented, so hunger-free most especially at night, for regular moderate meals during the day, which you choose to enjoy only in proper designated eating areas, far from media distractions like television, from smaller plates which you find more appealing and proper. Even just a small taste of chocolate is enough for you; you let it linger in your mouth; you savor the flavor and taste, enjoyably letting it linger there, rather than chewing it, as it melts in your mouth, satisfying you with one mouth-full, maybe just two, completely.

You are, in fact, learning to process your emotions better in ways that are more life-supporting to you, most especially you are free of overeating, even if you are or might be upset in any way, willing to deep breathe, and to drink a glass of water, rather than to stop yourself as it was in previous chapters, of your life, which are now over, as you are now unstoppably and forever, in a brand-new and better chapter of your life, lighter, thinner, healthier and better. You find yourself resting better at night, trusting in your life, and realizing the important fact that each and every day of your life is taking care of you, tomorrow will be just the same, as in this new chapter of your life all things seem to be working out in your favor, for you allow yourself to put the day on a shelf; today is done, it's nighttime, and you are supporting your head on the pillow, closing your eyes, and simply drifting off to sleep, as you have done so many times in your life; in fact sleeping comfortably right through the night like a small child, a baby resting wonderfully, feeling rejuvenated in the morning and optimistically ready to take on a new day in a more supportive way for yourself, as you are so easily able to rise to the top and become more unbeatable in your life than ever before.

You find yourself motivated and just a bit more energized, perhaps finding a new joy in body movement, able to get up and move around, truly starting to tune into and enjoy the way your body moves and reacts, just a few more minutes of exercise today, ever increasing, more movement, and walking, feeling like it's just the right thing to do. As a newer and lighter, more energetic you emerges and the weight just seems to be melting off on its own, you find your body is healing, and re-balancing itself, almost too as if that part of your mind is now healing your body. Your adaptive and always-working- in-your-favor, dynamic subconscious mind, is now inventing better ways to achieve all of this while promoting a more healthy, youthful, lighter, and thinner, healthier and better, clearer you, as you know unstoppably thrive within in new and budding, building sense of abundant health is now becoming your very own, and you're excited about it, almost as if you've received or have given to yourself actually, a special gift of a brand-new, empowered and inspired chapter of your life. The greater the challenge, the more easily able you are to rise up to meet any and all challenges as you are and you remain dynamically a master of your life and truly knowing this to be the truth from deep, deep inside of you, as your wonderful mind is now and forever making more of this so, day by day, and night by night. Of course you succeed and thrive, for that is your only option and truthfully you know it's true and within your grasp on each and every breath and heartbeat.

**Overcoming Night Eating and Getting Some Exercise** (Extras 2004) - You are filled and fulfilled, feeling full at night, you've eaten enough at dinner and have had enough to eat, feeling un-hungry, almost stuffed, feeling comfortable and happy all throughout the night, right into the next morning. Less is more, you fill up sooner, and even the sights and smells of the food fill you up, long before your first bite. Each and every dinnertime, you've had enough and almost feel a bit uncomfortable as you've had enough for the rest of the night right into the morning. Feeling motivated, you enjoy moving around; as a treat to yourself, you just get up and move around, just getting up and doing it, feels good, and makes you glad to be alive, happy to move and exercise, all of this becomes ridiculously easy for you in even surprising ways. You are learning with each and every breath and each and every heartbeat, you begin and remain taking better care of yourself, you enjoy moving and learn to enjoy just getting up to do it exercise-wise, to extend your health and long life, just getting up and doing, being happy and loving yourself and moving around, taking care of yourself now and conditioning yourself for your later years. You choose to eat healthy foods as part of taking care of yourself and loving yourself better. Your tastes are changing and improving in your favor; it just might be that you are losing your taste for fast foods and moving on, learning to enjoy smaller portions and filling up sooner on foods that are good for you, including fruits and vegetables, salads and learning to love it all as you take better care of yourself. You are just changing, growing up and improving, eating less fast food and eating healthy foods, making the best of all possible choices. You just find yourself choosing and drinking more water, as your tastes are now improving in your favor. Most especially, you are moving on in your life to a place where late night eating is just a thing of the past, fulfilled, filled up, having had enough, finding newer and better ways of becoming and remaining, lighter, thinner, healthier and better, just right through the night, moving on, free, fulfilled and un-hungry, having had enough.

# OPTIMIZING STATEMENTS

# Session Optimizing Suggestions

Add these to practically any standard session to increase your session's effectiveness,
generating greater impact and greater potential for improvement.

**Session Optimizing Suggestion 1:** You will only receive powerful and precise, highly effective and beneficial improvement in the most correct, potent, extremely effective, powerfully correct and fluidly adaptive ways from this. You are easily going into this wonderful relaxation state faster, deeper, stronger and better, with more limitless results in more unlimited dynamic ways every time you repeat this extremely enjoyable, wonderful, dynamic, highly effective and precise exercise.

**Session Optimizing Suggestion 2:** * The whole world works to support you in all of this, every sound, every noise that you hear from outside, including sirens, car horns and car alarms, (even barking dogs, etc.) each and every time you hear them instantly reinforce all of this. Even ringing telephones of any kind, every time you hear them are instantly reinforcing all of this, most especially your freedom and liberation from . . . (e.g. smoking, overeating, holding weight - gaining weight, your old habit, your fear, your phobia, etc.)

**Session Optimizing Suggestion 3:** In fact you feel like you've got the whole world in the palm of your hand. You are a winner. An unstoppable force of life improvement from deep within you has been forever activated. Your awareness grows, your life expands, you are both now and forever free and you truly know it.

**Session Optimizing Suggestion 4:** And your self-confidence, self-esteem and inner strength will immediately increase. You will detach completely from all conflicts, frictions and disharmonies, feeling forever free. You are empowered, successful and liberated. With every breath that you take, with each and every beat of your heart, your strength and dynamic empowerment increases, every suggestion and every beneficial solution and strategy instantly activates, amazing and impressing everyone, especially even you!

**Session Optimizing Suggestion 5:** You begin to take even better care of yourself, re-identifying and re-defining yourself as a new happier, energetic and lighter hearted person, by allowing newer and more empowered thoughts and inspired feelings of success, healing, wellness and health, each and every day to profoundly build within you like a giant reservoir of limitless energy and you allow yourself to bring forth the true reality, that you are whole, calm, comfortable, successful, lighter, better and complete.

**Session Optimizing Suggestion 6:** Your desire to succeed becomes a passion, your passionate desire becomes a truly committed unstoppable force, each and every day and night, you overwhelmingly succeed in truly inspired, effective, creative, amazing and successful ways, relaxing into a brand new better chapter of your life, winning in the most profound ways! You have no idea how easy this is going to be for you.

**Session Optimizing Suggestion 7:** With each and every breath you take, you are powerfully liberating the feelings, energy and sensations associated with these following thoughts, ideas and concepts into a vital and profoundly true reconditioning and redefinition of who you are, where you live from, how you respond and whom you grow forever to be into your life: you are feeling wonderful and forever improving by becoming (name the feelings, actions and reactions you wish to instill).

**Session Optimizing Suggestion 8:** (While they are deeply hypnotized) Nod your head for me because you now and forever truly know, that you've forever relaxed your way into a brand new and better chapter of your life and really know that all of this is true. (wait for their nod and continue).

**Session Optimizing Suggestion 8A:** (While they are deeply hypnotized) Nod your head for me because you know that this is true. (wait for their nod and continue).

**Session Optimizing Suggestion 9:** You trust in and truly know this fact: each and every moment of your life is improving and that things get better and more surprisingly and astoundingly wonderful for you in each and everyway.

**Session Optimizing Suggestion 10:** You are feeling a new, correct, true and profound sense of support from your life urging you ever onward into a lifetime of clever success.

**Session Optimizing Suggestion 11:** It might really even seem like it's been at least 12 or 16 years since you last (smoked a cigarette, overate, felt stressed, etc.), it's just so long ago, so forever ago, so far away from you, so far away your mind, your emotions, your habits and your life right now. In amazingly powerful, highly effective and important ways, you are truly liberated, cleansed, safe and forever free.

**Session Optimizing Suggestion 12:** Just as you've always done, you are doing everything you've unstoppably put your mind to, to get the job done, the most efficient of ways, most especially. . .(quitting smoking forever, losing weight, reducing stress, etc.).

**Session Optimizing Suggestion 13:** By becoming ever increasingly determined to feel good, you are surely feeling fine, wonderful and fantastic. So with each and every beat of your heart and with each and every breath that you take, you are relaxing deeper and further and your whole life unstoppably and forever improves.

**Session Optimizing Suggestion 14:** It's almost like you are jumping over the years back to a time when you were X (12) years old, and only this time, you are making powerful and forever commitment to yourself, so that even when you were X (13) , you were, remained and forever where, (smoke free, cigarette free, . . . or . . . lighter, thinner, healthier, better, more active . . . or calm, balanced, rising above and beyond any and all stress, etc.), for then, for now, forever and for always, living better, happier and more successfully in the very best and well deserved of ways.

**Session Optimizing Suggestion 15:** You will always remember to breathe deep and steady powerful soothing, breath; a calming, centering, stilling, harmonizing and balancing breath, and by doing so, you are easily overcoming any and all fear, doubt, worry and panic. That which once overwhelmed you, is now both easily and forever powerfully overwhelmed by you and the power of your breath, as you leave all fear, panic, and discomfort, far, far behind you forever. All fear, doubt and panic are now and forever forgiven, released, healed and vanquished.

**Session Optimizing Suggestion 16:** Now that you are proud of yourself and sure of yourself, you are amazingly unstoppable at all of this, feeling forever proud of yourself and permanently improved, taking your life back, truly getting amazingly successful, fluidly adaptive and precisely effective results from this highly proficient and enjoyable experience, going into this deeper, faster and even better results, every time you repeat this exercise.

**Session Optimizing Suggestion 17**: You are easily free of anyone throwing you off track by saying any words or even expressing any feelings, thoughts or actions that might stand in your way here. You are in fact feeling mighty and you are easily rising above and masterfully transcending any and all old limits, now in this brand new chapter of your life.

**Session Optimizing Suggestion 18:** The truest and most real point of view that matters to you is your own. In the long run, the opinions of others are just that, just points of view, to be learned from, embraced or even to be just put aside. You put aside everything and anything that interferes with your ever-growing success, whether it's opinions of others, stress, emotional feelings, mental patterns or even old blockages most especially any and all of the things that once caused you discomfort or distress. You are unstoppably becoming clearer, sharper, better, more fluid and adaptive, more flexible and unstoppably successful.

**Session Optimizing Suggestion 19:** Now that you are learning to truly appreciate yourself, you can do anything you've now and forever, set your unstoppable and effectively adaptive mind toward. Each and every thing you do and on each and every breath and on each and every heartbeat, you are cleverly adapting and succeeding at this as never before!

**Session Optimizing Suggestion 20:** You have now made up your powerful, adaptive, highly effective mind, which is only now working in your favor, getting stronger, better and more effective at reducing and eliminating any and all disruptive thoughts, feelings, actions and reactions, that once caused you to (name behavior), choosing now instead to deep breathe, to calm down and to thrive and succeed in their place. You are finding newer and better, more completely adaptive, fluid, skillful and eminently successful ways of reducing and even eliminating any and all old behaviors that once blocked you or stood in the way of your success now in favor of a newer and better well deserved life you now powerfully, effectively and adaptively create.

**Session Optimizing Suggestion 21:** Each and every beat of your heart and each and every breath that you take, is easily reinforcing all of this in the most powerful and potently adaptive effective ways. You are glowing on the inside with confidence for all of this limitless energy of inspired success.

**Session Optimizing Suggestion 22**: It's time to clean up your life, so you are and you are succeeding powerfully, adaptively, surely and with ever growing, more determined, creatively inspired, limitless success.

**Session Optimizing Suggestion 23:** In your past, one of your urges may have been to (name behavior: smoke, overeat, etc.). However now and forever, your greatest urge, an unstoppable urge that's building up to being at least 178 times greater, growing ever stronger is to remain healthy safe and free (name desired result: smoke free, cigarette free, etc.).

**Session Optimizing Suggestion 24:** Your greatest and most overwhelming craving is to become and forever remain healthy, happy free and safe, extending your life in ways that work for you best.

**Session Optimizing Suggestion 25:** Regardless of any and all past challenges, you truly and foundationally know right now, in the long run, a better day will surely dawn. That dawn begins right now, illuminating your life, going on forever, freeing you and healing you, making your life the very best it can be, as you feel content and smile happily from, deep, deep inside.

**Session Optimizing Suggestion 26:** It has been said, the one thing we never get back in life it time, every moment wasted on trivia, disharmony, imbalance and minutia, is a wasted moment of our most valuable asset, ourselves, our life, and our life-force. You are easily enjoying and employing all of your very best energies, to make the most of every well deserved and well feeling moment, thriving and doing your very best to seize the moment and truly life, and enjoy the very best of yourself and your life.

**Session Optimizing Suggestion 27:** The feel of a cigarette in your hand or mouth just feels so very uncomfortable and now for you, it's just plain wrong! You've moved on and are now and forever free and happy, moving forward in your life.

**Session Optimizing Suggestion 28:** Completely relaxing into this and past and beyond any and all former barriers, you now and forever unstoppably succeed and flow ever onward into a brighter and better life.

**Session Optimizing Suggestion 29:** * Each and every time you shake your head no, you are saying no to your past and moving into a better day. Each and every time you nod your head yes, you are saying yes to a newer and brighter, happier and better X (smoke free, lighter, thinner, healthier and better you, etc.) chapter of your life. Now sure of yourself, you are unstoppable.

**Session Optimizing Suggestion 30:** You are now unstoppably smiling inside with a true and real knowing, glowing confidence. You are sure of yourself and certain of your improvements, more than any other time in your life.

**Session Optimizing Suggestion 31:** Now that you know the truth, you are prevailing, dynamically and powerfully unstoppable in all that you seek to achieve. When you know the truth, you easily accomplish everything.

**Session Optimizing Suggestion 32:** You are effectively finding ways of removing old past blockages, most especially relaxing deeper now and releasing the fear of losing weight (change) and easily keeping it off, you are so mighty, powerful and effective at all of this, in fact it's easy.

**Session Optimizing Suggestion 33:** Truly you have enjoyed this, your powerfully effective Hypnosis session as only great, wonderful and beneficial improvements now come into your life from this, even in surprising and spectacularly beneficial ways just for you, powerfully improving all that you are, how you live and freeing up and powerfully activating only your very best effective inspirations and energies!

**Session Optimizing Suggestion 34:** As everyone knows, once you have unstoppably entered a brand new and better chapter of your life, things improve quickly and for only the very best. All things improve easily. You are so sure of yourself, that's where you are now and happily remain forever, in ever growing and glowing confidence. You are breaking through. You are truly unstoppable.

**Session Optimizing Suggestion 35:** You might have once thought things impossible to improve or change, but you now think to yourself and know, "I now know, I'm doing better and better and it's easy and amazingly simple." As always, my life is only getting better and better, I deserve this, it's now and forever mine. And so it is.

**Session Optimizing Suggestion 36:** You succeed easily, now finding even better motivated thoughts feelings and ideas, even finding excuses to succeed.

**Session Optimizing Suggestion 37:** It's really just amazing how easy it is for you to just . . . (melt off and keep off, 71, 86 and even 99 lbs. – remaining forever, smoke free, cigarette free, etc.).

**Session Optimizing Suggestion 38:** You know, it's just amazing to realize right now, that you've relaxed your way into a newer and brighter better way, as the weight just seems to melt off and you easily lose now, X Lbs.

**Session Optimizing Suggestion 39:** You are forever free of going to self-abusive extremes; your new extreme, is to extremely take the very best care of yourself and to simply thrive, work out, sticking now in your favor to what you know works and just doing it, in amazing and even surprisingly easy ways.

**Session Optimizing Suggestion 40:** You are now and forever forgiving and releasing all of the negative effects from your childhood, feeling upbeat even reinvented, having unstoppably entered a brand new chapter of your life, so super motivated, all of your very best thoughts, feelings and supportive inspirations just rise to the top as the unwanted weight just seems to melt off you as you make the time to feel better about yourself and be motivated to break though and succeed easily and amazingly at this as never before.

**Session Optimizing Suggestion 41:** All of the things in your life that ever once stood in your way have Right Now, just melted away and are gone. You are now and forever free to unstoppably move on, excel and succeed at any and all things needed to improve your life.

**Session Optimizing Suggestion 42:** The more in the past you once resisted yourself, the more in the future you work unstoppably and effectively in your favor to cleverly, abundantly and forever succeed at this. Nod your head yes for me because you know it's true.

**Session Optimizing Suggestion 43:** In this brand new and better chapter of your life, you only thrive and succeed at this. You breakthrough easily and skillfully and even surprisingly – clever, fluid and adaptive success is your only option here, and you know that deeply and truly.

**Session Optimizing Suggestion 44:** On each and every breath you take, and on each and every beat of your heart, you are released from past blockages that once ever stood in your way.

**Session Optimizing Suggestion 45:** You are forgiven, now knowing you are feeling whole, happier and better. You are healing, you are healed, you are moving on in the very best and most supportive of ways.

**Session Optimizing Suggestion 46:** Each and every thought, feeling, action or reaction is now working unstoppably in your favor to improve your life.

**Session Optimizing Suggestion 47:** You're smiling powerfully inside, with a warm knowing, glowing unstoppable confidence. You can feel and now truly know that all old blockages and hindrances to your success are now just seemingly dissolving and melting away, as you have now moved into a new breakthrough chapter of your life. Feel that smile, nod your head yes. You really know you've succeeded here, out of your own way, you've succeeded, you are unstoppable, you are unbeatable, you are free, feeling fine!

**Session Optimizing Suggestion 48:** With Cigarettes, you're just done and finished. You've moved on and into a forever healthier and better chapter of your life.

**Session Optimizing Suggestion 49**: Right now you are unstoppably free of any and all things toxic in your life, thoughts, feelings, memories, thought patterns, fears, worries and doubts. Now more correctly, more fluidly and powerfully unstoppable than ever before, you are thinking correctly and supportively, nurturingly and taking only the very best care of yourself, as your thoughts, ideas and actions, even reactions are now supporting you. Your feelings are pleasant and conducive to a happy life; happy memories are now supporting you.

**Session Optimizing Suggestion 50:** You are feeling fine, wonderful, even fantastic. You've just had a 5 hour nap and 3 solid hours of full body massage; you are feeling fine, your body, emotions, thoughts and memories and feelings, even your spirit, in a new and more powerfully profound and optimized, fully functioning harmony, feeling truly and deeply better than wonderful and excellent, on top of your World. Now and forever you are moving into the very best chapter of your life. Rising to the very top, you are thriving and succeeding, forever free of procrastination, activating and living your dreams and making them happen. You are unbeatable and rising to the very top, into a brand new and the very best chapter of your life, which begins unstoppably right now and forever, only getting better, stronger and more and more fluidly adaptive, all working only in your favor, now, always and forever.

**Session Optimizing Suggestion 51:** All things once toxic, are now released and resolved; all things once a hindrance, now are resolved and in their place. You are loved and supported, breaking through, freed, released and really wonderful as never before.

**Session Optimizing Suggestion 52**: All things that once stressed you out or upset you are now easily handled and even vanquished by you.

**Session Optimizing Suggestion 53**: Relax now barrier free and liberate new inspirations, allowing brighter, better and even brilliant ways of thinking acting, being and feeling to become a part of who you are. Melt and flow, relax and heal, get now inspired and allow a brilliant, new and more powerfully real series of new life supporting thoughts, feelings, habits, strategies and responses to forever emerge from your mind and into all that is your life. A brand new and better chapter of your life begins unstoppably right now!

**Session Optimizing Suggestion 54**: In fact, you might just come to now and forever know . . .

**Session Optimizing Suggestion 55**: You know, it's almost funny. You are now and forever so very free now and free from smoking and cigarettes, so firmly entrenched in a happy, healthy and better life, smoke free, cigarette free, it seems like the previous chapter of your life was yesterday and yesterday really just seems now like a million years ago – it feels great to be so free, happy, healthy, content and safe, smoke free, cigarette free. You smile inside and you just know you are contented, serene, happy, very sure and safe.

**Session Optimizing Suggestion 56**: Your new life now unfolds, in perfect and precise harmony, as you breakthrough here . . .

**Session Optimizing Suggestion 57**: All things and energies that have ever worked against you are now and forever turned back upon themselves, to reduce, remove and completely eliminate those negative and destructive energies and their limitations, removing and eliminating difficulties, while ushering in a brand new and better chapter of your life, possibilities for victories, triumphs, and advances expand as you make and take bold strides, opening up your heart and your mind unbeatably, while magnetizing and liberating only the very best of experiences, breakthroughs, successes and events into your life.

**Session Optimizing Suggestion 58**: Your powerful and adaptive mind is now creating flexible, clever, powerful and even surprisingly effective ways to dynamically and easily succeed at this. All of this, just getting easier and easier and more adaptive and more powerfully effective for you. You achieve and seize desired results with grace, ease and highest impact.

**Session Optimizing Suggestion 59:** It has been said, that little steps mean a lot; this time you are assuredly easily succeeding at . . .

**Session Optimizing Suggestion 60:** It's almost as if someone from deep, deep inside of you in this moment, has reset a switch, the dial, a thermostat, or a computer of some type, easily allowing you to. . .

**Session Optimizing Suggestion 61:** It's almost like someone from deep, deep inside of you in this moment, has opened a valve from deep, deep inside of you, draining away effectively any and all blockage and negativity energy; in fact, any and all in balances and blockages are now easily been drained away. What fills up the space right now, is a beautiful energy, an energy of inspired and creative life force, strength, adaptability, unconditional love, and inner light, which easily refills, in endless supply, focusing you, rejuvenating you, and liberating your mighty inner hero unstoppably.

**Session Optimizing Suggestion 62:** Your mighty inner hero, a part of you that knows no doubt, is fearless, courageous and mighty, has now and forever effectively been activated from deep, deep inside of you right now, powerfully and effectively, creatively, dynamically and adaptively, is right now unstoppably working in your favor to achieve your well deserved very own ultimate success. The part of you that is fully capable of saving children from great danger, like a fire or any other life threatening moments, is now actively working creatively and adaptively in your favor, from deep, deep inside of you, to break you through right here and right now into a brand new, freer and better chapter of your life. All of the negative, habitual, stagnating and limiting energies that once ever blocked you in any way, or stood in your way are now cleverly and effectively turned back upon themselves as you adaptively and heroically break-through here with ultimate success unstoppably.

# PERSONAL DEVELOPMENT

Also see ANXIETY, FEAR, PANIC:
    Overcoming Dizziness, Fear, Panic and Anxiety
    Overcoming Guilt, Fear and Shame
    Overcoming Panic and Learning to Trust Again in Life
    Overcoming Panic
Also see LEARNING ENHANCEMENTS:
    Learning Enhancement - Confidence
    Taking the LSATS
    Also see STRESS:
    Beating Road Rage, Self-Confidence and Forgiveness
    Stress Relief, Patience, Life Improvement
Also see RELATIONSHIPS:
    Better Parenting: Money and Better Organized
    Relationship Resolution – Trusting Instincts - Moving on or Staying

# Attracting Abundance - Eliminating Negativity & Sadness

You always knew your life was going to rise above any and all old barriers and limitations, any and all challenges, any and all negativity. So he you are in this brand-new chapter of your life, completely reconditioned, problem-free, challenge-oriented, you are and you remain, as you thrive and flourish abundantly, confidently, positively while blossoming forth in unlimited ways. Knowing who you are and seizing each moment effectively, you begin to think of yourself as an unbeatable winner in your life, a person who has taken on and met any and all challenges they have ever faced, and who is now boldly taking any and all necessary steps, to improve your life and to flourish in every thought, deed, and action, even reaction and so it is and effectively and skillfully, so you are. Thinking in new and better ways, you become problem-free and challenge-oriented, easily, skillfully, adeptly and adaptively, rising to the very top, finding and feeling newer and better ways to feel wonderful about yourself and your life.

You begin to realize, and actually in fact come to know, that you are doing better and better, and in this brand new, exciting, cleverly reinvented and improved and even better chapter of your life, you begin to adopt the philosophy that you have enough time, because in fact, in the grand scheme of things, you are in fact timeless, outside of time, having all the time you need.

In this brand-new, potent, and powerful chapter of your life, you're fine and doing better and better, loving yourself in more unlimited ways than previous chapters of your life allowed, allowing yourself to find and create methods, ways and means, to forgive, heal and release any and all, both known and unknown to you, critical and unsupportive, even destructive and hurtful self-judgments, which are now being released, supporting you better as you are experiencing more self-supporting and life-affirming thoughts, feelings, actions, and reactions, while you are awake, while you are asleep, even when you dream peacefully, sleeping wonderfully through the night, enjoying comfortable, life-supporting, inspirational dreams, as you now realize you are limitlessness, in fact sensing and seeing, truly knowing you are eternally young, yet wise, just right and fine for where you need to be, as a newer and better sense of true and eternal inner beauty shines from heart and mind, allowing you to realize you are timeless and are truly beautiful. Your heart and your mind now activating and finding, even realizing and actualizing, that this new, reformulated, and fortified balance of heart and mind, is forever, adaptively and unstoppably achieving a more profound and powerful internal wisdom which allows you to not only see the truth, and in more loving and self-supportive ways, moving beyond belief, to a place of true inner knowingness, moving beyond belief, even beyond faith, to a place of trusting inner knowing deep, deep inside of you, as your inner light shines, into all places where shadows once stood in your way, easily and forever vanquishing those shadows, as this eternal inner light now acts and reacts like a magnet, drawing to you, your ideal mate, who is just right for you, supportive, loving, and fun, and the most balanced, unstoppable, effective, undeniable and unconditional ways, as your life is now in fact, ever more self-supporting only unfolds, working only in your favor as you trust in all of this, in the most substantial and even surprisingly effective abundant ways. Each and every breath, each and every heartbeat, each and every thought and feeling you have now, effectively liberating from the universe and world; in fact, all that is your life, profound and perfect better energy around you, the manifestation and attraction of positive and unlimited self-supporting abundance, circumstances, friends, even new companions, as you are truly coming to forgive, heal, and release, truly coming to know, sense, feel, that you are in fact doing fine; the world around you is abundantly supporting you, and of course you are only magnetizing and attracting the very best of experiences into your life, easily able to repel the imbalance of shadowy negativity, as your inner light shines from heart and mind, now, always, and forever.

In moments from the past chapters of your life, where you may have felt sadness or negative thoughts, you now instead or doing even better, as you begin to truly relax, take slow steady deep breaths, and affirm to yourself a better story, even if your mind just wanders for just a second or two to make that happen, allowing your deserving self to feel happy, perhaps even a funny thought just pops into your head, making you laugh or perhaps even just smile and you begin to trust in the fact, that you are rising above, truly feeling better, while easily and effectively moving beyond, and adaptively succeeding in all areas of your life, even a little steps mean a lot, taking control of your life and your thoughts, as you easily forgive and release any and all blockage, regardless of whatever it came from, to better support a new and better sense of self love and trust in your life and in all that you create.

You now so easily able to handle, all events and circumstances that rise up to meet you, as you are unstoppably moving forward into a brand new tomorrow, as you now seize the moment, as a lighthearted, happier, more evolved, better you has now taken charge of your life. Every so often, most especially when needed, you effectively and easily get into positive, highly charged emotional state of serenity or happiness, to attract what you want, need, and deserve, as you deserve and create only the very best circumstances and situations are effectively and adaptively created, to achieve, to manifest, and effectively summon forth all around you, all that you now abundantly and self-supportively create, into the masterpiece of a life you are now orchestrating.

Redefined, reset, recalibrated, centered, safe, strong, fluid, adaptive, you are and you remain, almost as if someone from deep, deep inside of you in this moment, has reset a switch, the dial, a thermostat, or a computer of some type, easily allowing you to program and put forth, only your very best, handling any and all new challenges, embraced by unconditionally self-loving and healing force of forgiveness and release, allowing you to build, maintain, feel, experience, and truly even know the kind of reformulated, improved, sense of well being, truth, and the sort of a life you now and forever easily manifest.

And so it is, and so now and forever and cleverly it adaptively and effectively remains. You live a new truth, feel and experience a new and better sense of well being and trust in the way your life is formulated and created, and confidently smiling inside to yourself that all of this is only getting better and better as you have moved beyond survival into the kind of a thriving life you now effectively manifest, and create and feel embraced by, in each and every moment of your existence, now and forever, only getting better and better, as your recalibrated and creative mind is only creating the very best for you in all areas of your life.

## Belief in Yourself - Dynamic Magnetism

When you believe in yourself, when you truly know who you are and know and trust in yourself and trust in your life, you can and are able to do most anything, becoming and living, creatively super-motivated, doing all that it honestly takes to thrive and succeed. You are and you remain easily able to break free of any subconscious or unconscious striving for a comfort zone of inactivity that you once might have used to hold yourself back or even kept yourself from moving forward from where you want and need to be. You are so easily able to tap into your very best and to be more confident socially. You are easily able to feel a newer and better sense of your very own personal dynamic magnetism, becoming so very easily able to draw the world to yourself, by lighting yourself up inside, by knowing what you want and bringing it into your life, by either magnetizing it or even by just going out and getting it. With your new and improved, limitless, upbeat attitude, you are raising your energy and very best aspects to the top, to the surface, activating your very best energies, easily and skillfully raising and improving your self ideals, your self image and your self esteem to new and improved heights of greatness.

You are and you remain a confident person, knowing who you are, where you came from, and where you want to go; but now and forever, you are free of being lost, truly finding balance and direction, knowing who you are and where you are going, taking all the proper roads you need to take to get there. For from now on, even if you take one step back, it will always be followed by two or three steps forward and this is really just how it is and how it will stay from now on.

Moving beyond survival mode, you now flow and plan, just living your life skillfully, successfully and powerfully, doing all that it honestly takes to rise to the top and exemplifying only your very best, in flowing and fluid, skillfully-successful ways, tapping into your true and very best self. You rise to the top and flourish, thriving and gracefully succeeding as never before, feeling a newer, truer and growing sense of satisfaction and self-approval as never before. Relaxing now into this, you relax out of any and all past patterns, and light up your life as a shining example to how great life is and how great you life now becomes.

## Better Driving and Past Trauma Release

In this moment of deep, soothing and powerful life-changing relaxation, you are relaxing beyond, through, over and around, any and all old barriers of your life, into a newer, better and brighter, more powerful way of living, rising up, inspired by every past victory, triumph, breakthrough and success you've ever had. You are unstoppably entering a new chapter of your life, realizing and recognizing that you have inside of you an inner hero, someone who is capable of great things, saving children from a fire, helping to save a life. You are now liberating the bearer of great things, which you really and effectively are, into this very moment of your life. You relax and are now powerfully releasing, regardless of whatever bumps in the road, hurts, doubts, fears or traumas you might have once experienced, or re-thought of in your mind or feelings, now seeing them as powerful experiences you've been strengthened from, polished by, fortified by, and now rising up and beyond from, they are released into and they remain in past chapters of your life. You know deeply and truly that worry and fear are empty vessels. They do nothing; they are nothing; they are useless. You give no time or energy to them in any way, thought, feeling, shape, form, action or reaction to them in any way; you are powerfully past any and all of that now. I wonder if you ever realize how easily successful you are going to be at all of this. Almost like tapping into the energy, courage, strength and wisdom of the countless generations who have come before you, or even better, tapping into

Divinely-inspired breakthrough, might and wisdom, encouragement, you are now self-assured and unstoppable at overcoming anything that ever once stood in your way.

That same inner hero, you, is now coming up to the surface in the most powerful and potent of ways and is dynamically allowing you to thrive and right now, unstoppably enter a new and better chapter of your life while effectively and even easily allowing you to thrive, in everyday situations, and even stressful situations, not because I say so, but because it's in the nature of your own mind, thoughts, feelings and power to do so. The things you once gave power to, are now the things you now empower yourself over. Things you once were afraid of, are now things you easily and powerfully master, with pulsing and thriving knowing, glowing confidence, in heart, body and mind, with your very powerful, barrier-breaking, can-do spirit, strong, powerful and inspired courageousness. You are unstoppably breaking through, even mighty, fearless, or just feeling some fear and doing it anyway, with calm and balanced emotions, with regular, supportive and steady breath, you are more and more bold, you are thriving, succeeding and breaking through, yes, you really, really are! You have in fact right now, in this very moment, moved forward, into this new and ever stronger chapter of your life. You are reconditioned, rejuvenated; you are and you remain adaptively and effectively bold; you are mighty, mighty, mighty. Seizing the moment, taking charge, rising up and becoming mighty, just doing all that needs to be done, by just relaxing into better and brighter moments of your life. You find yourself rising up to meet any and all challenges, boundlessly determined to become mightier than your past. You are feeling powerful, yet relaxed, able, because you are. Easily able to (relax) cross bridges and (relax) go up onto high roads when you are driving. Of course you can, it's easy and you are centered, calm, safe and strong, so content, sharp, talented, able and serene, knowing you can and will do anything you've set your mind to, which is all, now and forever, working in your favor.

You learn to trust in your life, just as the Sun comes up each and every morning, the majority of your life you have been healthy, so today, even tomorrow is just like each and every sunrise. The light of your inner sun, shines and keeps your health up, feeling fine; only good things are happening to you; sure of this you are and you remaiAt each and every bedtime, even if you are almost asleep, you relax, relax, relax, and just put your head onto the pillow, just close your eyes and fall asleep, just like a calming, soothing blanket of sleep energy is laying its mantel of relaxation upon you, over you and all around you, Divinely-guided and protected, so very completely relaxed, you are at a deep state of rest and relaxation.

Even in places you've been, where bad things had once happened, they are all in the past, long, long ago, and you've moved on. You have been protected and safe;

all tomorrows, all tomorrow nights, taking care of you just the same. All old trauma is now releasing itself, as life is and has always taken the very best care of you. Mighty people survive, you have survived, and now you've unstoppably and mightily decided that it's time to thrive, and so you do, and so it is. Your breathing, now clear, so deep, so very regular, so relaxing, all around you supports you; life and this world are your playground; you are OK; you are thriving; you are, in fact, truly fine. Your powerful and deep and steady breath, and your ever deepening, deep relaxation, guides your way, as you thrive and succeed.

## Creating Self Confidence and Life Harmony

You are finding new ways to gain and maintain ever-increasing amounts of confidence, a new and supportive view of life, and a new and powerful unwavering sense and real feeling of trust. In fact, a new strength and a powerful and growing belief in yourself and in your life is easily and dynamically building and building, dynamically motivating you to unstoppably take on new challenges, allowing you fulfill your destiny, to live your dreams and to follow your excitement, in new, bold, courageous, imaginative, fair, effective and profound ways. You are either thriving or succeeding, and meeting new people, sharing your very best and most valuable asset, your most valued gift, yourself. You are effectively and potently forgiving and releasing anything or any blockages that had ever stood in your way, just flowing over, around and beyond any and all blockages. In fact, you are now feeling blockage-free, allowing release and forgiveness to recondition and revitalize yourself and your life, building a new sense of purpose and direction, with a budding and building sense of excitement about your life, your direction and your purpose, allowing you to blossom, to flow, to shine and to make this world a better place, surprising everyone, most especially yourself.

You are finding new ways to care for yourself, healing the past, powerfully forgiving any and all unpleasantness, even trauma or feelings of loneliness, even inadequacy. You are instead powerfully and effectively finding newer and better ways of reconditioning, compounding and building a reservoir of limitless love, affection and caring in powerful, correct, precise and ever-increasing amounts for yourself, to yourself, from deep within yourself and all around yourself, for yourself and for those you love, but most especially for yourself. All of those well deserved and well provided thoughts, feelings and true energies, build, build, build, truthfully, like a breath of fresh air, allowing you to give yourself all that if takes for you to thrive, succeed and expand your life. In fact, you are beginning to feel your connection to all that life provides you, to your life, to your world, to your Universe, to the Divine. You are feeling love in new ways and your intimate oneness with all things and with all people, most especially with those you love and care for, those you appreciate, most especially yourself.

You feel connected to life, to things, to all other people, to anything and everything you once found a challenge to connect to, because you are now thriving in profound and unstoppable ways, touching and being touched by life, connected, comfortable and at one with yourself and all things, free of ever feeling alone, being truly and forever a part of all things.

You are forever free of making limiting, judgmental, condemning or negative comparisons, whether they are physical, qualitative, quantitative, or financial. You are now choosing to enjoy your life, finding what you have to be correct and enough, finding balance and harmony, out of the "rat race," finding instead, a better peace, a better pace and a truer and longer lasting even forever freedom and happiness as you now have unstoppably chosen to flow with life.

You are magnanimous, generous, open-minded, being enough is enough You are happy giving and receiving, taking new strides to be happy and to generate happiness, finding fulfillment in giving and sharing, feeling fulfilled. When you give or do for someone else, it is from fulfillment and enough-ness, you do because you can and it feels good, you are forever free of doing, giving or pleasing from insecurity because you are secure, safe, strong, free, contented, balanced and harmonized. You are forgiving any and all blockages from your past, instead loving your way past anything and everything that had once ever stood in your way. You like and love yourself enough to do all that you need to do and all that needs to be done, getting pleasure from your generosity and wholeness, relaxing into brighter and better ways of being and thinking and doing, thriving unstoppably in balanced and harmonized ways as never before, feeling fine, great and on top of the world.

## Eliminating Excesses from Your Life

Now relax even deeper, and deeper and deeper and as you do you allow a really strong and empowered thought for a new day to come upon you. In this moment you have truly decided to release the idea of excesses from your life, because you have instead chosen to embrace and fulfill a more moderate and easygoing way of life and because you have chosen to find deep and powerful inner harmony and true inner fulfillment from deep within your life and from deep inside of you, because you have in fact, truly realized that you really are enough and that each and every day you are easily and successfully finding true and powerful inner fulfillment in your life. Right now and forever, better and instead of the old ways, you embrace moderation, calmness and conscious consistency as your new healthier way of life. You realize very powerfully that all excesses are excuses for not having felt enough at times in your past, so as you relax deeper and deeper, you release that thought right now, forgiving it, releasing and relinquishing it, until it is gone and gone forever. Instead, you relax into and embrace a healthier and more harmonious way of life, a calmer more balanced way of living, relaxing into and through all that you do, you are finding, each and every moment, each and every day and night newer and better ways to thrive, prosper, and most especially feel fulfilled. You release all old ideas and old ways of living that once caused you imbalance in the past, because you feel so much better without them, you find inner harmony free from them, including: (name habits and behaviors) because you are so much better off without them. You'll hardly ever be thinking about them, but even if you do, you'll be thinking of them in relation to how much better off you are without them and how much beyond them now You are because in this moment, you are free, liberated and truly empowered, blossoming into all areas of your life, flourishing in new, profound and meaningful ways, more and more each and every day and night.

## Finding Something Lost (A Non-Regression Method)

You are beginning to relax so very deeply, so very truly, just like having waves of calming soothing realization flow over you, around you and through you, allowing you to relax deeply, peacefully, easily and naturally. You are so calm, peaceful, and deeply relaxed right now, ready for inspiration and upgrade, memory activation, memory enhancement and upgrade and true motivation, recall and remembering. You are feeling relaxed, invigorated and able, ready to open up the powerful and most accurately precise filing system of your subconscious mind, most easily able to remember and recall in powerful and surprisingly powerful, absolutely beneficial ways.

It's almost like a time in the past, when you were trying, trying, trying to think of something and then, you just forgot about it. And just after a very few brief moments, just as soon as you stopped struggling and trying to attain, what you were trying to remember came back to you quickly and easily in precise and measured correctness, accurately showing you what it was you were looking for.

It's almost as if a light bulb has gone off and lit up within your head, just lit up over your head, just lit up your head and creatively sparked up your mind, a new idea, a better recall, a better memory, a recall idea. It's just like someone has thrown a switch or activated a powerful computer of some kind which precisely records, files and maintains a record of each and everything you've ever done or experienced in your life, easily solving any and all questions, supplying accurate and precise answers. Your recall is up and running, and all of this is only getting better and more precise and direct, more and more correct with each and every breath that you take and with each and every beat of your heart.

Think about how a canal, like the Panama Canal works, doors or floodgates open and water goes in and fills up. As you relax deeper and further, it's just like that; your mind is now being flooded with new and correct thoughts and information about all that you need to know, anything and everything you need to remember, whether you realize it or not.

As I count from 3 to 1, you relax 27 times deeper on each and every number that I count and only on the count of 1, you are about to have an A-Ha moment, while experiencing complete and profound true, deep, deep relaxation. An A-Ha moment is a moment of profound and powerful, deep and true relaxation and instant realization. On the count of 1, you are deeply and truly relaxing, deeper and deeper, relaxing all over. Your mind is now deeply, truly and profoundly open, whether you realize it or not; your powerful and dynamically now-enhanced rearranging and magnetic mind, now unstoppably is open and free, free to remember, recall, reactivate, rejuvenate, re-assimilate all information, just re-appearing, in ways you'll remember and in ways most obvious and meaningfully revealing to you and for you. You are remembering, recalling and realizing where it is, what was done with it, who was there, who saw it last, who touched it last just like when you found what was lost in the past, it simply and easily just popped into your head, it just came back. This is your A-Ha moment, 3, 2, 1. A-Ha! It's forming, just clicking in, kicking in, this recall thought, your recall thought. You are sensing it, it's coming back, it's there, right here in your powerful and cooperative mind, the image is forming, crystallizing, the movie (TV) screen of your mind, now becoming brighter and openly obvious, just letting it light up now and revealing all that it has to. You may even find yourself nodding your head (Note: Ideo-motor signaling- or raising and lowering your left - right index finger) where it's coming back is back in your mind, just where it needs to be, just where it belongs.

# Free of Writer's Block and Life Motivation

You are finding and creating very small amounts of time to affect positive changes in your life. Little steps mean a lot; unstoppably, you are finding and creating a few seconds each day or even just 2 or 4 times a week, to sit and write, sometimes nothing, but more often than not, you are easily exceeding those seconds, as seconds become minutes, minutes hours, as a passionate fire within you burns, drives you forward and allows you to unstoppably break through here. Just like a baby learns to walk, you learn to avoid falling down on your passionate commitment to write and liberate your thoughts and feelings, experiences and expressions into the world around you, enriching those whom you inspire, those of whom you touch, those of whom you are now sharing your experience and insights with, while all the time forgiving and healing yourself, loving yourself enough to break through here, rise up and thrive here, liberating your inner hero here, free forever of ever ripping people off by you not sharing your heart, mind and passions with, fully sharing and caring enough to open up and deliver this time. Your passion to write is bubbling up to the surface, almost like you have unstoppably activated a vale of creativity; all things you need, thoughts, experiences, ideas and inspirations flowing freely, not because I say so, but because you have decided to do so. Just like any and all past times you've risen unstoppably and undeniably to the very top, you know it's almost like the energy of every past victory, triumph, breakthrough and success you've ever had is now passionately bubbling up and driving you forward unstoppably in truly inspired and powerful ways, to drive you ever onward. And just like a snow-covered mountain melting in the spring creates a powerful yet adaptable river, flowing ever onward, you are flowing ever onward, this time, right now, beyond any and all old and former blockages, and inconveniences, beyond any and all things that ever once stood in your way, liberating your book, your creation, even just jotting down ideas and layouts. All of this seems to be burning, flowing and practically creating itself, almost taking on a life of its very own, with you as the captain of this ship, which sailed on to the end of the journey, towards fulfillment and completion; in fact, you've never been so sure of anything ever before in your life. You are now redefining terms to break through here . . . Any and all things you once called problems, as you are now and forever problem-free, are in fact, now and forever challenges, you rise up to meet and beat, whether spitefully or nobly, it matters not. Any and all things you once thought or felt were failures, are now redefined powerfully and forever as learning experiences, for now and forever, you either learn or succeed. Instead now, you are skillfully finding reasons and even excuses to find newer, more effectively and improved ways of doing all that it takes, as your inner passionate fire once and forever burns bright, burning away the obstacles of old. Any and all of this encourages you and motivates you to find reasons, to create within your life zones of success, treating yourself better and better, in body, emotions, mind and even spirit.

You take, make and easily create the time to exercise, to clear your head, and make your body, organs and joints work better, finding times and reasons to succeed just the same way as well, eating right; your right foods more appealing and tasty; all of your tastes changing in your favor; all things seemingly ready to work in precise and proper flow just for you, enjoying immensely, this soothing sort of deep relaxation. You move beyond kiddy foods, like breads and cakes, intended for children; all of your life becoming easier and more self-respectful, finding rewards in self enrichment and drinking lots and lots of water to wash you clean inside and to fill you up sooner.

## Get Up and Do It - Exercise Motivation

Relax, Relax, Relax. And as you relax, you realize from deep within a new thought is coming upon you, only getting stronger and better in every passing future moment, a powerful unstoppable thought and feeling. You are in fact beginning a new chapter of your life right now that only gets stronger and better with each and every passing day to completely improve your body, your emotions, your mind and each and every thought and all that is your life. In this new and more active, more empowered, powerful chapter of your life, it's time for you to begin a healthy and most beneficial new urge, new passion, a new powerful motivation. And just like an unstoppable force, almost like a nagging need, this passion, your passion, begins burning like a flame, a flame that slowly grows and burns strong and burns bright. Its time for you to get moving and start to exercise, in ways so healthy and just right, just for you. You can feel a warm, small powerfully determined glow beginning from within you, a happy and a passionate desire to exercise in ways so right, so perfect, so healthy, just for you. In the past, you may have found reasons, even excuses, to find other things to do, almost like when a child can find some excuses to not accomplish some chore or homework assignment. But better than that, you relax deeper, you powerfully and truly forgive those moments, flowing past over and around them, moving on and beyond any and all judgments upon those moments and on you, you relax, you release, you forgive forever right now. But right now and for the rest of your life, you are seizing the power and unlimited inspiration of all of your adult years of learning and experience, are upon you now, activating the energy of all of your past victories, successes, triumphs, and breakthroughs to motivate you to workout, performing a regimen you will enjoy in the most healthy beneficial ways, so right just for you, to exercise, to accomplish each and every step of the way, easily, successfully, precisely and carefully doing all that it takes, no matter what, to begin to give yourself the gift of exercise and all of exercises limitless health benefits, a better body, a healthier set of lungs and muscles, and a healthier heart, absolutely creating the kind of sculpted body you deserve and benefiting with tremendous and rigorous health, each and every day and night, only getting better, just feeling great physically, emotionally, mentally and throughout all that is your life, that you know is right and beneficial, just perfect and right, just for you. You absolutely recognize from deep, deep within and you even truly know you've begun this new chapter of your life in profound and unstoppable ways. You remember times from the past, that are just beginning to drift away now, when it was easy for just about anyone, even you, to find an excuse, to sit and do nothing or even be distracted. But those times are forever over! You detach from them and they are forgiven and released. They are just drifting away, drifting away, gone and gone forever. You truly recognize, that the superior person, will get up and accomplish all that it takes, slowly, deliberately, carefully, with skill, correct, careful, fluid and flowing precise movement and with creative, empowered, success inspired determination, to achieve all that is necessary. That person is you! You correctly think to yourself, "Just get up and do it!" That's right, "just get up and do it!" Right now, truly always and forever, you feel and truly are, motivated, successful, thinking creatively, achieving powerfully, always allowing for at least just a few short minutes a day to exercise, just getting up and doing it, allowing yourself this kind of benefit, succeeding and motivated, a motivated exercise person, just like some others you've met, you find the time to perfect your skills, always finding and allowing the time, to be the kind of motivated, goal oriented person you were born to be. In fact you are that kind of person. Your body slims down, your clothes fit better, your outlook on life is optimistic, clear focused and strong, you look good, you feel good, you breathe better, in fact, you are an inspiration, you are truly inspired, even inspiring others, even workout buddies to come along, just as if you've somehow magnetized them and they also become a powerful guiding force. Slow and steady wins the race, so with slow yet powerful determination, you succeed in amazing ways and it's easy for you now, in this new time in your life. With exercise, just a few moments a day, just a few times each week, an easy goal, even your little wins mean a lot. You feel like you've got the whole world in the palm of your hand, you are a winner, for an unstoppable force from deep within you has been forever activated. Your desire to succeed becomes a passion, your passionate desire becomes a truly committed, very powerful, unstoppable exercise force from places you didn't even know you had, each and every day and night, you overwhelmingly succeed in truly inspired creative successful ways, relaxing into a brand new better chapter of your life, winning in the most profound ways! Each workout is a win, each and every win allows limitless inspiration, drive and determination, to continue to rocket you along your path, to ultimate success, a new better brighter, healthier more limitless, deeply inspired, healthier, better, more powerful, more fit you begins right now, you always, just get up and do it and it feels great!

## Good Mental Health and Suggestions

Rather than being focused and fixed upon your old ways of being overly demanding of self-perfection in all things, you now learning to relax into a better chapter of your life and relax into each and every moment of your life. You are unstoppably allowing yourself moments and months of adaptability, flexibility and creativity. It's OKAY to learn, it's great to succeed, but in all things that now matter to you the most, you allow yourself to drift, to flow and flourish, growing and learning from any imperfections, real or imagined, sometimes even allowing yourself to shine your own perfection out into the world from the deepest recesses of your soul and spirit; you are just fine the way you are, growing, adapting, learning and liberating inner true wisdom, living in harmony.

You relax into a better way of living and being, moving into a newer and brighter chapter of your life. You evolve, and adaptively and effectively, even easily, move beyond being all things to all people, for being true and okay to yourself is enough. You find it is really and truly OKAY to leave some things undone; as your life evolves, all things get done in Divine order. You find newer, better and more adaptive ways to not only cope, but to find a new pace and flourish. All things in their proper time, your thoughts and actions easily allow you to do all that needs doing, but in ways that create comfort-ability and ease. You are enough, there is enough of you to go around, you honor time commitments, getting it all done, free of over-committing, finding your place and pace in your life and powerfully in your world. For all the "yeses" in life, there are also "no's." In this ever-developing program of life improvement you now and forever unstoppably create, you learn when it's time to put yourself first and to say no when you must to insure that you are taking proper care of yourself and to allow others to flourish, learn, gain, grow and succeed on their own, creating and instilling their own powerful and positive development in their lives. You make, take and find the time to take care of yourself, even scheduling time for yourself when necessary, as this is needed, necessary for you to thrive and succeed in each and every moment of your life. As there are things you've done regularly, there are now times for you to be re-excited about your world and your life, finding harmony in being free of monotony, even doing nothing regular in your life, keeping your positive anticipation and excitement levels high. You are easily finding it's Okay to just be yourself, and to love that self, all manner and regard, just as easily loving yourself when boring, inelegant, and sometime unattractive.

Thou shalt embrace life. You learn to be your best unconditional best friend in all moments, forgiving any and all past hurtful and negative past judgments, unstoppably, cleverly and adaptively learning to love all that you are, even the parts you once found most difficult to love, most especially when old habits once caused you to be your own worst enemy, now and forever, you are adapting, improving and learning to treat yourself the way a loving and ideal parent would a wonderful child. You are filled and thriving, flourishing and flowing, effectively and adaptively creating a new pathway in your life, easily and effectively activating unstoppable optimism, joy, love, comfort-ability in all and any thoughts, all and any feelings, all and any actions; in fact, truly and forever you know, you are creating and easily liberating ways to be all that you are, in your own perfection, enjoying each precious moment of your life, smiling on the inside, meant to be all that you are.

## Growing Up and Moving On

You are relaxed, feeling satisfied, in this deep and powerful form of relaxation. You find that being calm, you are better able to focus on only the very best actions, reactions, thoughts, feelings, and patterns that allow you successfully to move into a happier and better and healthier, more self-respectful place for now, and only even getting better into the future. You recognize from deep within, that all that you fix, improve, repair, is worth it, as the smallest of journeys start with one step, and like learning to walk, each step gets steadier and better, allowing you to arrive at the bright and happy future you deserve and actively liberate into the right here and now. Regardless of person, persons, people, events, or circumstances, you grow, you learn, you evolve, finding each and every day and night, you are doing better for yourself, to make your life's journey good, healthy, whole, complete, right, set up to support you in the very best of ways, always tapping into the limitless inner power and strength of any and all of your past victories, triumphs, breakthroughs and successes. You find inner balance; you are relaxing into major improvement in the ways you find peace for yourself. You find yourself at home wherever you are. There's nowhere to run to, nowhere to hide; you are strong and solid in your trust of your life as your home, wherever you are, a place of peace, transcending any and all past limits and blockages and it feels great. You express yourself clearly and cleanly, realizing that arguments in and of themselves are self-defeating. You'd rather explain, teach, lead to understanding, you tap your limitless potentials and unleash only your very best in the ways most proper and perfect for an adult you.

You are doing all it takes to succeed in your life, because you are finding new and better ways to appreciate yourself. You find yourself lovingly and unstoppably motivated and excited about your life, as it should be, finding joy and happiness in simple things, powerfully and unstoppably, a new chapter of your life has begun.

You see having it all as a powerful part of a step-by-step unfolding process; you take all necessary steps, beginning one step at a time, gaining momentum. You see an overview of your life, realizing powerfully that in time, you'll see all the steps you've taken, even though right now, you may not understand your reason for being here or there. And whether or not you're heard, understood or even appreciated, it doesn't matter, for you understand you, you appreciate you, you love you, you learn each and every day to take better care of you. You care for yourself the way an ideal parent would a loving and nurturing child in the most ideal ways, this only getting better and better, more creative, more inspired and empowered, each and every day and night, regardless of the thoughts and feelings of others, you take better care of you. You recognize that your life is full of choices and you are now relaxing into the moment you are living, maximizing every choice as a limitless opportunity.

You find limitlessness in all things you once considered limited. You find unconditional-ness in all things you once considered conditional. You are always finding new and better ways to liberate yourself, and that begins with forgiving the past, releasing and forgiving any and all past judgments, finding your sense of personal freedom expanding in ways of greatest significance.

## Healing Anger and Creating Forgiveness

You now and forever realize that your newer and more correct response to any challenge great or small in our life, is to relax through any and all barriers, choosing responses that generate healing, most especially whenever challenged by others, choosing to adapt, talking it out, while listening or explaining, generating openness, becoming flexible, adaptive, reducing stress while calmly deep breathing, taking a break, soothing anger energy responses by deep breathing, making time to laugh, exercise and in extremely prolonged cases of anger, writing letters you don't send, while giving yourself the benefit of the doubt and giving yourself a break, by forgiving yourself.

Inside everyone resides an inner hero and it's time to redefine yourself that way, so you now and forever do. Who you really are is a hero, capable of saving children in a fire, but past influences, actions, reactions and effects in old moments and in past chapters of your life, instilled or allowed you to define yourself as less than that. You are, now and forever, freed from what you once saw yourself as less than. You now unlimited, you now powerful, mighty, fluid and adaptive! From here on out, each and every thought, idea, feeling, concept, each and every plan or action or reaction, redefines you in the most supportive and self-loving, appreciative of ways. You now see yourself as capable, victorious, breaking-through, triumphant, successful and empowered, failure-free, succeeding and learning, you are empowered, forgiven, calm and peaceful, deep breathing, centered, truly a master of your life, serene, in the zone, unstoppable, undeniable, setting aside, things of lesser value and unstoppable. The power of your breath detaches from the moment, you dynamically achieve a higher place of being.

You are becoming personally mighty on a daily basis, beyond any and all challenges, while easily rising above old situations and blockages while powerfully and easily living from a newer sense of truth and inner power. You are dynamically achieving higher, more balanced inner and outer states of consciousness, love, true healing, compassion, calmness and limitless joy.

---

## Life Enhancement

You are truly beginning a new chapter in your life; you are determined to feel upbeat, and are finding new excitement in your life. You are finding new interests and finding new appeal; you are becoming unstoppably determined to take better care of yourself, the very best care of yourself, learning and easily and cleverly and adaptively finding and achieving newer, brighter and better ways of loving yourself, taking the very best care of yourself and finding newer and better ways to rise above any and all challenges from your past and moving freely ever onward. You are powerfully and forever determined to do anything and everything that it takes to be brighter and upbeat, not because I say so, but because it's the nature of your own unstoppable mind to do so; so you do. You are feeling like old positive feelings from the past are now emerging; you are beginning to take care of yourself the way an old and loving friend would; you are beginning to take care of yourself the way the most ideal and loving parent would a wonderful and beautiful child, feeling almost Divinely guided and unstoppably motivated and this is only becoming better and easier for you in the very best and most unstoppable of ways. Now think about a new morning, and a new sunrise: the golden white light of your sun always shines, but this time it's shining on you.

You find new and better ways to lead your life, trusting the very true fact that life always has supported you, does and will support you, in the very most amazing of ways; you may even find yourself saying this to yourself, and you'll feel great! For in this moment of deep relaxation, you come to a profound understanding: you've always either learned or succeeded, and in this and in every moment, you've decided to learn and to thrive in the most amazing and even imaginative of ways and it feels great. You let go of the 'what ifs' in favor of the love and trust and respect you have for yourself, in an endless and ever growing supply.

You relax into the flow and harmony that is your life. And you raise your consciousness, easily and effectively, seeing things for how they truly are. For your loved ones (children) you have thought you've stood alone; but in fact, the whole world has been rooting for your success and quite often you realize now and even recognize, support has come your way, sometimes very unexpectedly, just when you needed it and when it was appropriate. You summon up limitless inspiration of all of your past breakthrough moments, moments of victory, pride, empowerment, amazingly creative success and you feel that wellspring of limitless power, rising up, rising up, building up within you unstoppably.

And now it is time that you improve your view of money now. What is money? Some might say in reality, it's a form of energy, a representation of the energy that we are in our lives. The more energy you put out, the more it comes back. Just a like a rubber ball a child might throw at a wall, the more energy expended, the more energy is returned. You know, the Universe is full of energy, energy immeasurable, going on and on forever, in immeasurable, undeniable, limitless supply. Feel your oneness with this energy now; you recognize it and embrace it. For it is you and you are it. You are guided by this energy that neither seeks nor tries. It just flows on and on in endless supply, and so do you. You are trusting and flowing into all areas of your life. Trusting in the fact that your days of lack are over, you've begun a new and healthier and better chapter of your life. You know that you think clearly, now even better than before. You follow your intuition, making the very best choices, as you've always done, doing even better now, giving yourself a break, even the benefit of the doubt, loving yourself the way the very most ideal parent would a wonderful lovable child. You now have decided to nurture you above all challenges that may arise, or not arise. You are super-empowered and super-inspired to relax into your life and to be your limitless very best.

So now it is time that you improve your view of overcoming loneliness. From now on whenever you are alone, you will listen to the sounds of the world around you. You might hear noises, sounds of people, kids, happy birds chirping in the trees. In such a busy place, how on Earth could one ever be lonely? Each and every time you are alone, you've deeply and unstoppably and completely decided to make those moments time for you to get to know, love and appreciate you better and better, better than ever, being and becoming only your very best. You make the very best of relationships with yourself, and by doing so; easily attract only the very best of friends and people into your world and your life like some kind of people-attracting magnet. You find the perfect relationship with you and by doing so; create a powerful inner light, which in time attracts the perfect wholesome mate. All of this feels so good; it just makes you smile, both inside and out. And right now your courage builds, and everyone and everything around you can sense this level of trust, fearlessness, Divine inspiration and guidance, most especially animals. You go anywhere with ease, peace, centeredness, contentment, relaxed yet powerful focus, easily able to rise above anything and everything that once ever stood in your way, even getting past you, and it feels so great. The sun always rises; your light always shines past, through and into any and all darkness. You light up the world, and with just a few deep breaths, each and every day and night, your fear is releasing; you are moving forward, feeling great in every way.

## Life Improvement: Memory, Money and Success

Your mind is now relaxed and while relaxed, your powerful and active mind is now improving, whether you realize it or not, is now working in new, powerful, enhanced and improved ways to thrive and succeed in your favor, almost as if you are being Divinely-inspired and guided to thrive and succeed anew. Your thoughts are now powerfully and unstoppably reorganizing themselves to create better memory, recall, mental pathways and associations whenever you need any required or desired information, in laser-beam like focus and precision. Your mind is now readily repeating and recalling, anything and everything you need to know, like when you first meet someone, repeating their name in your mind subconsciously, 5 to 7 times, so you'll remember their name with ease. Upon hearing their name, or any important information, you'll easily and always think to yourself, this is what their name looks like to me, readily and steadily associating their face with their name. In any kind of class or training, your powerful, functional and very active mind, is now wide open and is a powerful and unstoppable memory bank of information and is now becoming like a sponge, absorbing anything and everything you need to know, but now even better, you are creating new pathways of information and memory and recall. It's just as if your brain is growing, expanding, in power and in precision, to perform optimally. You are easily succeeding in class; you are feeling fine and super motivated, wanting to thrive and succeed, allowing yourself and your very best abilities to come up and to come through, most especially during any test or examination, whether announced or given unannounced. You are absolutely ready to succeed and accurately perform, in fact, you are feeling truly empowered and inspired by every moment of past victory, triumph and success you've ever had. All of that important and unstoppable energy is powerfully releasing itself into your life, motivating you to understand and perform optimally. You think about seeing a newer and more successful you emerging. You liberate this vision of yourself and make it happen, making it so, making real and true to yourself right now and into your brighter future. Your sense of self confidence now supports, expands and embraces you, as you deep breathe a sigh of relief, because you are so sure of yourself and so focused and so very, very ready to thrive and succeed, so powerfully and unstoppably sure of yourself, stepping into this vision of yourself. A better, more whole and future you emerges right now, and you feel fine, wonderfully and unstoppably sure of yourself, growing ever more powerful from here on out.

All of your life as well is now pulling together right now. You are cleverly and precisely improving your view of yourself and of your life. You are feeling mightier than any challenge you might encounter, transcending any and all limits. Your view of money improves in your favor. You now see money, finances and financial planning as an extension of the work you do in the world the more energy you put out, the more money and abundance you create. The more you spend, the more you make back. Whenever you spend money, it's just like throwing a rubber ball against a wall, the faster it's thrown away, the faster it comes back, often in surprising ways as you are wide open to receiving in this way. You are magnetizing money; you deserve so you create the opportunities you deserve. You are ready and open to embrace the energy that is money as it abundantly returns into your life. You deserve abundance and you create it, as an extension of your life, thoughts and deserve-ability. You are learning to just go with the flow of your life and you are now, powerfully and unstoppably, trusting in the very real, true and important fact that life is always taking care of you.

You are problem-free, challenge-oriented, struggle-free, flowing and adapting to life and all and any circumstances, flowing like a mighty river, rushing down the side of a mighty mountain, always getting wherever it is you need to be or do, surprising and amazing everyone, most especially yourself. You live your dreams, getting in touch with your activated excitement. You are living your dreams, following your excitement, rising above any and all limits, apparent or unseen, real or imagined, easily getting out of your own way, moving on and feeling fulfilled, trusting in your life and sleeping right thought the night, just as you once did in your past, deserving rest, getting rest, at bedtime, just putting your head on the pillow, closing your eyes and going to sleep. You are now and forever relaxing away from and through any and all barriers, feeling a rejuvenated sense of excitement about the masterpiece of a life you are now dynamically creating, not because I say so, but because it's the nature of your own powerful mind to do so. You are becoming increasingly upbeat about your life, your world, your plans and living your dreams. You are so motivated, so successful, doing all the right things, not only for others but most especially for yourself. Your child-like sense of wonder is now active in your creative mind, your feelings so self supportive, your actions and movements so flowing. You are aglow with limitless possibilities and thriving in correct and directly successful ways, feeling on top of the world, loving yourself and releasing any and all past blockages. You are a winner, successful and unstoppable, flowing into the next and brightest days of your life in a brand new chapter of your life, as if a light now shines from you into the world, dazzling, amazing and impressing everyone who beholds you, most especially yourself.

## Making Your Way Into a Better Life (Pediatric)

You learn to get excited about your life, the world around you, and take more interest in things you find to be of interest to you. You are finding newer and better ways of becoming and remaining, sure, confident, secure and strong. You learn to follow the direction of others, most especially people who are more experienced and are only there to guide you to greater and better, lasting success, happiness and a better way of life. You give them permission to guide you; you accept that their leadership will guide you to succeed better in life, taking only the very best care of yourself, making your life the healthy, long and most successful place it can be. Your attitude brightens, and you feel happy and wonderful. For when you believe in yourself, when you trust in your life and those who care about you and are really there for you, you can do anything. You are good enough, just as good as anyone else; you are an important part of life and living; people know you as a good person, a worthwhile person, one of the good guys, and what you bring to the lives of others is important and valuable. You are as good as anyone else, in some cases better, and all that you are is worthwhile and important. In fact, you might just feel like you are on top of the world, smiling on the inside, feeling better than you have in a really, really long time, finishing all tasks, doing your very best to succeed in life and to become the very best at all that you do, all that you can be, determined to do all that it honestly takes to succeed in the very best, honest and most lasting of ways, feeling proud of yourself and your accomplishments. You are feeling good, just as you know you should, and everyone around you is proud of you; you are proud of yourself, and life is getting better and easier.

You learn to love and to like yourself, treating yourself better in each and every thought, each and every word, each and every action that you take and in each and every way, you are learning to like and love yourself, more and more, better and better. While you might be sensitive, you know when to be sensitive and when to toughen up in the most powerful and effective of ways that will and do work for you. You are motivated to do better and better, taking better care of yourself and your life, doing all that it honestly takes to get the job effectively done. You are easily and effectively succeeding at this, in unstoppable ways.

# Master of Your Reality and Your Life

In this moment of extremely deep relaxation, you are in fact relaxing beyond any and all imbalanced and disharmonious barriers that had ever stood in your way, and you are sure and certain that you now flow easily beyond those old barriers from a previous chapter of your life that once sought relief. In fact you are certain and sure you have begun a brand new chapter of your life, free at long last, feeling wonderful now, being released from the chains and anchors that were present within the previous chapter of your life. You are now feeling lighter, liberated, safe, and stronger, rejuvenated, reinvented, re-calibrated, upbeat, clear, in fact feeling fine, optimistic, upbeat, while dynamically beginning a brand new chapter of your life, making the conscious choice as well as a subconscious choice, in fact choosing in every way, to be happy and upbeat, seeking and seeing the silver-lining in every cloud is an opportunistic possibility for the realization of a happier, brighter, upbeat view in a newer and better chapter of your life. Within your mind, within your emotions, you serenely allow yourself to bring back the memory and a sense of a time in your life when you felt upbeat, optimistic, even jubilant, perhaps when you were younger, on a holiday, or perhaps a birthday, when delighted, happy jubilation and joy seemed to bubble up from your stomach, from your heart and mind spreading a warm, contented glow through your entire body, and even beyond. Feel that experience as if you were there right now, and memorize what it feels like to feel so very great and know yourself and your life now, so balanced, so wonderful, and so good. It is time to re-experience that joy in your life, right now and keep it there, to rise above, and to embrace and become one with the centeredness and belief in the world around you, as you are meant to be here, you are vital, as well as you being a vital part of everyone's life that your life touches. It's almost as if from deep, deep inside of you a recalibrating switch, dial, thermostat, valve, or thermostat, has been powerfully, adaptively, and forever reset, overwhelmingly liberating a brighter, better you, while you are now and forever so easily transcending any and all challenges from previous chapters of your life that had ever stood in your way, ushering in unstoppably and forever this brighter, better you, certain, centered, peaceful, serene, determined, recalibrated, reset, and definitively freed, ahh, freedom at long last, seizing every moment as an opportunity to do better and better, while allowing yourself moments of relaxation, release, cleverness, fluid and skilled successful adaptation, while your correct response to any and all old challenges from your past is to relax your way beyond, over, and through, into the masterpiece of a brighter and better life, you now abundantly, adaptively, and cleverly, create and liberate, effortlessly, practically Divinely-inspired, feeling truly upbeat and even unbeatable.

Your days of sadness, your nights of sadness, your moments of uncertainty and sadness, are forever shunted and released into a past chapter of your life, almost as if the dark clouds from those days have being blown away and swept away, as a new dawn of sunshine arises forever in your life, and your inner light glowing from your heart and mind makes each and every one of these enhancements so. Sure and certain you are of the following fact: that a feeling is just a feeling, and a thought just a thought, an idea just an idea. And so far in your life, a feeling or a thought or an idea has never destroyed you, you're safe and sure. But even better right now, you are inspired by greater ideas and ideals, enhanced with life- supporting thoughts and emotions that unstoppably usher in a brand new chapter of your life, the masterpiece chapter of your life, now dynamically liberated and growing, which inspires you in the very most profound of ways to step forward, to live your dreams, to break through, to do all that it honestly takes to succeed, step by step, making surprising progress with adaptive and flowing ease, in knowing, growing, glowing, budding and building confidence, most especially in your relationships, just being yourself, most especially the relationship you have with yourself, being fine and OK with yourself, content to be who you are and who you are growing into, the very best you have to offer anyone, feeling and sure you are enhanced, released, forgiving, healed, improved, realizing your dreams, easily rising above, overcoming, and vanquishing, any and all old feelings of upset or stress, easily now handled by you as the Master of Your Reality and Your Life, inspired unbeatably and unstoppably to remain in a higher and greater harmony, enjoying and employing only a truest, best and most liberating of inspirations into the world around you, seizing the day, as well as the night, with a new sense of prowess, determined to turn around to work in your favor. Any and all things that ever once stood in your way, are now and forever done, you now, the mighty master of your life, even if the challenge is complex, usual or unusual, and even more so, an everyday event. For the more challenged, the easier it is for you. Each and every night, while you are awake or even while you are asleep, each and every morning while awakening, you are unbeatably, and undeniably, and unstoppably determined to improve your relationship with yourself, finding adaptive and clever ways to do this, not because I say so, but because it is the nature of your own mind to do this and so it is. As an extension of your improved view of life and yourself, you find your relationships with others, guided and inspired by an intuitive wisdom and understanding of who they are, tempered by your new and foundationally improved relationship with yourself, just going better and better. All of this right now seems to flow, in a brighter, better harmony, guided by an ever-expanding belief, trust, faith, and even knowingness within the rhythm and harmony of your life. For surely and for certain, in this moment, only growing stronger on each and every breath and heartbeat, the relief and the shedding of the energy, and uncomfortable embrace of the static, imbalanced and disharmonious energy from the last two or three years, is now and forever shed, gone and leaving you as a brighter, brilliant, inspirational, healing, recalibrating, re-harmonizing energy is now flourishing abundantly all around you, supporting you and caring for you, all of it flowing, budding, building, floating, all around you. You notice and sense this vibrant energy's embrace, as a profound inspiration, adaptively and fluidly harnesses this energy, right now it readily and easily flows through heart and mind, unleashing and activating only your very best.

In this new chapter of your life, you more easily rise up to instinctively and effectively blow off the imbalances, for the more challenged you become, the more adaptive, effective, stress-free and more fluid you are, skillful and with unstoppable passion, creativity, and enhanced mastery, you now calmly and skillfully rising up to meet all challenges, for the greater the challenge, the more motivated, skillful, clever, and adaptive you are in successfully breaking through as needed, for each and every moment, you are certain, serene and sure all of this is becoming easier and easier, as you've now released into greater places a passion and success into each and every moment that is your life.

# Motivation & Relaxation: Creating Balance and Healing

Your powerful and cleverly adaptive mind is both now and forever always working things out in your favor. Your determined and unstoppable mind is now willing to relax you beyond, over, beyond and through any and all old barriers that you may have been encountering, creating a new balance and harmony to your life, a can-do and willing spirit, activating your truly unstoppable ability to rise above all limitations, either real or imagined, even to the point of restoring and healing, beyond what others around you have told you are capable of. Just like noticing a paper cut, long after you've experienced it, and then experiencing discomfort, you're beginning to now realize that any and all former discomfort is now completely and totally under your control, that after just a few deep centering breaths, it's almost as if someone from deep, deep, deep inside of you has reset a switch, a dial, a computer or a thermostat of some kind that is only easily allowing you to balance, heal, restore, reset, recalibrate, rebalance, almost as if, any and all discomfort from your past, both real or imagined, is now easily under your control, forgiven, healed, released, let go of. Now you are feeling free and steady, after taking a few deep, steadying, life-giving, recalibration breaths, you can actually feel yourself restoring, pleasantly making numb, whenever you need to, forever liberated and freed from any and all former blockages from a previous chapter of your life. Truly in fact, it's almost like, that your brain is actually re-circuiting itself, to allow you better coordination, healing, strength, balance, fearlessness, inner strength, inner wisdom, feeling, noticing and truly coming to know, that you are mightier and more powerful than any challenge that has ever been presented to you. You are rising to the top; you are unbeatable; your healing is paramount; it is being accomplished, like a martial arts master or skilled acrobat, you're finding a new sense of balance, harmony, inner strength, and you are unstoppably rising up to meet any and all challenges presenting themselves, from the raw determination and the abilities you have, to remain determined, to be unbeatable at any and all of this, because you can, you will, and you are, rising above all challenges. You are relaxing beyond and through any and all challenges, rising to the top, realizing you will and do master your old and useless and now forever vanquished and under your control discomforts, creating pleasant numbness as needed, realizing that you'll find new balance within yourself, almost like you're making a game of it, for the more challenged you become, the more clever and adaptive you become, to get back on your feet, discomfort-free, stronger, better and mighty, almost as if the mighty inner hero from deep, deep inside of you, the part of you that is capable of saving children from great danger, is now unleashed in working only in your favor, to seal, to heal, to lubricate, to make pleasantly numb, to re-circuit you, while allowing you unstoppable determination to rise above any and all limits from the previous chapter of your life, now that you are in a brand new chapter of your life, finding better balance, healing, newer pathways to unlimited success both in and outside of you. In fact you're allowing all that you are experiencing to work in your favor, most especially any medicines that you're on, allowing them to work to your limitless and precise benefit, and the most profound and most dynamic of effective ways, they are absorbed properly and working just right, just right for you, while you now know and you are completely open to their greatest potential beneficial effects, as they work in perfect harmony and concert just for you. The greater and the mightier challenge once was to you in a previous chapter of your life, the mightier you are as your inner hero is unleashed, to allow you to smoothly and safely walk, walk up or down a flight of stairs, in safety, in harmony and in balance, because while it might have once been OK to fall, you are doing better than that, and from the greatest and strongest place is deep, deep inside of you; you know better and are doing better for yourself. Your mind and in fact all of you, is now unstoppably creating adaptive and clever life-supporting and self-supporting ways, to tell your muscles effectively, precisely and with great success, in ways that work for you to suit your best, you now, stress-free, and anxiety-free. You are and you remain strong, centered, balanced, focused, serene, and sure that you are effectively and unstoppably in a brand new balanced and comfortable, fully functioning exciting chapter of your life, almost as if you've just had the experience of fifteen to twenty years worth of powerfully effective healing, just knowing that you're doing better and better and better, worry-free, in balance, fearless, doubtless and mightier than you have ever been, as every thought, feeling, experience, breath and heartbeat, including all medications, are now working unstoppably and effectively, even perfectly in your favor to break you through here, not because I say so, but because you are more determined than you have ever been before to do this and so you are doing it, and forever onward so it is.

## Motivation for Success

Relax even deeper now and as you do, you realize that something wonderful is happening to you, something you may have hoped or even prayed for, but very powerfully, it truly is happening to you and its unstoppable and it feels great. As you relax even deeper and deeper, you feel almost as if, a wonderful energy is enveloping you, a limitless energy of inspiration is coming upon you. You can feel it in your skin, a happy yet powerful excitement is building from deep within your stomach area, your heart rate is calm, yet strong. You have decided to open up your life and you have decided to absolutely thrive. You have actually begun to open up your life and to liberate the best and most potent potentials in your world, in the most beneficial inspired thoughts, ideas and solutions are beginning to activate within you right now. I wonder if you are feeling bold, a bit more and more fearless, completely expanding your horizons, really truly liberating your most powerful potentials. You are less and less fearful of shortfalls in your life actually, both now and forever, you embrace and easily rise above them. For instead right now, you focus powerfully upon and truly activate into your reality, more and more each and every day and night, the benefit of the lessons in your life you have learned from, feeling yourself thriving from all of the benefits of your years of powerful learning experiences, free of all past judgments, thriving from the limitless benefit of everything that is your life. All you have ever pictured, imagined or have even experienced, you have learned from and you are still learning from your past experiences. All of these experiences have polished you, allowed you to grow and when you really think about it or even look back on it in any way, you've always met your challenges sometimes easily, but always powerfully and successfully. All of your life has taught you and motivated you. And whether you've realized it in your past or if in fact you are realizing it right now, all that you've done has been necessary in your life process. Even if you've realized it or not, many, many times you've helped to light up the world with the power of what you've done. So, right now, as you relax, you draw upon all of the power of your beneficial past experiences, to empower yourself, to succeed, to thrive, to benefit, to actively create, better and better experiences, actually magnetizing only the best successful opportunities and very best experiences that life willingly shares with you.

Beginning right now, you absolutely stop trying, you relinquish struggling and even better, you relax and liberate into your life, all of the energy that will motivate success in the most vital areas of your life. You find and you take the time to begin to record your very best most inspired ideas, you start making a plan, you follow a schedule and you begin to build upon each inspired moment. You and everyone you know, actually begin to notice, you seem to be getting better and better, in fact better than you have ever been. You begin to truly recognize, you are the power in your life. You are always there for yourself, just as you've always been there for others, unleashing your limitless inner power, living from this power. By you just being an important part of this world, even in some small way, you are helping to light up the hearts and minds of everyone you meet, your positive outlook and attitude, is unstoppably beginning a chain reaction from you outward and into others. You also recognize you have been liberated from any restrictions you may have once suffered from in your past, your past is only a memory, the secret is that your past's real power is in how it has polished you. You are becoming each and every day and night, challenge-oriented and completely problem-free, anger-free. You cleverly and correctly have chosen to convert any and all problems into challenges. And you know challenges are things you can improve, change, grow and learn from, so even they support you, in your success. Any and all old feelings of anger are being converted now in this process, their energy, becomes like rocket fuel, accelerating you into new vistas and dynamically into all that you aspire to in your life, even into better places and circumstances, than you've ever as yet, had realized were possible. You have set out to rise above any and all challenges and you can, you will, in fact, you do, just as you've really always done. And all of your best inner wisdom, inner beauty, inner harmony, inner hidden abilities just flow out of you into the world in an endless supply, manifesting and magnetizing all of your success, bringing it right here into the right now, bursting forth into your life. All the success you deserve, create and have to share, more powerfully and magnificently, because its always been your nature to do so, right now you feel good throughout all that You are stress-free, peaceful and in harmony with the world and with your life and all of those whom you love and with all that needs doing and will get done, having set a wonderful stress-free pace and tone to your life and your world, you function smoothly, relaxed, calmly, determined, creatively, effectively, you're unstoppably successful, you succeed powerfully in truly new and amazing ways and its so very easy for you. And it only gets better and better in any and all future moments. So feel the embrace of all that You are body, emotions, mind, relaxing, thriving and succeeding, for that's who You are you made a breakthrough, you are victorious, successful, limitless, completely re-adapted, re-paced, re-identified, harmonized, stress-free and you win! You relax and go into every moment of your life, stress-free and peaceful, a winner in every way, trusting in your life, trusting each and every circumstance, each and every event, each and every moment, and you win, forever and always, stress-free.

## Overcoming Clutter

So right now as you relax, you deeply and truly realize that you have made a very important decision, a decision that you have made and that you are going to stick with. You have truly decided to forgive your past and all of its hurts and all of its traumas. And by forgiving your past, you are also forgiving and releasing any and all of its fears and feelings of inadequacy. Your life right now truly supports you in the most wonderful of ways, because there's always enough, for you, for your family and those you love, most especially even you. You are finding, newer and better ways, of letting go of any feelings, whether you realize what they are, whatever and wherever they are, because you are absolutely letting go of the concept of lack within your life. And what is replacing it, are powerful, stronger feelings, feelings of being fulfilled, having succeeded, having triumphed, having been polished by any of the adversity that you may have once encountered, because you have succeeded and perhaps even thrived. In actuality, you have always succeeded and thrived in your life, in spite of events or circumstances. You have survived many amazing challenges, but that's the way you see them and saw them, as challenges. Something that was there to rise up from and to learn from and to be polished from and you've always succeeded in that, so its time right now to give yourself credit for that, so right now, you feel like you can smile in the inside and even on the outside, because you have always gotten through anything and everything life has thrown your way. You even might recognize, that you are even more than the sum of your experiences, you are the master of your life and you are living a life that each and every day and night, nurtures you and supports you in the very best ways. You always have enough these days, feeling enriched. Each and every day and night, you are always being supported, you are always cared for, you are free from the moments and days from the past, when you had to scrimp and save anything and everything. Because beginning right now and for the rest of your life, you have truly begun to live from and very truly and most powerfully begun to know, that your life is supporting you better and it is taking better and better care of you each and every day and night. Your life has always supported you and in each and every moment, you have either learned or succeeded. Things might have been hard or tough, but you are absolutely releasing that concept and all of its ramifications, because you are focused upon how life is always supporting you, taking care of you and how you are supported by your life, your loved ones, your beliefs, and most importantly, how you support yourself. And as you unclutter your home (office), you unclutter your thoughts and your feelings and your life. You relax right now and in all future moments, into a happy more peaceful way of living, being clear, safe, happy, content, supported by all that your life is and all that your life will bring. The rainy days of your past are gone, the skies of your life are forever clear, bright and sunny and as you recognize this, you are feeling better and better each and every day and night. You recognize, that You are able to release all things that are not completely necessary from your life and your world, just throwing away things that you will never be served by, this also includes all old and useless thoughts and feelings that may hold you back from enjoying your life to its fullest, any and all old fears from your past, so you right now release all and any doubt, any and all old cluttered emotions that had once created fear, you are far too important, powerful and mighty and have come through too much to allow fear to grip you in any way, because you have always succeeded and thrived in the most wonderful of ways. And you truly feel like you can pat yourself on the back, for always having risen up in each and every moment of your life, a good and decent person who has been there for others when he - she was needed, but right now, even better, being there for yourself, empowering yourself to all relinquish and release all doubt, disharmony and discomfort, having given yourself complete and total permission, to relax through and release and any and all clutter in your life, its going, going and its completely gone! Because you love yourself and all of your family and friends too much and you always provide a safe and clean environment for yourself and your family, all of those whom you love and let the clutter of the past, physical things or any items, even emotional or mental aspects or in any other area of your life, to stand in the way, of the clearness that is today, the today that is clear and supportive. And in your powerful and pivotal place of calm determination, you are absolutely determined to support and love yourself, in the most creative, amazing and impressive ways possible, throwing out or even better, liberating yourself from all things that would slow you down or even interfere with the kind of a relaxed, calm, peaceful, well ordered and happy life you deserve. By removing clutter, you are truly supporting yourself, your family, your loved ones and freeing yourself and them as well, of those burdens in every form. Burden-less, burden-free, you are and now and you forever remain. Throwing out the blockages from past, makes room for the brightest of futures and shows the world, your family, (coworkers), friends, loved ones and most especially even you, the trust and support you have in your life, your beliefs and in yourself, and you bask in the glow, of the power that shows through from this new and most empowered you!

## Overcoming Procrastination

And as you relax, deeper and further, further and deeper, you realize from deep within a new and truly-inspired motivational thought is coming upon you, and it's only getting stronger and better in every passing future moment, this powerful unstoppable thought and feeling. You are, in fact, beginning a new chapter of your life right now that only gets stronger and better with each and every passing day, to completely improve your body, your emotions, your mind and each and every thought and action, truly improving all that is your life. In this new and more empowered, highly effective and reconditioning, powerful chapter of your life, it's time for you to begin a better harmony with your life, so each and every thought is now realigning itself, allowing for a better pace in your life and an improved series of steps and actions to take place. You are truly building a healthy and most beneficial new urge, new passion, and a new powerful motivation. And just like an unstoppable force, almost like a nagging need, this passion, your passion, begins burning like a flame, a flame that slowly grows and burns strong and burns bright.

It's time for you to get moving and start to take better care of yourself, as a proper person should, just like a proper adult, and you now do. You are setting up your mind, emotions and thoughts to unstoppably take better care of yourself in ways that matter most for you to succeed in any and all areas of your life. So you are finding, making and creating the time needed to do all the things you once resisted doing, relaxing into a better and more adaptively successful way of life and of living, getting all chores and tasks done early, so things get done on time and in the most effective ways. It might just be writing out and paying your bills on time, just setting aside the time to sit down and do something because it needs to be done and you deserve to have it done on time because you are too important to avoid doing this, so you succeed at this skillfully, effectively and successfully, so you relax into this newer and better rhythm and just get it done. It's almost like you are feeling super motivated to just get up and do it, so you do and feel happy, proud and even relieved when it has been done to completion.

You will and can feel a warm, small, powerfully determined glow beginning from within you, a passionate desire to move beyond putting things off and just getting things done, because your sense of self-value and self-worth is going up and up, like someone from deep, deep inside of you has reset a switch, a dial, a computer or thermostat of some kind, super-motivating you and allowing you to win and thrive at this, because you deserve to and you are unstoppably determined to do so, and because you unstoppably deserve this as you are far too important to do anything else that might have ever once stood in the way of your success. You are feeling a new and better, more profound sense of support from your life, urging you ever onward, building a new and more powerful regimen and skill at succeeding at this.

In the past, you may have found reasons, even excuses, to find other things to do, almost like when a child can find some excuses to not accomplish some chore or homework assignment. But better than that, you relax deeper now, you powerfully and truly forgive those moments, flowing past, over and around them, moving on and around any and all once uncomfortable judgments, upon those moments and upon you.

So you relax, you release, you forgive those past moments forever right now. But right now and for the rest of your life, you are seizing and bringing forth all of the unlimited and highly effective power and unlimited inspiration of all of your adult years of learning and experience. They are upon you now, the energy of all of your past victories, successes, triumphs, and breakthroughs, to motivate you, to get things done, performing all needed tasks you will now enjoy getting done in the most healthy beneficial ways, so right just for you, to completion, accomplishing each and every step of the way, easily, successfully, precisely and carefully doing all that it takes, no matter what, to begin to give yourself the gift of better timing and being highly effective at moving beyond old, and now and forever, drifting-away patterns of procrastination for you to now and forever take better care of yourself and to find a better pace and to now and forever adaptively succeed, in the very best, well-timed and most highly effective of ways. And you feel great, wonderful and fantastic, even better than excellent. Each and every day and night, you are only getting better, just feeling great physically, emotionally, mentally; feeling wonderful and fantastic throughout all that is your life, that you are creating and knowing that you are proceeding in ways that are right and beneficial, just perfect and right, just for you. You absolutely recognize from deep, deep within and even know, you've begun this new chapter of your life in profound and unstoppable ways. You remember uncomfortable times from the past, that are just beginning to drift away now, when it was easy for just about anyone, even you, to find an excuse, to sit and do nothing or even be distracted. But those times are forever over! They are just drifting away, drifting away, gone and gone forever. You truly recognize that the superior person will get up and accomplish all that it takes, slowly, deliberately, carefully, with skill, correct, careful, fluid and flowing precise movement and with creative, empowered, success-inspired determination, to achieve all that is necessary. That person, is you! You correctly think to yourself, "It's time to just get up and do it!" "That's right, just get up and do it!" Right now, truly always and forever, you feel and truly are, motivated, successful, thinking creatively, achieving powerfully, always allowing for at least just a few short minutes to just get up and do it, allowing yourself this kind of benefit, succeeding and motivated, a motivated exercise person, just like some others you've met; you find the time to perfect your skills, always finding and allowing the time, to be the kind of motivated, goal-oriented person you were born to be, now living as that person.. In fact, you are that kind of person. You are now and forever getting it done and doing all that it takes. In fact, on each and every breath that you take and on each and every beat of your heart, you are cleverly creating newer and better ways to succeed at this, unstoppably, an easy goal, even your little wins mean a lot and you feel fine.

## Public Speaking - Corporate

You are feeling fine, so calm, so peaceful, so relaxed. You are feeling inspired now, capable, comfortable, able to take on any challenge, completely inspired and ready to thrive. It's almost as if, the energy of every past victory, triumph, breakthrough and success you've ever had is flowing down like a blessing upon you. It's almost as if in fact, truly, someone from deep, deep inside of you has thrown a switch, reset a dial, activated a computer or a thermostat of some kind, easily allowing you to become and remain calm, cool and collected in your thoughts, within your ability to express yourself and to convey your knowledge in creative, bold, gripping and powerfully effective ways. Your thoughts are calm, you are feeling, glib, persuasive, determined, free-flowing, smooth and convincing. For truly now you empowered and deeply and passionately inspired to convey all and any points with comfortable ease. Your heart rate, body and skin are all calm, soothing, rhythmic and balanced. You now and forever release and forgive any and all past blockages, uncomfortable memories and any and all pain. In fact, you are moving on into a brighter and more brilliant future, easily able to express yourself in any situation articulately, with grace, poise, skill, ease while easily magnetizing and generating interest from all who hear your words and gain from your knowledge (most especially when you have to enjoyably give a speech or when sitting in senior level meetings, even while in social settings when dealing with managers or executives you feel calm, relaxed, and balanced, just flowing and melting into new waves of comfortability and also at times you relax, you take it easy, you are so very calm, so in your zone). Your correct response to any and all old modes or stress or tension, is to rise up, to become bigger than the challenge at hand and to rise above it powerfully and dynamically, stress free, balanced, focused, relaxed, calm, clear and precise ways. All emotions, thoughts, ideas, action and feelings are working unstoppably in your favor to support you and to allow you to succeed, and it feels great. You are in fact now re-identified as a person who has moved on and is able to speak at anytime and in any place and you deeply and truly certain and sure of this. The only opinion of you that matters is your own, and you know you can do it. You respect yourself and know you have limitless reserves of talent, tapping into those reserves whenever you need to.

You only allow your very best to come through in the most self-assured of ways. All that you have to say gets easier and better as you feel so in our zone, so comfortable, so calm, so relaxed, so peaceful and so very richly inspired. Each person there to hear you, is truly a fan and a supporter. You are so sure of your self, you know it now and forever. Your words just seem to flow, breathing so very calm, so very balanced and so very relaxed, throat open and words just so easily flowing. You are highly efficient and effective, so worthy and deserving of praise, so self-starting, so self-supported, so ready, willing and able, so ready, skin so comfortable, so ready, so peaceful, so having moved on, so ready each and every day, each and every moment before and even during the week before. You are so ready, you are sure of yourself and your abilities in a newer and brighter and happier chapter of your life, just like you've begun anew. You are the focused, yet from now on and only getting better and easier and more powerful, you have newer and better thoughts and feelings that support you in profoundly better ways. You are allowing yourself to either thrive and succeed or just to communicate freely and clearly, breaking through the past and becoming victorious in all future speech giving opportunities. Your concentration and your focus are laser-beam like precise.

You see yourself as a superior as a teacher, a leader, one who leads another to knowledge. All who are listening to you are deeply interested in what you have to say, as you lead them to the knowledge and the wisdom your words have to impart to them to enlighten and enliven, to streamline, make more efficient, to create and to make better. Like a model family and wonderful friends, those who listen to your words are supporting you. You know from deep down inside they want you to succeed. They are rooting for you, they are on your side, they want you to succeed, so you do, in newer and more creative and brilliantly powerful ways. And everything just seems to flow, for your ability to communicate, clearly and confidently, successfully, succinctly, directly, with cool and calm emotions, harmonized and balanced thoughts, each and every self-supporting action, just works. All of you is just freely flowing, you are supported, by your very own thoughts, words and emerging talents as your thriving confidence just seems to build and build. You feel like you've got the whole world in your back pocket, like you are ready to communicate to the world or at least to some of the people who have come to hear your important brilliance flow out from your words and thoughts. You are and you remain so relaxed, so determined and so very cool and calm in the most brilliant and powerful of ways, communicating, clearly, you are balanced, you are a self assured and unstoppable force, appreciated, calm and forever succeeding.

## Public Speaking – Media Success

A new thought is beginning from deep, deep inside of you; a thought that is now becoming glowing, growing stronger and more and more fluidly adaptable, more and more comfortable to you, for you to easily and forever bring up only your very best and powerfully mighty inner hero; the part of you that knows no blockage, no hindrance, is unstoppable, undefeatable; the part of you that knows no defeat, only knows success and the ability to rise to the top; not only because I say so, but because, in fact and indeed, it's only the truth, that you are now and forever ushering in a newer and better chapter of your life, which allows your inner superstar to rise to the top and just flow in any and all circumstances around you, finding a safe and powerful inner space, an inner place of calm, direction and inner peace, one in which you are free of over thinking, over-analyzing. You are truly, in fact, serene and up personality-wise, finding a few friends in any crowd that allow you to express, share, and succeed, because you deep down know truly you were meant to be there. Speaking in public or to large groups, while calming soothing breath, keeps you cool, calm, collected, focused, articulate, glib, only at your very best, fluent, chatty, easy, flowing, confident, assured, reassured, as if from deep, deep inside of you, a switch, a dial, a thermostat, a computer or a valve of some kind has been unstoppably and forever activated, working in your favor, in simple, complex and even amazing ways, allowing you to break through here, forgiven, healing and healed, centered and focused, re-identified in all of these ways, forever and always in a brand new chapter of your life, freed from the now broken chains of the past, forever freed and forgiven at long last, your inner celebrity just rising to the very top, now and forever just knowing what to say, cool and calm, up and happy, delighted to be there, each and every powerfully supportive and precise heartbeat and soothing breath are all calm and balanced. You now re-identified as mighty, remembering your lines, easily doing better than you ever imagined, seizing and now using once that once was negative energy, to your powerful and forever harnessed advantage, truly just glowing inside and out. Each and every calming and relaxing breath, soothing you, zoning you in. Fearless and mighty, flowing and glowing, you are and you remain. You, now just being confident in your auditions and knowing that you did a great job, of course you have, cutting yourself a break this time, free of over-thinking in any way, succeeding in amazing ways; of course you can, so you do! Taking the energy of the fear from the past and other chapter of your life, harnessing it, and turning yourself into the one who is mighty and bigger than any old challenge, problem-free, challenge-oriented, accepting and taking on any and all old challenges. In fact, truly with each and every breath, and each and every heartbeat, you are shining light into the shadow that was any fear and vanquishing all shadows with your inner light, which shines from your heart, your mind and from your face, lighting up any room you enter. You just seizing all of the very best offers and many roles, accepting into your life and very existence, all great opportunities, embracing it all. As you exhale now slowly, feel the new chapter of your life beginning, reaching and flowing beyond your goals, and you are just doing so much more!

For you are unstoppably and forever more empowered, stronger, more confident in your mind and even with the choices you make in your life. You have a fun life, an easy life, an exciting life, and now effectively create with surprising ease-- by relaxing beyond any and all old barriers-- the more stable, fulfilling life you deserve and career you now artistically create, regret-free. You create your very best dreams; you live your dreams; you seize opportunities, investing in real estate, modeling, travel, starting a clothing line, meet the coolest people, you the coolest of the bunch, being promoted by a PR man for magazines, TV, radio, just more comfortable and at ease in front of the camera, just creating the confidence to do more, and so it is, and so you do. As you are pretty cool and comfortable with photography, so too, you can see it's more than speaking; you are doing fine, little steps like giant strides. The consummate professional within you is now active and thriving, alive and living, rising up to the top and working only in your favor. Shed and now set aside, are the childish fears you once had that stood in your way, as you move on easily, directly and powerfully.

## Self-Confidence (Teenage)

You relax into a better and brighter way of life, and firmly begin to know who you are in your life, opening yourself to the limitless possibilities and joining in the joys that are life, empowering yourself and trusting in your life, loving life and yourself in most effective and powerful ways, leading the kind of happy and well adjusted life you deserve to have and now unstoppably create. You are adapting to finding newer and better ways of adjusting to releasing any and all critical and harsh judgments by way of forgiveness, from yourself, from others, but most especially yourself. Now liberated from that past and free, you are flowing ever onward past any and all things, any and all people who would have steered you off course, feeling centered and focused, grounded and re-calibrated, moving into brighter and better horizons and vistas for yourself and for those you love, completely re-conditioned, just doing better and better, trusting in your life and those who love you, trusting in and loving yourself and knowing the truly and powerfully deep-down right things to do for your life and your future. In the past it might have been easy to say I don't care, but have secretly deep-down did care, but now in reality, you do care and are easily and mightily rising up to meet each and every challenge, easily and effectively and brilliantly activating only your most inspired and very best to seek the best of all possible outcomes for yourself, your life and for all of those concerned, succeeding in glowing and brilliant ways, while activating inner wisdom, with the truest and best of intentions and greatest and most wonderful outcomes.

You now begin to activate your own inner leadership qualities, trusting in your own thoughts, and judgments, self- reliant, self-approving, truly and unstoppably knowing who you are, and loving who you are, becoming all that you are, rising up to be the very best you can be, meant to be here and rooted into your life. On top of the world, upbeat and relaxing through any and all barriers, into brighter and better days and nights, fulfilling your dreams and unstoppably moving on in your life.

You begin to take better care of yourself, trusting in the fact that you are moving yourself into better places in your life and planning on taking excellent care of yourself for your health and upkeep, treating yourself in every way like someone you love, heal, forgive and take better care of. As you begin to love yourself more and more, taking better and better care of yourself, just cutting yourself a break and simply just deciding to take better care of yourself, in the long and short term, you begin to see something of yourself in other people and begin to take an interest in them as well, finding better and improved ways to be kind, outgoing and more patient. You are feeling at one with yourself, people, animals and things in your life in newer and more improved ways, just treating yourself and others in the very best and most caring of ways. You are growing up, almost like you are evolving in your life 5 years into the future, and allowing yourself to thrive, succeed and do better, forgiving and releasing any and all harshness from the past, finding inner peace, harmony, comfortability, healing and truly, whether you realize it or not, inner wisdom, harmony and balance, creating a more fluid, more adaptive and flowing, adaptively powerful center within yourself. It might have been easy to feel down, and once, you did that; but now, even better, you've adaptively moved into a brand new and better chapter of your life and easily allowed yourself to thrive, not because I say so, but because it's the nature of your own powerful mind and personal improvement and upgraded system that is allowing you to thrive in newer and better ways, responsible ways, because you deserve it. You come to learn to love, trusting your own inner wisdom and judgment, most especially and in spite of those influences and opinions of others, the most important opinion of all is yours, and following your own inner guidance and wisdom, you become and remain steadily and powerfully focused and balanced, trusting, loving, healing and rising above, activating talents and abilities, truly enjoying your life's path, in spite of and because of all challenges, because you are more determined to create inner harmony and guidance, than ever before, while allowing yourself to be wonderful and fantastic; truly, you are learning and allowing yourself to flourish and become better and more and more amazing, better and better than ever before.

## Self-Confidence and Re-Excited About Life

You have more and more limitless confidence in yourself, building, building, building in a new and powerful ways, in an unstoppable flow. You are re-excited about your life, finding new ways to enjoy yourself, and to live and to create greater abundance in your life in all of the very best ways possible, finding, making and creating more time for yourself to win in your life; in fact, you feel lively, energetic, motivated, empowered, inspired, vigorous, and powerfully full of life. Your ability to concentrate becomes so very active, and you find yourself easily able to concentrate with laser-beam like precision, for you've entered into a brand new chapter of your life. All of your best just easily flows, every thought, feeling and idea, each and ever action, just constructively flows, in clear and precise communication, clearly, cleverly, and sharply, healing balancing, healing, activating and restoring all that you are to surprisingly powerful, newest, best, potent potentials. You learn to like and even better, now and forever love yourself, learning to cut yourself a break and love, trust and take care of yourself in all the ways you know you should. You are now and forever easily able to stop caring about what other people think and so very easily able to stop yourself from letting other people bother you. You now and forever know and truly learn that what they think of you is none of your business and now that you are feeling fulfilled, taken care of and supported with an ever-building sense of self-worth, and a true and knowing belief in yourself. You are feeling upbeat and on top of the world.

You are finding newer and better ways of becoming, and forever remaining now and forever, free of ever and in any way getting hung up worrying over what others think. You are learning to speak your mind when it's appropriate or to correct a situation, so easily able to take and make the correct and appropriate actions needed, because you're now confidently self- assured, even fearless; what you think and feel is what's important to you, and healing to your world and life. All of this powerful, unstoppable and profound improvement is now working in correct and precise motion to enhance and improve your personal and professional life. You are finding and easily achieving newer and better ways to build and forever increase well-structured Self Confidence. You are finding and easily achieving newer and better ways to build and forever increase well-structured Self Esteem. You are finding and easily achieving newer and better ways to build and forever overcome useless habits from your past that once hindered you, easily moving onward to brighter vistas and horizons in your life. You are feeling so upbeat, so motivated, so powerful, so victorious, so breaking-through, vanquishing all doubt and fears, feeling motivated to thrive and succeed in your life, or at least just this, and it's easy. So you dynamically and cleverly create a new and forever improving attitude adjustment. To be more relaxed and positive of a person, is who you are, what you are about, and how you now and forever successfully thrive and succeed in your life, improving unstoppably.

# Trusting in Life and Divine Support

It has been said that a thought is just a thought, a feeling is just a feeling, and so far no thought or feeling you have ever had, felt, imagined or experienced has ever destroyed you; for in fact, you know you have been and actually are Divinely-supported and guided, and truly in fact, are now and forever empowered to rise above any and all thoughts, feelings, and ideas that might have ever stood in your way. In fact, right now your mighty inner hero is being freed up, liberated and unleashed to a greater and grander, mightier place, where in fact truly and forever, your mighty inner hero is now liberated, both safe and strong, rising to the very top; in fact, undeniably, you are unbeatable. The part of you that is capable of saving children from a fire or from some sort of severe danger is now being unleashed; you are rising to the top as your mighty inner hero is unleashed, from places deep, deep inside of you, creating a more naturally unlimited you, the powerful part of you that knows only power and truth, doubtless, fearless, while truly inspired and empowered in fluid, completely effective and adaptive ways, all of this energy and inspiration is now allowing you to face down any thought, any doubt, any disturbance, any disharmony or discomfort from your past; for in fact, you, like a mighty and unbeatable warrior or an unstoppable master of olden times, is now rising to the top, more unlimited, dynamic, and determined, to break through here, in the most unbeatable of ways. Your clever and completely correct response to any and all old patterns that caused you stress or discomfort in any way, is to relax yourself and your way, by deep breathing yourself into a calmer, more balanced, more trusting, more empowered, and Divinely-protected and guided series of loving thoughts, ideas, and feelings. With God on your side, there is nothing to fear; you are truly taken care of. Your powerful subconscious mind is now unstoppably working in your favor, to allow you and your soothing, life-supporting breath, to de-stress you while instilling a sense of comfort and powerful protection, as you're embraced by a higher protective light. Your powerful, always-working-in-your- favor subconscious mind, is correcting any and all thoughts and imbalances from the past chapter of your life. You're now sure you are in a brand new chapter of your life, better protected, more caring, more loved, more supported, and better taken care of, more than ever before. Any and all things, thoughts, feelings, ideas, actions and reactions, that ever worked against you, are now reversed back against themselves, working only in your favor, to only allow you in the most unlimited of ways to break through here and become free, as each and every thought becomes more serene, tranquil, trusting, you now and forever, better taken care of, and self-supporting, and in the most beautiful of ways, as an anxiety-free and more comfortable you is now and forever unstoppably emerging, and you know truly, adaptively and actively that you are and remain, all throughout the day and even more so at night, more easily able, as all of this just getting easier and better for you on each and every slow and steady breath and regular, soothing heartbeat, for it is your time to feel wonderful, and you know that you're supported and taken care of, now and forever, and so it is.

Your light and life-force, both inner and outer, is now forever vanquishing any and all shadows. You develop new and better ways of thinking, acting, reacting and feeling, not because I say so, but because it's in the nature of your own dynamic mind to achieve this easily, for your own good, and so it is and remains forever. Your mind relaxes, your breath relaxes and reassuringly flows, as you relax and flow through and beyond any and all old barriers from previous chapters of your life, because you are solidly, most assuredly and completely into a brand new chapter of your life, and ahh, it feels so good to be there.

In the perfection of our hindsight, as our lives go by, we come to know, that all things are as they should be, working out in our lives. You know where you should be, all it takes is looking down at your feet. You trust in the fact that you are where you should be. Should any life improving change need to take place, you trust in yourself and make whatever adjustments need to be there, feeling wonderful, supported and guided. It's almost like you're jumping back over the years to a time fifteen or sixteen years ago, seeing where who you are now merging with who you were then, and making a powerful and forever life improving decision, to completely trust in your life and to rise above all limitations, shining a light from your heart and your mind in balance, which creates wisdom, to guide your way.

## Weight and Life Motivation

Your relationship with food is now improving in your favor; each and every thought, habit and action in this brand new and better chapter of your life, now sees and reacts to food as a source of nourishment. Less is more, less is more; you fill up sooner and know when you've had enough. You are now learning and completely determined to take the very best care of yourself, as the weight just seems to melt off and you are enthusiastic about the power and effectiveness, the ease and grace you now discover from deep, deep within yourself. You are problem-free, challenge-oriented, rising up to meet all challenges wherever they come from with the courage and drive of a mighty, mighty hero, just like you've always actually done. You are forgiven, healing, healed and released from the ways and patterns of the past; not because I say so, but because you have once and for all, once and forever put your foot down and taken charge of your life here.

You are motivated to move beyond the ways of old and move into a newer, better, more motivated way of life and living, being true to yourself, maybe even energetic and re-enthused about your life and your world. It's almost like someone from deep, deep inside of you has reset a switch, a dial, a powerful and-or effective computer of some kind, allowing you to get motivated, lively and re-excited about your life. You find joy in little things, newer things, things of enjoyment, even things involving work, because you realize now that life is about living and living is something you are determined to do; upbeat, happy and clear, you are moving forward unstoppably. You begin to believe in yourself, trust in your life and a new thought dawns upon you: your life is now supporting you in better and truer ways, just as it always has, only in this brand new chapter of your life, even better and better than ever before. You are willing to feel good, even great about yourself, in this brand new, dawning chapter of your life. You find things to enjoy, laugh about, be upbeat and clear about, focused, working toward new goals that are not only interesting, but also thrivingly support and excite you. You heal, you forgive, you take better care, you trust in your life and knowing who you are and how you are there to take the very best care of yourself, just relaxing beyond any and all old barriers from your past into the very best days and nights, opportunities you now create and embrace, making all of this your very own, feeling directed, healed, forgiven, released and taken care of in your life and in your world and in each and everything you are thinking, doing, feeling and acting and reacting to, moment by moment, with each life-giving and life-supporting breath you are taking. With every move you are making and with each and every beat of your heart, you are doing better and better, just fine, learning to not only just live your life, but to thrive and to savor the joys of each and every moment, making the whole experience a Masterpiece. You know who you are; you are excited about your life and your world, and you know who you are and what you are interested in and excited by, and do all that it takes to accomplish your life goals, which are surprisingly more and more apparent to you. You take on new things with ambition, pacing yourself, taking care, loving yourself and those around you, but most especially yourself, as if the floodgates of love and healing within you from, deep, deep inside of you are now opened to provide limitless support, forgiveness, healing, heroic courage, wisdom, energy, vitality, passion, joy and the ability to rise above the old ways, creating a passionate paradise for you right now, as things are seemingly falling into place, easily and precisely accomplishing all that you now set out to do, and that you do, and all that you will do, unstoppably, rising to the top, doing all that it honestly takes, because you now know you can.

# You're About To Have A Breakthrough

Relax, relax, relax, and as you relax, profoundly, powerfully, deeply and truly, a wonderful feeling is beginning to spread throughout your stomach area, a feeling of unknotting, release, a very joyous and wonderful sensation, a feeling of wonderful and happy anticipation, a feeling of wonderment, even maybe joyous excitement, just like the times when you were a kid, when it might have been your birthday or a holiday or perhaps a time when you felt triumphant, victorious, a time when you were just about to gain or win in a surprising and wonderful way, a great time, the very best time, a time when you just knew, something wonderful was about to come your way, a wonderful time of receiving gifts and receiving adoration, a time when you really truly felt wonderful, with happy and profound optimistic excitement, limitless joy and a wonderful happy anticipation. You feel the inspired happy, supportive, energy of all of those moments beginning to flood you and you feel an unstoppable smile starting to begin, (smile) yes you can, yes you do. You feel this joyous energy building unstoppably from deep, deep within you. You are really smiling very powerfully on the inside and it's building, it's building, it's building from places deep within you, it's there inside of you, growing stronger and stronger. And yes, it's starting to overflow, this smile, your smile, your wonderful smile, is starting to leak out into your face now and across your lips and your smile is unstoppable, it's moving across your mouth, you just can't help it and very soon, even now, your whole face is smiling and it feels like this joyous smile is spreading all across your face, unstoppable, all across your face and even throughout all that is your body and your emotions and your mind and thoughts and even most powerfully and assuredly throughout all that is your spirit, you can't help it, it's happening and it feels so good, so wonderful, so perfect just for you, so right, so life changing, that you just know from deep, deep inside for you, that something wonderful is just about to happen, something wonderful is about to come your way, that it has to and will happen, because it must, something so right, so happy, so intense, so perfect, so harmonious, so unstoppable, that it can, it will, it must and in reality, that it absolutely will, you are feeling so good now, so wonderful so relaxed, so positive, you just know, that something unstoppably wonderful has been set into motion, that it's here upon you right now, always and forever! All of this joy, all of this happy energy has changed something, transcended something, perhaps even shattered an old way of thinking, an old way of being, an old way of feeling, corrected an old way of reacting, has truly released an old way of feeling stuck and that all of this unstoppable joy, has genuinely and absolutely in fact, created right now in this moment, a major positive breakthrough in your life, because your joy is unstoppable, your happiness is growing moment by moment and in fact, the way your are feeling, you've never been so sure of anything in your life. Yes, you are certain, you've broken through right now. All that you are feels this, really truly knows this and lives this. In fact, you've begun a brand new chapter in your life, you've released your past, your mind has set up, whether you realize it or not, a brilliant new strategy, in your calm yet very powerful successful determination, in bold and clever ways, whether you are precisely aware of it and how it works or not, because you now and in any and all future moments are succeeding unstoppably and amazingly. You are cleverly surmounting and overcoming, everything and anything that once stood in your way blockage free, flowing over, around and through anything and everything that had ever stood in your way. And you feel and deeply and truly know the joy and wonderful happiness that is truly yours right now, ahhh yes, you've done it, by correctly having chosen to relax into to this brand new beginning. And here You are happy, relaxed, moving on, on with your life, you are forever determined to move forward and onward, a winner, successful in all that you have moved away from and both easily and successfully flowing into the next chapter of your life, free, free at last! And in your mind, see the happy faces of those in the world who acknowledge your very important powerful step forward in your life and most especially the support your feel from them, but most especially, the acknowledgment and support you give absolutely and powerfully to yourself, as you have truly and forever re-identified yourself, successful, empowered, triumphant, breaking through and victorious, succeeding as never before! Congratulations!

---

# Extras – Personal Development

---

NOTE: This is a section of additional suggestions I've written for various sessions. As with the rest of this text, please read and select or adapt the suggestions that apply to your client (patient) to fit their specific needs. By using this section, you are agreeing to pre-reading, rewriting, adjusting and adapting these suggestions to individual and specific needs.

**Life Improvement: Home and Business – *Extras* -** You relax into your life, and into your world and your work, enjoying your life, living and fulfilling your dreams, taking care of all that you must, making the best of each moment enjoyably, in calm and happy determination You're appreciative of all that you have and now better create. Each and every day you are finding yourself more relaxed in the most amazing of ways. You are willing to listen, in calm detachment, finding it easier and better to deal with and handle people in the most creative and effective of ways. You are free of taking the day-to-day stuff, personally. You keep the small stuff small, as it's all small stuff to you emotionally. You are finding, creating and thriving in a state of ever growing and glowing fulfillment and inner peace. You feel and truly know you are a success and that by relaxing your way through rough spots, you are thriving and succeeding in amazing ways. You relax and flow into your work and your life. You delegate, you express, you find balance and dynamically and effectively create harmony in your life, with your home life, with your partner and in general. You strengthen your partnership by expressing creatively only the very best and most constructive communication in the correct and best understood language, guiding, leading to knowledge and to better and improved harmony, the very best ways to formulate balance in your work load and responsibilities, in fact, truly and even happily, you smoothly handle your share and you smoothly share what you handle. You find better ways to communicate at home and find a true sense of inner peace, harmony and balance. You guide, explain and communicate correctly, powerfully and peacefully. You maintain guidance and discipline, you express yourself clearly and directly, clearly even when expressing yourself indirectly, getting your points across in positive terms, asking for what you want constructively, in the very best and no-nonsense of ways to your kids. You find only the very best ways to communicate, to teach, to train and to love your kids by guiding them effectively. You trust in the fact that the future gets easier and better, you begin stepping into that bright future right now feeling great. You are guided and inspired and you carefully create the best future in the very best and most effectively precise of ways, and you are sure of this and very sure of yourself. You unstoppably encourage and win. You create better time for yourself and your spouse (husband / wife), strengthening your marriage relationship, structuring your time more carefully. You find the time, you make the time, you schedule the time for one on one moments, calm and happy moments, moments of intimacy, laughter and closeness, making the most of each and every moment. Your health is good, and you trust in this important fact and it's only getting better and stronger, each and every day and night. And as you relax even deeper and further right now, your immune system is being turned up, tuned up, almost as if in fact, someone, from deep, deep inside of you has actually has in fact, reset a switch or a dial or even some type of computer or thermostat within you somewhere, allowing you to comfortably and easily have more vitality energy, better calmness, better health, a powerful and fine tuned immune system, longevity, calmness and happiness, your worry-free, guilt free and you live in the most healthy ways, clearing any and all toxins, creating better health, so right, just right for you.

**Self-Confidence – Extra** - You are unstoppably, adaptively and creatively, in surprisingly powerful ways, remaining calm, cool and collected, in each and every circumstance. You trust in life; you are enough; you are a valuable person and your life is important, and you were meant to be here and a part of it all. In each and every circumstance, you are finding newer and better ways of remaining calm, balanced, and better. Your correct response to any and all challenges is to breathe, slowly, calmly and powerfully, relax all over and feel wonderful, relaxing your way through any and all challenges, while believing in yourself and feeling fantastic and wonderful. You are and have always been there for yourself; you are unstoppably trusting in the fact that your life is unfolding in the way that it should, and you are learning to enjoy and love your life as never before. You live your dreams, following your excitement and are more often than anything, feeling fantastic more than ever before, believing in yourself, trusting in yourself, allowing yourself to glow on the inside and on the outside too, activating greater and greater levels of confidence while trusting in life more than ever before.

# RELATIONSHIPS

Also see ANXIETY, FEAR, PANIC:
  Overcoming Separation Anxiety – Children

# Better Parenting: Money and Better Organized

You are finding newer and better ways of getting your children to listen, learn, understand and obey your wishes; you become a guiding force, a light in their lives, rising above any and all conflicts, you move onward in well thought-out ways, free of just simply reacting, getting to and achieving your goals and methods of guidance, clearly, cleanly and directly, in ways that work, in ways that are and remain, calm, balanced, relaxed and stress-free. In fact, you begin to trust in life, taking the very best care of yourself, seeing your world and your life as a place of encouragement and support, knowing that life truly supports you, just it has each and every day and night. And as you trust in life, you begin to improve the ways you think about money. You see money as energy: the more energy you put out, the more it returns. And just like throwing a rubber ball against a wall, the faster it is thrown, the faster it comes back. Every time you have to spend money, you are making way for new money to come in and to enter your life, because your life always takes care of you, and you know this as a deep and powerful profound truth. Whatever the challenge, you are handling it skillfully and well, even remaining detached emotionally when you need to be, in order to handle everything and anything you have to, even if it involves dealing with your son getting in trouble in school, dreaming up newer and better ways of teaching, healing and guiding him to better ways of living and behaving in his life while you remain stress-free and calm, easily and cleverly finding new ways to rise above and to deal with each and any thing that might come up, while doing all that it takes. You are teaching your children to respect themselves, each other, yourself, your husband and others, becoming a guiding force, free of being taken advantage of while maintaining the upper hand, as a parent, as an adult, as a guiding force. You learn to take things step by step; in fact, your organizational skills are starting coulisse, logically you think, you plan, you take all the steps necessary, you get the job done; logically you think, you plan, you take all the steps necessary, you get the job done, feeling fine, wonderful and fantastic, balanced, truly harmonized and healed, stress-free, struggle-free, a sea of calming tranquility in the midst of any possible storm, always finding better ways of achieving this unstoppably.

# Coping With A Difficult Family Member

Relax now barrier free and liberate new inspirations, allowing brighter, better and even brilliant ways of thinking acting, being and feeling to become a part of who you are. Melt and flow, relax and heal, get now inspired and allow a brilliant, new and more powerfully real series of new life supporting thoughts, feelings, habits, strategies and responses to forever emerge from your mind and into all that is your life. A brand new and better chapter of your life begins unstoppably right now!

And as you relax, beyond any and all old barriers from previous chapters of your life, you are unstoppably, whether you realize it or not, easily and dynamically, brilliantally and effectively while in differently inspired and precise ways, overcoming any already known or as yet unknown selfishness, egotism, difficulty or harshness of your (family member or difficult person) and people that you know. Your powerful and now only always working in your favor subconscious mind is actively and cleverly relaxing you through, over around and beyond any and all things that can or might ever had once stood in your way while a new chapter of your life so very easily begins and a dynamic newer, powerful, mightier inner hero within you is forever released. You are now easily yet precisely liberating the powerful hero that you actually are. The inner hero that is capable of saving children from danger like a fire is now released and actively working out success strategies to allow you liberate everything that has worked, will work and ever more so, newer and better strategies of dealing and coping with any event, challenge or circumstance, old, new or different so you are more easily shining through to a brighter and better day, a brighter better way, a brighter, better healthier and more masterfully powerful, effective you! This new and more balanced, calmer, more masterful you, is profoundly rising the top, unbeatable and is dynamically choosing to be happy and calm, upbeat, most especially whenever challenged by the habits and actions of other people, most especially by the smaller minded and more needful people in your life. You rise up, like a parent with a child, to explain, correct, course correct and challenge while sticking to your truths, even knowing when to walk away at just the right time for optimal outcomes, just seeing your way through, truly now, just seeing yourself as a true and real leader in your life. So easily able to now blow off the disharmonies and refocus your calm and centered self on other better areas of your life, fearlessly while feeling strong and reset.

In this new Chapter of your life, you see this future in a victorious fashion, all of it's success and all of it's energies, while generating and creating a focus on happiness within yourself, because of and most especially in spite of anything that's meant to take that way from you. You are speaking plainly and calmly, free of resorting to guttural language and happy about that. You so much better now, ahhhh, lighter and better, just like a giant weight has been lifted off your shoulders, completely free of embarrassment, just succeeding or learning, happy with who you are, and happy with her being whom she is, happy with whom they are.

Whenever you are or might be feeling the old energies of upsetment, that old energy is now harnessed, and is turned around and utilized powerfully, now in your favor, becoming the energy that allows you to unstoppably rise to the top, as you learn to lead and direct here. Any bully is in fact a frightened child, some are cowards, now never able to stand up to the strength and light of your heroic presence. In fact, truly you have most assuredly and undeniably let go of any and all old patterns of victim-hood, instead rather you are choosing to feel fine. Research has proven, when someone screams or yells at another, they are seeking a similar scream or yell back in return. You had choices to make, only now instead you are making the very best of choices, simply refusing to yell back during a fight. Your voice is steady and calm, free forever of playing that old game, knowing when to walk away, perhaps coming back at the more appropriate time to draw out communication in others, to open hearts; to open minds. You are ever growing in love for yourself and now your abundant and ever increasing health is now only allowing you greater strength, serenity, peace and calmness. All things that once stressed you out or upset you are now easily handled and even completely vanquished by you. You are and you remain more than ever before, calm and determined to be happy, safe, centered and in your zone, regardless of challenge or challenging events and people, your health and happiness are of paramount importance to you and so you stay strategically connected or disconnected, attached or unattached, in each and every circumstance, all thoughts, actions and feelings are there in only the very best ways to support yourself, your goals, your thoughts, your ideas, your dreams, your feelings, regardless of event or circumstance, most especially whenever challenged. You are focused, carefree, serene and fine, knowing you are doing better and better, little steps meaning a lot.

## Coping With A Snoring Mate and Getting Better Rest - 1

Tonight is the very beginning of a very special and new night, a new and better night is coming, one of your own creation, one in which you rest more peacefully, more powerfully, more soundly than ever before and only getting more sound, more powerful, more beneficial at each and every bed-time. You are going to allow yourself to sleep, more peacefully, more comfortably, more soundly, than ever before. You are going to enter a land of rest and peace, just like you've done before, so many, sleepy times in the past, when you just put your head on the pillow, closed your eyes and went to sleep. You just put your head on the pillow, close your eyes and go to sleep, a deep and powerful soothing sleep (3X). Prior to getting this sort of sleep, you've done and will do all that allows you peaceful rest, you've turned off the TV early, about an hour or so before going to bed, perhaps reading instead, listening to calming music or a relaxation tape or even just relaxing You unwind, in body, emotions and thoughts pleasantly becoming relaxed and unfocused. You've used the bathroom before going to bed, allowing your body comfort, rest and ease. And you've put the day and all of its cares away, far, far away from you, because as you are relaxing, as you are releasing, as you are letting go, learning to let go, deeper and further, deeper and further, more and more you are doing any and all of the right things to allow yourself to get better and better sleep. You relax deeper and further now, you let go of all of the day's cares and emotions, you've put them on a shelf, yesterday is resolved, today took care of you, tomorrow will be just the same. And as you've let go of the day, you let go of cares, you relax into the perfection that is your powerfully unfolding life, trusting in your life, all of its support, all of its inspiration, you truly feel that all is well. You are beginning to realize and re-identify from deep, deep within, that you have a powerful, successful and highly creative mind. This mind of yours is a powerful tool, creating your life, your world, all that you do, all that you see, all that you imagine and feel. This mind of yours is now beginning to access new, powerful, soothing, healing and better ways of tuning into restful sleep, beyond any and all past frustrations and challenges. You are forever, only getting better and more successful, each and every night, becoming completely able to powerfully tune out any and all disturbances that would interfere with a good and safe, peaceful night of powerful rest. This powerful mind of yours is now releasing any and all patterns of past frustration, any and all anger, any and all past patterns of blockage and interference. You are calmly yet powerfully determined to successfully rest each and every night, especially in spite of old annoyances and challenges, even snoring, for your powerful mind can change that sound into a whispering, soothing lullaby, because it can, you will and you unstoppably choose to do so. And slowly now, your powerful, successful, re-interpretive mind is clearing, changing, improving any and all sounds you might have once found disturbing, to sounds that are relaxing, sounds that are pleasing, sounds that allow you to relax. Any and all formerly disruptive sounds might seem like a gentle symphony, a whispering, soothing lullaby, those sounds might even slowly begin to sound like gentle rolling waves flowing in from a beautiful beach, wave after wave, wave after wave, wave after wave . . . allowing all that you are to relax as those sounds begin to fade into the distance as you let go, your body relaxes, completely and totally, your emotions relax and begin to fade as they too begin to sleep and rest. Your mind at rest, feels so calm and deserving of rest, you are so relaxed and so very tried, so drowsy, so sleepy, so relaxed, so able to sleep, ever deeply, ever profoundly, ever better. Thinking is a daytime activity. You are now resting at night to fall asleep, your thoughts just drift away, drifting away, on wisps of clouds on a starry, soothing night sky.

You really and truly love yourself, only getting better and better each and every day and night. You really and truly love your Spouse (husband / wife / mate). The power and strength of this love, is enough to get your through anything, including giving yourself the power to rest, sleep and dream, right through the night and joyfully awakening the very next morning, fully refreshed and happy. You deserve your rest, enjoying this fact, free of over analyzing or analyzing in any disruptive way. You begin to see your spouse as an extension of yourself, finding harmony and oneness, healing and hope, strength and peace, together through limitless and growing unbounded love. All of the very best that your mutual strength provides you both, allows you to comfortably allow sleep and rest to come your way each and every night, only getting better and stronger in every possible way, even in ways you've yet to imagine. You have chosen to relax into a new truth for a new day and new night in your life, a new and profoundly powerful truth in your life, your world, your universe, beginning right now and for the rest of your life, you have correctly chosen to relax through any and all adversities, challenges and frictions in your life, no matter how important or even overpowering they might seem to be or how important they seem to have once been. For right now in this moment, you have correctly chosen instead, to empower yourself the most beneficial ways possible. Tonight, from here on out, with this only getting easier and better each and every night from now on, you trust, you relax, you rest, you sleep. Your realm of sleep becomes an unshakable refuge of rest and relaxation.

So from this place of real, true and permanent support, as you relax even deeper and deeper, you begin to think and to see within your mind, a beautiful place, perhaps a beach just at or after sunset. You are standing on this beach, right by the water's edge, in your bare feet, calm, comfortable, relaxed all over, feeling really, really good, calm and relaxed all over. You feel the gentle waves by the salt water's edge touching your toes, you imagine the smell and almost taste the salt air, the gentle breezes touching the rest of your skin, the calming embrace of the warm water as it first touches your toes and the rest of your feet. You feel almost as if the water is a form of soothing, even healing energy. As it comes in and touches your feet, you can feel an almost magnificent energy, moving up from your feet, calming you, soothing you, maybe almost even healing you, moving up from your feet and moving up your body. As the water recedes again, you can actually imagine, that all old unwanted, unneeded, unnecessary energies from your body, draining out and far,

far away from you. Your focus is calm, ever relaxing and pleasantly unfocused. You look out upon the water, you see far away, the lights of a ship off near the horizon, yet in another direction, a buoy with a light on its top, marking the waterway for ships and you look down and see your toes again, embraced by a magical relaxation energy contained by these water. You even feel different as the light and gentle breezes touch your skin in various ways, how different scents of the seawater seem to you as the breezes blow. And truly recognize how remarkable it is to be able to and how you really can, focus your attention, on whatever it is you wish to notice, or to feel, or even not notice or even ignore. So in this moment and in all future moments, you further realize that you easily and truly have a powerful ability now, a power, in a powerful yet very relaxed way, to successfully focus your attention, or to even de-focus your attention, on whatever it is you wish to concentrate upon or ignore. And in this moment, you have correctly, really and truly chosen from deep, deep inside of you, to extend this ability to the area of your hearing. That's right, you have within you the ability to tune into a voice, a sound, a noise, or to tune it out completely as you wish. And in this and all future moments, you have chosen to tune out any and all sounds, any and all noises, both everything and anything that sounds less than pleasing to you or that has in any way, interfered with your rest or happiness in any way. You know, it's almost as if someone has in fact, or really indeed, turned down a switch or a dial within you somewhere, lowering the volume of a sound or a noise that you have correctly chosen to relax out of and far, far away from, you have relinquished it and powerfully released it from your life. Or perhaps even tuning you to a frequency you just can no longer hear, a frequency well outside of the human range of hearing, both now and forever, but it really is of little concern to you, because you achieve true and limitless success, through the power of your subconscious mind and from the dynamic healing power of all that you are. And each and every night you have absolutely and correctly chosen to tune into all the things that are wonderfully pleasant to hear, (perhaps the whispers of gentle lullabies) and to tune out all the sounds and unnecessary noises, putting them out of your head and all that is your life, that you are now each and every day and night, retuned, re-set, re-adjusted, becoming free, free, free at last, both always and forever.
You can actually feel a happy and deeply relaxing shift in your consciousness and throughout all that are your thoughts and all that are your emotions, a forgiveness, a release, really just feeling the old energies from the past, rising up, off, off and far, far away from you, right now, always and forever. And from deep, deep within your powerful and dynamic mind, most especially your subconscious mind, you have made a very real, very true, very powerful, most successful choice, to begin, with each and every beat of your happy and healthy heart and with each and every breath that you take, to begin to heal, realign, re-tune, readjust, re-calibrate your sense of hearing, better and more comfortably, than ever before, better and better each and every night, in the ways that are most powerfully and dynamically beneficial to you,

allowing you to relax, rest, heal, release and be supported by all that you are or are not hearing, in all the most beneficial ways possible, daytimes, nighttimes, while you are awake and even while you sleep, now, always and forever!

## Coping With a Snoring Mate – Better Rest - 2

You are easily finding and creating newer and better, more appropriate and easily adaptive, highly effective thoughts, feelings and responses to create a wonderful and right-through-the-night type of sleep. Each and every bedtime, you put your day's cares up on a mental shelf, storing them away, all of them just being stored away, feeling calm, balanced, relaxed, easily able to powerfully forgive and release past blockages, flowing ever onward into a blissful and joyous, well deserved, invigorating night of nurturing and healing sleep. You are correctly and even amazingly finding newer and better pathways of joy, ease and peace, comfort and ever deepening rest, only anticipating a joyous night of rest, easily, correctly, adaptively, skillfully and deeply sinking beneath any and all sounds, all cares just drifting away, resting peacefully, just like being rocked to sleep like a baby, slipping beneath a soft and comfortable blanket of healing, nurturing sleep energy. Even if you should awaken, any old and useless feelings you once had about the noise that might have disturbed you in any way, are now really becoming more and more meaningless and unimportant; as what becomes ever more important, fluid and adaptive, is your new and adaptively functioning, ability to sleep deeply and right through the night, even falling back to sleep, easier and faster, deeper and easier. Any and all once disturbing noises, now become like a gentle symphonic lullaby, allowing for peaceful and undisturbed rest, allowing you to sleep in the places you should, most comfortably. You begin to open up your life, to relax into the dawn of a newer and brighter, better day in your life, deeply and truly re-identified in the deepest and most foundational recesses of your mind, as you are trusting in life and the ever growing support that life is always giving you. You are taking all of the appropriate steps necessary to truly and profoundly re-identify yourself as calm, peaceful, relaxed; calm, peaceful and relaxed, trusting in life and bringing into your life, all that needs to be there to support yourself powerfully, absolutely and totally, each and any time, day or night. You develop a new zest for living and for life, now easily and truly learning to anticipate only the very best, calm, peaceful and just flowing with life, trusting in all that you create and manifest. You are learning to do what is right for you to do, in spite of the reactions of others; however, carefully and skillfully getting all of your points across and just like a skillful parent or guiding teacher, getting your points across, calmly, clearly, powerfully and deliberately, seeing things from their side, getting them to see things from your side, with calm and balanced emotions, regardless of their reactions, calm within yourself, getting all points across until the job is done. You are calm, peaceful, blissfully relaxed, disturbance-free, moving things to a newer and brighter level, any and all old disturbances you once were hindered by, you now just flow over, around, beyond and deeply under, relaxing into a better nights rest, of joy, ease and peace, and a brighter and better day, a powerful and more brilliant way, just looking forward to it, setting things up to succeed at this easily and now relaxing deeper down and achieving it with skill and creative adaptability. All of this is only getting easier, more flowingly adaptive and powerful for you, each and every day and night, with each and every breath that you take, with each and every beat of your heart, with each and every thought and experience that you have, as you now have effectively moved into a brighter and better chapter of your life, easily sleeping in peace, undisturbed, uninterrupted, continually, all of this only getting better and easier for you, each and every bedtime..

## Coping With A Snoring Mate and Getting Better Rest

Tonight is the very beginning of a very special and new night, a new and better night is coming, one of your own creation, one in which you rest more peacefully, more powerfully, more soundly than ever before and only getting more sound, more powerful, more beneficial at each and every bedtime. You are going to allow yourself to sleep, more peacefully, more comfortably, more soundly, than ever before. You are going to enter a land of rest and peace, just like you've done before, so many, sleepy times in the past, when you just put your head on the pillow, closed your eyes and went to sleep. You just put your head on the pillow, closed your eyes and went to sleep, a deep and powerful soothing sleep. Prior to getting this sort of sleep, you've done and will do all that allows you peaceful rest, you've turned off the TV early, about an hour or two before going to bed, perhaps reading instead, perhaps listening to calming, gentle music or just relaxing. You unwind your body, emotions and thoughts pleasantly becoming relaxed and unfocused. You've used the bathroom before going to bed, allowing your body rest, comfort and ease. And you've put the day and all of its cares away, far, far away from you, because as you are powerfully and effectively relaxing, as you are releasing, as you are letting go, learning to let go, deeper and further, deeper and further, more and more you are doing any and all of the right things to allow yourself to get better and better sleep. You relax deeper and further now, you let go of all of the day's cares, you've put them on a shelf, yesterday is resolved, today took care of you, tomorrow will be just the same. And as you've let go of the day, let go of cares, you relax into the perfection that is your powerfully unfolding life, trusting in your life, all of its support, all of its inspiration, you feel that all is well. You are beginning to realize and re-identify from deep, deep within, that you have a powerful, successful and highly creative mind. This mind of yours is a powerful tool, creating your life, your world, all that you do, see, imagine, and feel. This mind of yours is now beginning to access new, powerful, soothing, healing and better ways of tuning into restful sleep, beyond any and all past frustrations and challenges and you are forever, only getting better and more successful, each and every night, to be completely able to powerfully tune out any and all disturbances that would interfere with a good and safe, peaceful night of powerful rest. This powerful mind of yours is now releasing any and all patterns of past frustration, any and all anger, any and all past patterns of blockage and interference. You are calmly yet powerfully determined to successfully rest each and every night, especially in spite of old annoyances and challenges, even anyone's snoring, for your powerful mind can change that sound into a whispering, soothing lullaby, because it can, you will and you unstoppably choose to do so, effectively and only getting better and easier each and every night in the future. And slowly now, your powerful, successful, re-interpretive mind is clearing, changing, improving any and all sounds you might have once found disturbing, to sounds that are relaxing, sounds that are pleasing, sounds that allow you to relax. Any and all formally disruptive sounds might seem like a gentle symphony, a whispering, soothing lullaby, those sounds might even slowly begin to sound like gentle, rolling waves flowing in from a beautiful beach, wave after wave, wave after wave, wave after wave, allowing all that you are to relax as those sounds begin to fade into the distance as you let go, your body relaxes, completely and totally, your emotions relax, and begin to fade as they too begin to sleep and rest. Your mind at rest, feels so calm and deserving of rest, you are so relaxed and so very tired, so drowsy, so sleepy, so relaxed, so able to sleep, ever deeply, ever profoundly, ever better. Thinking is a daytime activity, resting at night to fall asleep, your thoughts just drift away, drifting away, on wisps of clouds on a starry, soothing night sky.

You really and truly love yourself, and it is only getting better and better each and every day and night. You really and truly love your Spouse (husband / wife / mate). The power and strength of this love, is enough to get your through anything, including giving you the power to rest, sleep, and dream, right through the night and joyfully the every next morning, fully refreshed and happy, you deserve your rest, enjoying this fact, free of over-analyzing or analyzing in any disruptive way. You begin to see your spouse as an extension of yourself, finding harmony and oneness, healing and hope, strength and peace, together. All of the very best that your mutual strength provides you and allows you to comfortably sleep and allow rest to come your way each and every night, only getting better and stronger in every possible way, even in ways you've yet to imagine. You have chosen to relax into a new truth for a new day in your life and a new and profoundly powerful truth in your life, your world and your universe. Beginning right now and for the rest of your life, you have correctly chosen to relax through any and all adversities, challenges and frictions in your life, no matter how important or even overpowering they might seem to be or how important they seem to have once been. For right now in this moment, you have correctly chosen instead, to empower yourself in the most beneficial ways possible. Tonight, this and every night, from now on, you trust. Your realm of sleep becomes an unshakable refuge of rest and relaxation.

So from this place of real, true and permanent support, as you relax even deeper and deeper, you begin to think and to see within your mind, a beautiful place, perhaps a beach just at or after sunset. You are standing on this beach, right by the waters edge, in your bare feet, calm, comfortable, relaxed all over, feeling really, really good, calm, and relaxed all over. You feel the gentle waves by the salt waters edge touching your toes, you imagine the smell and almost taste the salt air, the gentle breezes touching the rest of your skin, the calming embrace of the warm water as it first touches your toes and the rest of your feet. You feel almost as if, the water is a form of soothing, even healing energy; as it comes in and touches your feet, you can feel an almost magnificent energy, moving up from your feet, calming you, soothing you, relaxing and unwinding you, almost even healing you, moving up from your feet and moving up your body. As the water recedes again you can actually imagine and even feel, all the old unwanted, unneeded, unnecessary energies from your body are draining out and far, far away from you. You are so centered, so calm, ever relaxing and pleasantly unfocused. As you look out upon the water, you see far away, the lights of a ship off near the horizon; yet in another direction, you see a buoy with a light on its top, marking the waterway for ships and you look down and see your toes again, embraced by a magical relaxation energy contained by these waters. You can feel the light and gentle breezes touch your skin in various ways, how the different scents of the seawater seem to you as the calming, soothing, gentle, soothing, relaxing breezes blow. And you truly recognize how remarkable it is to be able to and how you really can, focus your attention on whatever it is you wish to notice, or to feel, or even not notice or even ignore. So in this moment, and in all future moments, you further realize that you easily and truly have a powerful ability now, a power, in a powerful yet very relaxed way, to successfully focus your attention, or to even defocus your attention, on whatever it is you wish to concentrate upon or ignore. And in this moment, you have correctly, really, and truly chosen from deep, deep inside of you, to extend this ability to the area of your hearing. That's right, you have within you the ability to tune into a voice, a sound, a noise, or to tune it out completely as you wish, just like turning down a dial or turning off a switch as you wish. And in this and all future moments, you have chosen to tune out any and all sounds, any and all noises, both everything and anything that sounds less than pleasing to you or that has in anyway, interfered with your rest or happiness in anyway. You know, its almost as if someone has in fact, or really indeed, turned down a switch or a dial within you somewhere, safely lowering the volume of a sound or a noise that you have correctly chosen to relax out of and far, far away from; you have relinquished it and powerfully release from your life. Or perhaps it's as if someone is even tuning your hearing away from the noise to a frequency you just can no longer hear, a frequency well outside of the human range of hearing, both now and forever at each and every bedtime. But whatever it is, it really is of little concern to you, because you achieve true and limitless success through the power of your subconscious mind and from the dynamic healing power of all that you are. And each and every night you have absolutely and correctly chosen to only tune into all the things that are wonderfully pleasant to hear (perhaps the sleepy whisperings of gentle lullabies) and to easily and effectively tune out all the unpleasant sounds and unnecessary noises, putting them out of your head and all that is your life, that you are now each and every day and night, re-tuned, re-set, re-adjusted, becoming free, free, free at last, both always and forever. You can actually feel a shift in your consciousness and all that are your thoughts and all that are your emotions, a forgiveness, a release, really just feeling the old energies from the past, rising up, off, off and far, far away from you, right now, always and forever. And from deep, deep within your powerful and dynamic mind, most especially your subconscious mind, you have made a very real, very true, very powerful, most successful choice, to begin, with each and every beat of your happy and healthy heart, and with each and every breath that you take, to begin to heal, realign, re-tune, readjust, re-calibrate your sense of hearing, better and more comfortably than ever before, better and better each and every night, in the ways that are most powerfully and dynamically beneficial to you, allowing you to relax, rest, heal, release and be supported by all that is your hearing, in all the most beneficial ways possible, daytimes, nighttimes, while you are awake and even while you sleep, now always and forever!

# Overcoming a Breakup – 1

You are so very willing to flow with life and excel. You are ready to move on and into a brighter, better and happier chapter of your life, the next chapter of your life. You are willing to forgive and flow beyond anything and everything that once brought you discomfort, willing to unstoppably relax into a newer, better and brighter chapter of your life. Each and every day and night, you are more willing to take better care of yourself, giving yourself a break and you are completely willing to forgive, to heal, to move beyond, to allow, to see anything and everything you've once experienced as discomfort, as a learning and polishing experience. You are moving on with your life, healing, even whole, taking loving care of yourself and becoming more and more willing to love and care for yourself in newer, more effective and better ways. You relax deeper and further now, all the way down deep now, relaxing into newer and better ways of feeling, acting, reacting, thinking, experiencing your life, willing to feel good, sometimes even great, finding more things to laugh about, more things to feel lighthearted about, tapping into the memories and feelings of happy times, supportive times, times of joy and inspiration, enthusiastic about yourself and your life, finding newer and better thoughts and feelings, just flowing and moving on like a mighty river or ocean, eternal and forever in your flow of life. You are activating joy, ease, contentment, peace and comfortability. For your future lies ahead, in all next moments, all next days and nights, all new experiences, all supportive actions and experiences you find yourself more easily moving on into this future, smiling on the inside, feeling better on the outside, getting back the support you once more easily built up and more freely gave to yourself, feeling and re-experiencing feelings of being and even better and more easily remaining, cool, calm, balanced, serene, unruffled, composed, happy and at ease. More and more each and every day and night, you are moving on with calm and blessed, balanced determination, unstoppably determined to feel good, move on and feel great, because you can, you will and you do. You're doing just fine when you are with others, feeling even fine, even great when you are alone. In fact all of this is building, building, building, like a giant reservoir of limitless inspirational energy. This is a desire, a drive, your unstoppable determination to be happy, to be whole, to be safe, to be free, to succeed at moving ever onward in your life. Your real, truest and best option, profoundly realizing that you are enough, you are feeling more whole and you are relaxing into this newer and better way of living and feeling, you are free, you are living, you are healing, you are acting while taking positive actions, in fact feeling great. You now and forever deeply and truly understanding now, that to feel happy you are forever free of needing anybody next to you. You, by yourself are enough. The best way of winning any competition is to be competition free, by relaxing into happiness as a way of living, healing and being, just feeling great in newer and better ways, the very best ways to thrive, remaining competition free. You take delight in your life. All around you can think about seeing beautiful things. People are happy and laughing. Children are laughing and are happily delighted nearby, just like when you were a child, birds are singing joyously. Only right now, you are finding newer and better, more easily powerful and forever ways to feel glad, happy, at ease, comfortable, learning better and better each and every day and night, to take, make and activate joy into your life, finding in smilingly happy ways to feel unstoppably glad and free, free and glad. Truly, in reality and in fact, you've gotten to feel like your needs are filled and fulfilled. You need only one person back, to enjoy everything again and you've got her / him. You are there, you are enough, you feel light and free, almost as if someone from deep, deep, inside of you has drained off any and all old emotional trauma baggage, drained off all unpleasantness and discomfort, allowing all that you are to be free, to be happy, to be calm, to be light, to be fulfilled, with a new and resounding feeling of ease and powerful comfort, balanced, and stable, just flowing. Succeeding at this truly, unstoppably, easily, deeply, naturally, creatively, inventively, precisely, effectively, feeling and even knowing, you are truly forever living from a pivotal and powerful place of new starts. Living in a new chapter of your life, a place where you are happier now, more than ever, ever before. Tapping into all of the wonderful, supportive and very best experiences you've ever had, feeling limitlessly inspired. You are tapping into the very best feelings and inspirational energies all of the past victories, triumphs, breakthroughs and successes you've ever had. All of this incredible energy, driving you foreword, you're free, You're liberated, you're re-identified, you're moving on, thriving, willing to be better, do better, so you do, in even surprising, more powerful and better more balanced ways.

---

# Overcoming a Breakup – 2

You are relaxing and are determined to remain, relaxing your way through any and all past adversity as you move on. You begin to think bigger and better ways, moving on with your life, striving to succeed and thrive into a happier life, a happier way of being, as you continue to move on while elevating your sites. You are getting on with your life, powerfully releasing, forgetting, devaluing and maybe even forgiving anything, everything, most especially yourself in powerfully effective and real ways. You are releasing, forgetting and forgiving anything and everything that has blocked your way from happiness and living your life, now enjoying and living your life to it's very fullest. This is the very best way to settle any old score. You deserve to enjoy yourself and your life while finding enjoyment in all that you are, all that you do and in the very best ways. You live and provide for yourself lovingly. You find ways to romance yourself, treating yourself in the very best ways, just as an ideal love in your life would. You fill yourself and fulfill yourself with the very best support that life has to offer you, becoming free of need. You are feeling so abundant. You are an ever-building reservoir of happy fulfillment. Feel the calmness that this state of deep relaxation brings. You are so calm, so free of anxiety, feeling so supported and reassured. Your emotions, balanced, calm, serene and relaxed. You find your center, choosing to forever live there. In your center, you truly find peace, calmness, power, control, balance, ease, pleasantness, serenity and harmony in newer, more profound and unstoppable ways. You release any and all negative or painful situations, feelings or old strains. You now truly and powerfully realize that anything and everything you've very experienced has polished you, allowing you to move on. So you heal yourself, you forgive yourself, forgiving, healing and releasing any and all past harsh judgments, judgments upon yourself or upon on others, because you are better than that. You now and forever realize that forgiving, healing and releasing, is truly what's best for you. So you move on, to create a better life, thrive and succeed, feeling better and better, feeling wonderful, joyously moving on right now and forever into the very next, brightest chapter of the masterpiece of a life you are determined to make your life into forever. You relax deeper now, releasing any and all old blockages to your happiness right now, deeply and truly re-identifying yourself, as clear, free, brave, valiant, blameless, wide open to newer and better experiences. You are free of past bad feelings, those feeling being forever washed away. You'd rather be and in fact are successful, happy in ever increasing amounts, tranquil, peaceful, forgiven, forgetting the impact of past pain, polished, finding a new love of yourself, for yourself, in new imaginative and boundless ways. And, as everyone knows, when you love yourself, the world will beat a path to your door, wanting to share in that happiness. You are getting back to being, self-assured, cheerful and confident, happy, peaceful, rising up to meet any challenge with ever increasing success. You are re-energized, re-started, re-balanced, relaxed, having learned from all past experiences and doing all of this better every time. You are problem free, challenge oriented, learning or succeeding and polished by your life. You are feeling forgiveness, relaxation and peace, floating ever onward, relaxing your way through any and all unnecessary self-criticism, doing better and better for yourself, you feel the embrace of this world, a love of yourself profoundly building, unstoppable and unshakeable and in endless in supply, coming from yourself, to yourself, giving yourself a break, a newer sense of caring building, mightily putting the past behind you now, you are moving on.

Now project your thoughts and your feelings to a more emotionally happy and stable place, say ten years into the future. You've healed. You've moved on. You are on with your life. All of the things that happened in your break-up are hardly even a memory. In fact, you hardly ever think about them but if you do, you think about them in relation to how easily you've moved on and succeeded in your life. Perhaps there is happy news, new and building excitement, maybe your are involved with someone else and all of this past trauma has moved you on, propelling you into this brighter and happier future, actually having polished you up for the kind of happy future you deserve and have in this future you've effectively created. The past from ten years ago is always so easily forgettable and always so insignificant in perspective. You only remember the good, best and happiest of times. Your standards are higher. You've grown and reshaped your life, it's a masterpiece right now. You are glowing, growing and moving through your life happily, maybe even beyond your wildest dreams from your past. You are safe, calm, happy, secure and comfortable, glad to be alive. Now move those feelings and thoughts, easily activating feelings of health and support from that time into the right now and making them your own right now, For they are yours solidly, foundationally, right here and right now, growing only every stronger, flexible, effective, adaptive and functional. You are whole, healed and complete, ahhh, and it feels so right, so real, so right now and forever.

## Overcoming A Breakup – 3

You are easily, powerfully and effectively finding newer and better ways to not only just cope with your divorce, but to easily and effectively move on. It's almost as if you are now five years down the road, having healed and having moved on, feeling great, just as you deserve to be. The past is over, you've moved on, tomorrow is yet to be, right here and right now is your point of transformational power and in this moment, you have unstoppably decided to move on and to freely flow and thrive in your life, polishing up your life, determined to heal and to move on in the most unstoppable of ways, growing more and more determined and driven to succeed at this than ever before, braced up by the energy of every past victory, triumph and success that you've ever had in your life, in fact, you are so adaptive, so effectively focused, so done with the past, more and more, on each and every heartbeat and with each and every breath that you take, you can only move on, and you've never been so sure of anything in your life. You begin to trust in your life, as you move on and effectively succeed, willing to trust in your days and in your nights, taking all of your cares, and putting them on a shelf at night. Today has taken care of you, you've learned and succeeded, even been polished. Every past yesterday has done the same; tomorrow will do the same as well. You now put all of your thoughts, feelings, even anxieties and cares on the side and breath easily and deeply, willing to rest right through the night, almost as if in fact, a Divinely guided and perfectly brilliant blanket of healing light has laid its mantle of healing and balancing restorative light upon your entire body, allowing you to truly and peacefully relax, unwind, sleep, rest and dream. And in the morning when you awaken, you awaken fully refreshed, more and more upbeat, and ready to take on the world. You trust in your life and the way it takes care of you, you believe in yourself, with a new and budding sense of inner strength, easily and dynamically asserting yourself when it's needed, treating yourself right, treating others right, finding better balance and strength, courage and wisdom, fortified with drive and determination, seeing who you are as a valuable person, interacting with others and finding a new flow in your life, becoming one with others and trusting in yourself, trusting in your life, feeling fortified and feeling a new and greater connection to yourself, to others and to the world, in a brand new and ever growing stronger chapter of your life, all of your very best coming to the surface, driven, determined, healed from the past, moving on, feeling fine.

## Overcoming A Breakup - 4 (male)

You are easily, powerfully and effectively finding newer and better ways to not only just cope with your break-up but to easily and effectively move on. It's almost as if you are now five years down the road, having healed and having moved on, feeling great, just as you deserve to be. The past is over; you've moved on; tomorrow is yet to be, right here and right now is your point of transformational power and in this moment, you have unstoppably decided to move on and to freely flow and thrive into your life, polishing up your life, determined to heal and to move on in the most unstoppable of ways, growing more and more determined and driven to succeed at this than ever before, braced up by the energy of every past victory, triumph and success that you've ever had in your life; in fact, you are so adaptive, so effectively focused, so done with the past, more and more, on each and every heartbeat and with each and every breath that you take, you can only move on, and you've never been so sure of anything in your life. You begin to trust in your life, as you move on and effectively succeed, willing to trust in your days and in your nights, taking all of your cares and putting them on a shelf at night. Today has taken care of you; you've learned and succeeded, even been polished. Every past yesterday has done the same; tomorrow will do the same as well; you now put all of your thoughts, feelings, even anxieties and cares on the side and breathe easily and deeply, willing to rest right through the night, almost as if in fact, a Divinely guided and perfectly brilliant blanket of healing light has laid its mantle of healing and balancing restorative light upon your entire body, and throughout all that you are, allowing you to truly and peacefully relax, unwind, sleep, rest and dream. And in the morning when you awaken, you awaken fully refreshed, restored, more and more upbeat; you are completely ready to take on the world. You trust in your life and the way it takes care of you; you believe in yourself, with a new and budding sense of inner strength, easily and dynamically asserting yourself whenever it's needed, treating yourself right, treating others right, finding better balance and strength, courage and wisdom, fortified with drive and determination, seeing who you are as a valuable person, interacting with others and finding a new flow in your life, becoming one with others and trusting in yourself, trusting in your life, feeling fortified and feeling a new and greater connection to yourself, to others and to the world, in a brand new and ever-growing- stronger chapter of your life, all of your very best coming to the surface, driven, determined, healed from the past, moving on, feeling fine.

It has been said, the one thing we never get back in life is time; every moment wasted on trivia and minutia, is a wasted moment of our most valuable asset, ourselves, our life and our life-force. You are easily enjoying and employing all of your very best energies, to make the most of every well-deserved and well-feeling moment, thriving and doing your very best to seize the moment and truly live, and enjoy the very best of yourself and your life.

The time for upsetment and old useless regrets is now unstoppably and forever gone and over, as you are unstoppably determined to feel upbeat, calm, confident, relaxed and most especially upbeat and harmonized, whole and balanced, truly just moving on from any and all past and present regrets, and you knew you wouldn't be feeling this way forever; so just as if and in fact, you've gone through 5 years of healing, you in fact have accelerated your healing, 5 years into the future; you are really just there now, feeling everything there is to feel and knowing you are just there, not because I say so, but because you have, in fact, truly made up your powerful and dynamic mind to do so, most unstoppably. You are just fine with yourself, whether you are with someone or if you are alone; you are just fine, feeling fine and whole while allowing yourself to become better and better in each and every way, in even more powerful and even surprising ways, finding newer and better ways of just feeling solid for yourself in spite of and most especially because of circumstances from your past, becoming a pillar of strength from within yourself, just as if you've activated newer and recently recharged, reactivated energies from deep, deep inside of yourself, like self reliance, self appreciation, as if becoming a well of certainty for yourself in even newer and more surprising ways. You are so ready to move on from uncomfortable situations, circumstances and feelings, while releasing hurtful and disharmonious thoughts, feelings, imbalances, actions and reactions, in favor of yourself and a better life, as you are readily and easily becoming even more able to rise up, to rise to the top, to feel tip-top, and to begin again anew, into a newer and more improved chapter of your life, free, free at last, thriving, liberated and moving on, OK for yourself and more fluidly adaptive for yourself in each and every way, circumstance and event, having less and less time for discomfort, while generating more and more time for comfort, joy, ease, improvement, empowerment, harmony, healing and ascendancy, even taking more and more joy and balance into your life each and every day and each and every night, with each and every breath and each and every heartbeat. All of you is now improving and restoring, balancing and healing, harmonizing and improving in body, emotions, mind and even in spirit. You are taking better care of yourself, even sometimes when appropriate, joyously and pleasantly hungry, interested in life-giving nutrition and sustenance, finding newer and better ways of becoming and remaining re-energized and re-excited about your life and all of its optimism and limitless possibilities. You are powerfully reconditioning yourself to begin a new and better chapter of your life, energized in the days, easily finding newer and better ways of resting deeply and peacefully at night, easily able to fall back to sleep at night, calm, balanced and relaxed, comfortable and free, adaptively finding newer and better ways of releasing old blockages and moving on to a brighter day and better night, most unstoppably, trusting in the future, that each and every powerful thought, action, reaction and feeling, more powerfully and supportively brings. Forever free of blame, and trusting in the support that life readily brings you. Truly trusting in the inescapable fact, that each and every tomorrow, is taking care of you, even better care of you than each and every yesterday, finding and feeling better things to be unstoppably happy about, because you and your life and each and every moment you have is worth it, truly recognizing and trusting in the way your life is unfolding, for the very best of all possible outcomes and events, even if you are as yet, unaware of the final outcomes. You are determined and relaxing your way back onto the path that is your life, learning and allowing yourself to flow into newer and better places, thoughts, ambitions and feelings, activating all that you know you should and will, honestly and in the very best of ways, flowing like a mighty river down the side of a mighty mountain in Springtime, flowing past any and all old blockages, into ever-thriving, better and more brilliant tomorrows, sure, safe, confident, thriving and serene, learning to love yourself better and better, taking the very best care of yourself, as if you were becoming and truly are, an endless reservoir of abundant enough-ness, love, healing, harmony and life-force. Willing to truly thrive and live, feeling, knowing and truly creating from deep, deep inside, more comfort, ease, gentleness, strength, openness, joy, ease, centeredness, truly able to be embraced by life, as if bringing up the energy of any and all past moments of these wonderful energies from your past, into the right here and right now. Making time for fun, more and more laughter, more and more enjoyment, more and more passion, for yourself and for all that is your life, emerging now into a better and better place, thriving, relaxed though any and all frictions and moving ever onward to brighter and better vistas, making time for fun, friends and all the joyous passions that are life, focusing your presence and brilliantly moving on, re-labeled in the very most abundant, whole, and healed, harmonized of ways, trusting, loving, living, even making time to thrive, relaxed, released and restored, rising to the top, free and balanced, casting aside all things that ever once stood in your way, like a breath of fresh springtime air, revitalized and renewed, really and truly feeling mighty, liberating only your very best, amazingly and impressing everyone, most especially yourself, sure and confident of yourself, moving ever onward.

Now, remember the energy, the feeling and the power of a time, when you were and remained completely bound and determined to accomplish something. You, so determined, so assured, so direct, that no matter what it took, you would unstoppably get any task done. Be now in that moment and activate the energy of that moment into the here and now, into this moment, instilled with this power and ability in even greater and ever-growing dynamic amounts. Right now and in this moment, only getting stronger and better, more and more adaptive and powerful, more and more focused and effective, more and more certain, you are powerfully determined to heal, feel greater and greater self-forgiveness and release, moving on into your life better than ever before, because you must, because you will and right now, because, whether or not you realize it, it is in fact truly happening, in spite of and because it's needed to strengthen you, heal you, because you need it and you deserve it, and it's yours. And it does in fact happen, in order for you to better love, heal and powerfully forgive and release any and all situations, releasing any and all blockages and doubts, allaying and removing completely any and all harsh self-judgments as it's strengthening you, balancing you, truly and completely healing and releasing you into a brighter and better day for yourself, and for all and anyone, and anything involved. You are now moving into a brighter, better day; a brighter, better night; a brighter and better life, as a brighter and better you forever unstoppably emerges.

## Overcoming A Breakup - 5 (male)

You are moving easily into a place in your life where you are and you forever remain happy, safe, secure and comfortable, even if you are alone or with others, but most especially when you are alone. In moments from the past when you used to feel discomfort, you are now remaining calm, deep breathing slow and steady breath and allowing yourself easily to feel calm, relaxed, even soothing yourself, whether it's daytime or night, (most especially when it's 6 PM and beyond) when it's light outside or even most especially when it's dark. As you know, every night becomes another day, and deep inside you the light that is your very life-force, is guiding your way into brighter, better days and nights, while finding and adapting to newer and better, more powerful ways of becoming and truly remaining, calm, balanced, comfortable and relaxed. Truly and powerfully re-identified as becoming and truly remaining, calm, balanced, comfortable and relaxed, releasing, resolving and liberating any and all discomfort and imbalance, truly and powerfully feeling deeply restored, as if after a night of good, deep and healing sleep, truly now and forever freed, flowing with a newer and more joyous upbeat optimism, clearly and truly, better than ever before. Your personal dawn of healing, now and forever rises within you, only getting better and better, as you become and truly are more and more whole and healed, unstoppably feeling better and fine, dynamically and profoundly accelerating your healing and feeling fine.

You are beginning to become more concerned about living your life fully, more focused and more fluidly, adaptively creating success, peace and happiness, and in a more whole way, only allowing thoughts that instill your very best of all possible futures from deep, deep within. Each and very day and night, is getting better and better, easier and easier. Beyond limiting hopes that once were used to stand in your way, you are now unstoppably getting out of your way and allowing your hopefulness to expand your vistas and horizons, working now in your favor, to allow you to right now, and forever, only getting more and more clearly powerful to put your past chapter of your life behind you, and let go of those things that no longer serve you and to move on forever into the very best life you now are so super motivated to create, and now . . . just do. You are forgiving, releasing, and just sweeping aside and forgetting about looking for and seeking out anything, anyone, any item, from the past chapters of your life that creates disharmony in the here and now. More than resisting temptation, you are even better and more correctly relaxing your way through moments of emptiness and into moments of fulfillment, and you are absolutely full of resolve and perseverance to move on, free of seeking out anything or anyone who would stand in your way of you completing, harmonizing and fulfilling your life, moving beyond looking for (her car, computer tie-in's, etc.). You now think much more often about how to live more fully, more completely, more powerfully in healthy ways, physically, emotionally, mentally and spiritually. Free of and releasing temptation, you are moving ever onward, and sure of yourself and the serenity you create. It might have once been Ok to have felt bad, but now you are sure that time is over, and it's truly, practically and powerfully, most assuredly time to move forever onward. And as you do, you cut yourself a break; you toughen up; you bring greater peace to yourself, a greater and better peace to yourself, loving and respecting yourself way too much to ever backslide into the past chapter of your life, as this newer and better chapter of your life is way too enjoyable, important and filled with newer and more limitless opportunities, so upbeat and released, forgiven and healed, pulled back together again, breathing easier and free, free and long lasting; you are feeling better truly than you have in years.

## Overcoming A Breakup – 6 (male)

You relax into a brighter and better way of being, thinking, feeling and living. You now choose to think about better and more supportive ideas, moving from destructive thoughts and feelings, to forgiving the old and any and all people involved, to now and forever more easily finding yourself in a better place, in a better space, having found closure, free, free at long last! It's like you've found that closure and have now fluidly, adaptively, and forever moved on boldly forward in your life, almost like you had that closure and have moved 15 years forward in your healing process. On each and every exhale you release; you are releasing your past and are forgiven and healed, looking forward into the very best you are now enjoying and living from, for most unstoppably and undeniably, you are free of old thoughts, doubts, fears and thinking patterns, having moved into a brighter and better day and way of living and life. It's almost like someone from deep, deep inside of you has thrown a switch, a dial, a computer or a thermostat on in your favor, having reset and having freed you of any and all of the old barriers that have ever stood in your way.

Old thoughts and patterns that once stood in your way, old uncomfortable actions, feelings and reactions, are now drying up and evaporating, far from your present, and into your past, far, far away from you. Things in the past like old songs, even your favorite songs and artists reflect that the sentiments that you had once held for her, in a past chapter of your life, are now and forever gone. Simply old songs, new and more supportive meanings and feelings are now emerging. Even if you hear any of those songs, you enjoy those songs and are now finding powerful and clever ways of becoming and forever remaining free of any and all of the attached emotions and reflections regarding your past; it's done, it's over, you are creatively and adaptively moving on forever, finding newer and better ways of moving on, rising up and absolutely thriving, in place of old ways. Your newer and better choice is the breakthrough here, unstoppably and succeeding, polished, shiny and new, a fresh start is yours right now. In fact, truly, it's now just becoming easier and better for you to just heal, relax beyond all old barriers, having had enough of the old ways, now in the brand new chapter of your life, finding your life more enjoyable, upbeat, more willing day by day and night by night to rise up and laugh more often. Right now you are unstoppably free of any and all things toxic in your life, thoughts, feelings, memories, thought patterns, fears, worries and doubts. Now more correctly, more fluidly and powerfully unstoppable than ever before, you are thinking correctly and supportively, nurturing and taking only the very best care of yourself, as your thoughts are now supporting you. Your feelings are pleasant and conducive to a happy life; happy memories are now supporting you. All things once toxic, released and resolved; all things once a hindrance, now are resolved and in their place. You are loved and supported as never before. You are easily able to effectively shut down the past and open and activate the new, in your wonderfully resolved and restarted life, able to go anywhere, feeling comfortable, feeling fine, most especially whenever you may or might be passing or visiting a place where you had once been, feeling carefree, and glad to be healthy and alive, discomfort-free, feeling happy, calm, safe, at peace, centered, loving yourself, finding peace, healing, and joyous. All of this is becoming easier and better each and every day and night, on each and every breath, and with each and every beat of your heart. Your focus is upon healing and health, well-being and your now active and innate ability to resolve and transcend any and all things that had once ever been put in your way, by others but most especially by yourself, you know, all of the old barriers that once stood in your way are now more easily being resolved and truly and completely released. All things of old that ever once hindered you, now are your greatest source of strength, as they seem to be just creatively melting and evaporating. All old hindrances are just now gone; you find yourself reset, easily able to have feelings for others, feelings of love and healing for yourself, relaxed and trusting, your life just moving on, able to have any feelings for other women, as new thoughts and feelings just rise to the top, powerfully supporting and re-propagating your life and completely revitalizing you. The old things that once ever held prominence in your past, now diminished, the new things, thoughts, feelings, experiences, just seem to flow. It's almost like the old hindrances and feelings in your life have been so lowered, so turned down, so diminished, it's practically or even truly like they had never occurred. You are feeling wonderful, only doing better and better, almost like you are going back in time, just drifting back in time to an earlier time, say 7 or 8 years ago, almost like just leaping over those years to the right-now, free of any and all past effects you had once experienced, now and forever freed in powerful and forever ways, relieving and releasing any and all past recollections that ever caused you discomfort, moving wholly forward into the very best that your life can, will and does offer you in abundantly loving, self-nurturing, supportive supply.

# Overcoming Cravings

It's almost like any and all unneeded cravings, any and all unwanted cravings, truly, any and all unnecessary cravings are now being activated by a valve of some sort from deep, deep inside of you. And as the valve is opened and they are flowing, any and all cravings are just flooding out and are bubbling up, bubbling up and coming up to the surface in a flood right now, like water or energy just flooding up and out to the top, and now they are fully flowing out completely ready to be swept away.

Now imagine the ever rising and forever unstoppable light of the golden-white sunlight just warming the cravings up and just evaporating them away, drying them up, drying them away, as they heat up and are dried away from you and forever dried up from your life, now, always and forever. And now yet another valve from deep, deep inside of you is now opening and now fully opened. You are being flooded with new and better, more supportive thoughts and energies, the limitless energies of inspiration, an unstoppable can-do spirit, the ability to easily rise above anything and everything that once stood in your way because you can, because you must and so you now and forever do. You instead choose correctly forever to generate better and more supportive feelings of empowerment, liberation, triumph, victory and success, almost like you are shining a mighty light of golden-white sunlight from all around you and this light, your light is being turned up, tuned up, turned on and is forever and always vanquishing any and all doubt and cravings, with the light of knowledge, with the light of healing, with the light of enlightenment, with the light of love, with an unstoppable blinding light that vanquishes the old cravings as you are unstoppably flowing into any and all situations that once used to cause cravings, removing and forever vanquishing those cravings from yourself, from your life and from your world, both now, forever and always. Blockage-free, you flow joyously ever onward in remarkable and wonderful ways, even surprising yourself at how easy this is becoming.

You begin to realize that cravings in and of themselves are nothing and you are truly the mighty one. Right now, you are self-empowered, always and forever, you are ever more empowered to rise to the top and to completely relinquish and vanquish unhealthy cravings in whatever form they used to take by becoming empowered, mighty, old-craving-free, dynamic and by unstoppably rising to the top in the most magnificent and brilliant of ways.

Those unneeded and unwanted old cravings are like an empty vessel with a hole in it, they do nothing, they hold nothing; in fact, very truly, your old cravings are nothing, as you are now empowered, inspired and mighty, doing all that it takes, easier and better because fantastically, you've unstoppably moved on and are free, free at long last, not because I say so but because it is the nature of your own empowered mind and spirit to do so, unstoppably and relentlessly. You've decided to rise up and become mighty in all that you do, in all that you need to do, and just get it done, forever free of excuse or blockage, and you knowingly win, thrive and succeed. You have made up your powerful, effective, clever, adaptive and dynamic mind to thrive and succeed here as you are more determined to win at this more now than ever before; so you do. Your greatest and most overwhelming craving right now, is to become and forever remain healthy, happy, free and safe, extending your life in healthy ways that work for you best.

## Relationship Resolution - Trusting Instincts Moving on or Staying

You are finding newer and better, more trusting ways of thinking, feeling and acting in your life. A powerful and adaptive part of your deep and powerful subconscious mind is now actively trusting in your truest instincts and finding powerful resolution in your life and in all that you do. Trusting your first instincts, your deepest and most true responses, is a newer and better pattern in your life that is, now and forever, unstoppably emerging in correct and balanced ways. For from the deepest and truest places inside, you know what to do, based upon what it is you need and want. You begin to, and gain strength at allowing yourself to, clearly see what has been going on, what is going on, what will be going on in the future, and as you inhale deeply and exhale slowly now, with each and every breath that you take, you are allowing yourself to calm down, get centered and to truly know what to do, just as in past times when you were in your zone and on top of the world, truly knowing what it is that needs doing and taking any and all necessary steps to get resolution, clarity, balance, harmony, and power, from a deep and truly foundational part of who it is you are and are evolving into. Just like when sharing your very best guidance, clarity, direction and information with a great friend, you are now open to sharing this information with yourself, giving and taking your very best advice and following through to boldly create the next chapter of your life, making it the very best it can be. You might just find that physical attraction is coming back, or truly that it is yours right now. Or you might find that you might just be moving onto the next level, in ways so very right just for you, while finding acceptance, while realizing that you gave it your best shot and are now and should be, moving on. Your first instinct is your best, most trustable and truest; you are forever free of over-thinking it, you simply are in a place of power, empowerment and trust now, and just like waking up in the morning from a dream that creates obvious clarity and improved-forever direction in your life; you are now waking up to the possibilities of a greater and better life; a greater and grander you, is right now unstoppably emerging and it feels just great now, doesn't it? All of this is not because I say so, but because it's the nature of your own powerful mind and inner wisdom to do so. For in all things now, you are gaining more patience with and compassion towards everyone, most especially yourself while rising to the very top in your life, doing what you know you will do, must do, and are doing to balance and enhance your life, in the most potent and powerful of ways. You are building confidence, clarity and strength, purpose and direction, enhancing and improving your life, easily adaptive and learning from the deepest and most true of places to live with your decisions, forever free of looking back and questioning them, as you are in a new and better, more dynamically improved chapter of your life. You learn to sleep peacefully and powerfully right through the night; even your dreams are now working in your favor and with every morning upon your waking up, you are feeling truly revitalized, reactivated, rejuvenated, resting peacefully and powerfully right through the night, easily able to fall back to sleep whenever necessary after just a few deep, slow and steady breaths, giving yourself gifts of better energy, powerful and better rest and a recharged libido, optimistic, clear, confident, powerful and strong, re-circuited, re-defined, unlimited, more unconditionally loving, most especially to yourself, and re-balanced, flowing ever onward into a newer and more potent, powerful chapter of your life. So very sure of yourself and rising to the top, you are powerfully and forever self re-identified, dynamic, clear, successful and more motivated, moving into brighter and better vistas, on top of your game and truly living your life in more focused and direct ways, better and better than ever before.

## Spouse Infidelity Fears and Trusting in Life

You are finding newer and better, more supportive and relaxingly effective ways to thrive and succeed in your life. You are effectively, powerfully, adaptably and amazingly giving up old habits of fear, doubt, rage and panic, completely giving up all uncomfortable patterns that create stress and most especially you give up trying and struggling, learning better how to trust in your life, your world and all that you create and in all that you experience.

You are beginning to feel better about yourself, learning to tap into the feelings, thoughts, experiences and emotions of any and all times when you felt and truly were feeling truly mighty, easily able to re-identify yourself as mighty, rising to the top, now and most passionately remembering to activate the energy of every past victory, triumph, breakthrough and success that you've ever had, allowing all of that to think of yourself in more unlimited ways, and truly and profoundly coming to the realization, more and more, each and every day, each and every night, on each and every breath that you take and with each and every beat of your heart, that you are in fact fine, looking good and feeling fine, both inside and out, truly and most unstoppably, you are and you remain determined to release any and all blockages that you ever experienced, that ever stood in your way to that now-and-forever inevitable goal. You are trusting in your life no matter what, you are fine, you are doing better and better, and even amazingly, learning, remembering and knowing in fact forever, you will be fine, regardless of event or circumstance. You are now finding ways to believe in yourself, trust in life and making the most of every moment as if a switch or dial, a thermostat or a computer of some type, from deep, deep within, has been powerfully and forever reset, allowing you to thrive, trust and rise above any and all circumstances, as your thoughts, feelings and emotions are now being powerfully reset to take the very best care of you. The new thoughts and feelings that now prey on your mind are correct and supportive ones, that strengthen, comfort and heal you powerfully. Regardless of what anyone else is doing, might be doing or may be doing in any way, you are unharmed, strengthened and polished, and you know this. You let go of problem thinking, becoming challenge-oriented, rising up easily, effectively and powerfully to deal with any and all events and circumstances with precision, ease and clarity, in the more beneficial and effective of ways. You are looking good, feeling fine, trusting, living, enjoying, unfazed, adequate enough, determined, sure of yourself, trusting in your life, feeling inspired and almost Divinely guided and taken care of, loved by yourself and others in the more heartfelt and abundantly felt and highly effective ways. In fact, truly, you are relaxing into a better and more carefully crafted masterpiece of a supportive and more pleasantly happy life that you create, you deserve and that you are safely living within.

## Spouse Infidelity Fears and Trusting In Life

You are finding newer and better, more supportive and relaxingly effective ways to thrive and succeed in your life. You are effectively, powerfully, adaptably and amazingly giving up old habits of fear, doubt, rage and panic, completely giving up all uncomfortable patterns that create stress and most especially you give up trying and struggling, learning better how to trust in your life, your world and all that you create and in all that you experience.

You are beginning to feel better about yourself, learning to tap into the feelings, thoughts, experiences and emotions of any and all times when you felt and truly were feeling truly mighty, easily able to re-identify yourself as mighty, rising to the top, now and most passionately remembering to activate the energy of every past victory, triumph, breakthrough and success that you've ever had, allowing all of that to think of yourself in more unlimited ways, and truly and profoundly coming to the realization, more and more, each and every day, each and every night, on each and every breath that you take and with each and every beat of your heart, that you are in fact fine, looking good and feeling fine, both inside and out, truly and most unstoppably, you are and you remain determined to release any and all blockages that you ever experienced, that ever stood in your way to that now-and-forever inevitable goal. You are trusting in your life no matter what, you are fine, you are doing better and better, and even amazingly, learning, remembering and knowing in fact forever, you will be fine, regardless of event or circumstance. You are now finding ways to believe in yourself, trust in life and making the most of every moment as if a switch or dial, a thermostat or a computer of some type, from deep, deep within, has been powerfully and forever reset, allowing you to thrive, trust and rise above any and all circumstances, as your thoughts, feelings and emotions are now being powerfully reset to take the very best care of you. The new thoughts and feelings that now prey on your mind are correct and supportive ones, that strengthen, comfort and heal you powerfully. Regardless of what anyone else is doing, might be doing or may be doing in any way, you are unharmed, strengthened and polished, and you know this. You let go of problem thinking, becoming challenge-oriented, rising up easily, effectively and powerfully to deal with any and all events and circumstances with precision, ease and clarity, in the more beneficial and effective of ways. You are looking good, feeling fine, trusting, living, enjoying, unfazed, adequate enough, determined, sure of yourself, trusting in your life, feeling inspired and almost Divinely guided and taken care of, loved by yourself and others in the more heartfelt and abundantly felt and highly effective ways. In fact, truly, you are relaxing into a better and more carefully crafted masterpiece of a supportive and more pleasantly happy life that you create, you deserve and that you are safely living within.

# Beating Road Rage, Self-Confidence and Forgiveness

You are finding new and better, healthier, more beneficial, truly life-supporting and more self-gentle ways to process your emotions, by deep breathing, soothing, relaxation breath, while easily and dynamically achieving deeper levels of relaxation, while letting all imbalances drift away, forever releasing struggle mentality, even laughing out loud, allowing all that you are, to feel better and better about who you are, not because I say so, but because you deserve better in your life and, therefore, you are adaptively finding newer and more clever and even surprisingly effective ways of doing all this, simply and without over-thinking, just getting it done, more and more easily finding, achieving even better results, that function to liberate you effectively and precisely and even more clearly, allowing you limitless, beneficial results. Free you are now and forever remain, free of ever holding in the emotions and feelings that would work against you as they once did in the old and useless previous chapter of your life, which is now and forever over, as you are firmly and forever empowered within the embrace of a brand new and better chapter of your life. So each and every day and night, you are finding newer and more incredibly effective ways of working to your benefit, physically, emotionally, mentally, even spiritually, in even surprisingly effective, fluid, and adaptive ways, easily and comfortably achieving desired results, relaxing beyond, through, over and around any and all old barriers from the previous chapter of your life into brighter better vistas and brilliant inspirational horizons in your life. You are calm, you are safe, you are serene, finding the effective strength of relaxation and the power of deep and steady breath, that is forever bringing you refuge, whenever, wherever, however, from the emotional turbulence that once might have been your past, and is effectively now an oasis, deeply within you, from the world's turbulence, most especially while driving, you are calm and unstoppably staying focused, calm, peaceful, happy, upbeat, perhaps singing along to the music, soft or loud, staying safely in your zone, as you stay comfortably in a zone of peacefulness, finding clever ways to do this, that work best for you; the greater the challenge, the greater your ability to resoundingly bounce back and remain focused and calm, while driving skillfully, calmly and peacefully just like a pro; for what they know, you know, what they do you do, and you, more cleverly, effectively and easily do. You know, it's almost like someone from deep inside of you has opened up a valve of some sort, draining off all emotional imbalance, frustration, upset, while allowing this new clear space within you to find inner peace and harmony, in ways that are working out truly in your favor, whether you're realizing how this is working or not, creating inner strength, serenity, peace, and the ability to master any and all situations, which in reality you've always done, and now only getting better and more precise, skillful, and adept, all things now working only in your favor. As you are doing all of this, it is becoming more commonplace, more easy, more skillful and you now, more skillfully adept, more adaptive, more working in your favor, easily and effectively, as you achieve all desired results, establishing a new and better rhythm emotionally and mentally within yourself, as this newer and better chapter of your life is strengthening you, almost as if someone from deep, deep inside of you, has reset a switch, a dial, thermostat, or a computer of some kind, which is activating your mighty inner hero, the part of you that is doubtless and fearless, the part of you that is capable of unlimited, mighty great things, like saving children from danger or a fire of some sort, strengthened, redirected, and focused, by the limitless energy and inspiration of every past victory, triumph, breakthrough and success you've ever had, as a new inner light from heart and mind is forever shining brightly and boldly into all areas of your life that matter most to you, even especially areas you once found a challenge. You now just doing better and better, feeling fine.

As your relationship with your life and yourself now and forever improves, it's like all of this energy within you is becoming a magnet for better friendships, relationships, and even romance, as a new improved and polished you is now and forever emerging unstoppably.

Your dynamic mind now opens, your thoughts clear, your correct response to any and all old barriers from previous chapters of your life is to relax beyond and through them, relaxing beyond the challenges of any and all stress, while remaining completely calm and serene, speaking your mind, drinking in knowledge, breeding better results, forgiven forever, letting go of harsh judgments, most especially self-judgments, forgiven forever and released from the boundaries of the past, in fact polished by them. You shine ever onward doing better and better. Sure and certain of yourself, you are unbeatable and unstoppable at all of this, relaxed, forgiven and healed, smiling from deep, deep within, you notice a knowing, glowing confidence, calmness, inner strength, is undeniably, fluidly, adaptively, actively and effectively there forever.

## Overcoming Road Rage - Aggressive Driving

Relax even deeper now and just allow all that you are, body, emotions, mind and even spirit, to memorize this feeling of relaxed inner and outer balance. It's just like riding a bicycle, having the fun and happiness and finding that balance, just like when you were a child. This relaxation is a balance you can easily return to each and every time you need to. So while you are relaxing, just imagine or just think about the times in your life when you felt most relaxed, think about a happy, pleasant safe vacation, to a beautiful beach or a lovely mountain area, so peaceful, so serene; how good you felt and how good your are feeling right now. You are determined to keep these and other good feelings. It just feels like you are being embraced in the calmness, the gentleness, the serenity, the peacefulness, of those moments right now, as you relax, even deeper, even further.

Now, imagine or just think about riding in your car. You might be alone or even with others, or in heavy or even moderate to light traffic. It might be slow or it might be moving fast. But this time, for you, it's going to be better, more balanced, more peaceful, more relaxed. Because in this moment and from on, and it's only getting easier and better in all future moments, you are going to rise above your past and begin a new, better, emerging forever chapter of your life, becoming more balanced, calmer, happier, relaxing into a stress-free driving chapter of your life. In fact, you've decided to drive safely, competently, correctly – you are at a peaceful, safe, determined and happy place from deep, deep inside of you. A powerful and balanced, rising above place in body, emotions, mind and even in spirit. And you are powerfully and successfully tapping into your wonderful ability to rise above any and all challenges, to be at your very best, allowing all of your skill, all of your calmness and emotional and mental balance, all of your focus, all of your reactions, to be at their very best, living your life the way you know you should, to be the very best you can be. In fact, it's almost like you are so calm, so peaceful, so detached emotionally, so focused, driving clearly and calmly, relaxed, attentive and allowing any and all of your very best driving skills and years of experience, to come forth in perfect action and harmony and everything just flows. It's almost like you are on a separate planet, a separate plane of existence, its like you're an observer, your breathing is safe and deep, you remain neutral, so focused, so separate, so calm, so happy, so peaceful, so detached, so powerfully and deeply, truly relaxed. What others are doing is their business, even if they are drifting out of their lanes, driving dangerously or even gesturing in unpleasant ways. Their emotional reactions are their business, those actions or reactions absolutely none of your business. You keep your power with calmness and certainty and you are powerfully, absolutely determined to do so. You keep your power and sturdy sense of self-control within, that they would try to manipulate, laughingly keeping abundant good feelings within yourself. You may actually feel anger-free which is just fine with you, regardless of what anyone else is about. Each and every moment, you make it better and better.

So take a deep breath now and powerfully allow yourself to completely memorize this deep and powerfully profound feeling of a correct and comfortable way of existing, relaxed powerfully, deeply, truly, in all that You are body, emotions, mind and you even feel the relaxing empowerment of your spirit to balance, restore and guide you, above and way beyond any and all challenges, that can, might or even may arise. So take a deep, relaxation breath and count down silently in your mind, from 3 to 1, relaxing deeper on each and every breath, each and every number, 3, 2, 1 . . . And just after one or two or three short, deeply soothing, calming wonderful relaxation breaths, you relax powerfully, remain sharply and powerfully focused, laser-beam-like in your correct and powerful precision of emotional detachment and relaxation, you emotionally detach in the most complete, powerful and successful ways. And better ideas, supportive ideals, thoughts and feelings occur to you, for complete safety, getting bigger and better than any possible situation. So you are just letting it all go, relaxing and releasing any and all anger and any and all upsetment and any and all feelings of (name feelings) desperation, mistreatment, self-justification, getting even and unfairness, just letting it all go, going, going, gone, far, far away from you as it melts away. For you are truly knowing from powerful, real and substantial places deep, deep inside, you have absolutely nothing to prove, you trust in yourself and in your life and what others are doing or driving like around you is just fine with you. It has absolutely nothing to do with you as long as you are safe, safe right now, safe for you, safe for the ones you love, safe for yourself right now, you are healthy, safe and detached, calm, happy to prove nothing, content, peaceful, within yourself, safe and calm and completely detached and extremely relaxed, completely able to arrive alive, safe, at your destination, able to arrive home, to the ones you love or even with the ones you love, peaceful, calm, focused, balanced, harmonized, relaxed and most importantly, SAFE! Healthy! Each and every time you drive, you do better and better, anger-free, you are in control of your car as well as your feelings, and you are very determined to feel good in every way, regardless of event or of circumstance, finding your own powerful center and living from it. Safety is your best defense, you are powerfully free of anything to prove, you're safe, centered and grounded. There you are, with your car in a whole, safe undamaged and complete condition. And even more importantly with you and even the ones you love, intact, whole, peaceful and comfortable, in a whole and safe, undamaged, complete condition. You are doing all the right things to do, the better things to do, the only things to do, a new chapter of your life, happy, healthy, safe, calm, peaceful, detached, liberated, mature, free, larger than any challenge, problem-free, motivated.

# Overcoming Stress, Life Challenges and Alcohol as a Crutch

You have powerfully and unstoppably decided to take a new tack in your life, to get back on track and to succeed in unstoppably adaptive and effective ways. Your correct response to any and all stress is to first deep-breathe and to rise above it by relaxing your way through it. Just as you've always been able to work well under pressure, you are now finding clever and adaptive ways to rise above the pressures of your life, even if it includes increased case loads at work, finding newer and better ways to deep-breathe, relax and to adaptively and cleverly reduce your stress. Quite often in your past, just some deep-breathing was enough to bring down stress, and you'll just find yourself doing that, while successfully bringing down stress levels most effectively, doing anything and everything that needs doing or has to be done, feeling a new and ever-building sense of empowerment, so committed to success and in the most effective of ways, you are most assuredly succeeding unstoppably, turning once-elevated stress levels around for you to work with in your favor. You make time to flourish in your life, making time, scheduling and adaptively succeeding to make time for romance and intimacy with your spouse (husband / wife) in your life, regardless of change of life cycle or regardless of any event or circumstance, now even better, truly, effectively, cleverly, adaptively and relaxing into the joys of increased intimacy in your life; you make it important, you take and make the time, and it becomes a priority in your life, just doing what needs to be done there. You are becoming upbeat, capable, inspired, flexible and adaptive, easily able to relax and create insights about how to deal with and rise above vindictive and vicious people, allowing yourself time to cleverly succeed and to adapt, allowing your very best insights to come through, while remaining emotionally detached from events and circumstances to provide a clear way and to guide others on your path of clarity, to focus while leading them to better places and better harmonies, often by your own example, always unleashing your very best, wisdom, guidance, thoughts, feelings and perspectives, allowing the most powerful wisdom of your inner therapist to come through, in each and every moment, and this only gets easier, better, faster, more successfully adaptive and effective, in each and every moment and each and every time you are challenged this way, as you succeed skillfully as never before. You rise up and vanquish all hostilities, for you now know and truly remember, you are mightier than any challenge you might encounter; you are and you remain, problem-free, while staying challenge-oriented, shining light, direction and clarity, into the wisdom of the decisions and choices that you make. The light of the love you have for your family, always guides you to the very best decisions, choices and successes, you both now and forever create. You find yourself discussing and creating harmony in all moments and situations that matter the most, most especially when discussing the upbringing of your kids as you are both seeking the very best outcomes; you together, by your design and by your mutual love, always calmly discuss and arrive at the very best of all possible adaptations and decisions, allowing all of the very best choices and decisions that you mutually work out, to transcend any and all disharmonies and challenges. You are talking your life back, rising up and making the very best and most of your life, activating your very best, as if someone from deep, deep inside of you is forever and always turning on a switch of some kind. You are taking your past inner weaknesses and turning them into strengths, polishing up all flaws, remaking yourself shiny and new, powerful and focused, loving yourself in place of destructive self-judgments, forgiving and releasing the past, rising up to become mightier than any and all challenges you have or might be presented with, loving yourself in place of the old habit of beating yourself up, filling yourself up with a new sense of "can do" spirit and now truly, allowing yourself to thrive, doing all that needs doing, and smiling at how cleverly, adaptively you are succeeding, activating new inspirations from the deepest and truest places from your heart, mind and life, with precise and adaptive focus, with calm and balanced emotions, in the very best and most amazing of ways. Skillfully avoiding old and new pitfalls, you are finding new joys and life-supportive experiences, flowing ever onward.

# Post Traumatic Stress and OCD – Pediatric

**Note:** You must be a qualified and certified Clinical Hypnosis professional and have a written note of authorization to perform this or any other complementary hypnosis session from the attending physician, psychiatrist, psychologist, etc., no exceptions.

You now find you are really, truly and powerfully enjoying your life, with each and every move you make and each and everything you do and each and everything you have to do, whether at home, outside, or in school. School and going to school is going to be, and truly becomes and each and every day and night will be, getting only stronger, better, more and more truly, actually and effectively, an experience you look forward to, as you move into the next chapter of your life. You are calm, peaceful and relaxed, your correct response to anything you once worried about, is to relax your way into a better way of solving that challenge. You are now, more than ever, trusting in yourself and in your life. You truly know and now live from and even more importantly think and feel from the following truth: yesterday has taken care of me; in fact, all of my yesterdays have taken care of me. Today has taken care of me, and I am now more certain than ever, tomorrow will be the same, even more so. You are finding newer and better ways of trusting in your life, trusting in your life, which you make happen in only the very best of ways. You are trusting in your health, because in the past if you ever got sick you always got better, just as you will, today, tomorrow. So each and every day and night, you are doing better and better, getting better and better, feeling better and better, thinking only thoughts that allow you to feel better and better. You begin to let go of and allow yourself to have melt away from you, any and all past unpleasant or unhappy or untrusting thoughts and feelings; you are just letting them drift away, drift away, drift away, they are going, going, gone and gone forever. You begin to think right now, like planting a seed into the ground and watching it grow: my life is getting better and better, my life is doing better and better, I'm feeling better and better in new and better and more unstoppable ways. All of your functions and thoughts are balancing now, free of worry, free of fear of things you imagine; instead you imagine your body and powerful mind now working with you, in your favor, to allow you to move into a brighter and better chapter of your life, a chapter in your life where you live only your very best dreams.

Now relax ever deeper and further and as you do, I want you to begin to think of a time you felt your very best: your body felt great, your feelings were great, your thoughts worked out in such a way to make you feel on top of the world and really happy, and you were really feeling great on the inside and great on the outside. Your health was fine, is fine in every possible way, getting only better and better, like you are lighting up on the inside, with abundant, plentiful health. The thoughts you have make you feel good, the feelings you have make you feel good, most especially and even more importantly the properly prepared and healthy foods you eat, you trust in, are supporting you and taking care of you, in truthfully and real powerful ways. Your family is there to take care of you and is really going nowhere but back to you in time, even if they have to go away from you at times to take care of you and live their lives. Your Mom and Dad are always there for you and you powerfully find more new and real and true ways to trust in life and in this very important fact. You are enough, your health is enough, you are clean enough, you are taken care of by life and you are completely certain, you are doing fine, only getting better and better.

You are most especially sure, more sure than ever before, you are going to be fine in the very next chapter of your life, as you happily graduate and move onto your new school, because there, you'll surely and really thrive, grow, win, learn, be successful, enjoying all new learning, all new opportunities to gain, to grown and truly enjoy all new learning. You make your life a happy and joyous adventure, as you succeed and thrive, enjoying your life and your living, truly succeeding, a happy, trusting, relaxed and powerful winner in life.

## Rising Above Abuse and Stress - Staying Above It ALL

Now as you relax deeper and deeper, you allow a new thought for a new day to emerge and grow. A very new, very true and very powerful thought, is beginning now and for the rest of your life, you to begin to breathe and relax your way through any and all challenging situations in your life, both now, always and forever. It really doesn't matter where the stress is coming from or whatever the challenge is to you, because you recognize that you are in charge of your life and you are allowing yourself to remain detached, balanced, clear, calm and focused, even if it means allowing yourself to take on the role of a leader, a teacher or even an instructor in a given situation, because you allow yourself to explain and even ask for, or perhaps demand what it is you want, what it is you need, what it is you deserve. So you powerfully commit yourself to buy out of the emotional games that other people would have you play, because you know better and you are smart enough to do better and to know better as you thrive in yet un-imagined ways!

In this moment, you have decided to react in a bigger and in a greater way in this and in every stressful moment. You rise above, you maintain your focus, you stay centered and grounded and remaining within your foundation throughout all that you wish to accomplish, all that you will accomplish and all that you actually do accomplish, truly and in reality, powerfully and unstoppably beginning a brand new more empowered chapter of your life, allowing your life to be a place of peace and inner harmony it deserves to be, bringing it right here into right now. It really doesn't matter if you are cast into or relax into the role of being a leader, or if you allow another to take charge, because what matters is your ability to communicate and to express yourself, clearly and directly, even indirectly, relaxing into properly and correctly phrasing your words, sentences and thoughts, asking for what you do want, rather than asking for what you don't want; even if it means leading with patience and perseverance. You help to explain, instruct or even train an individual person to be the best that they can be. You are always clear to express yourself in calm, positive, direct terms and choose your words carefully and precisely to get all of your points, thoughts, concepts and ideas across, clearly, expressively and with maximum impact, result and effectiveness, to achieve the optimum outcome, in a clear, focused, calm, relaxed fashion, because, you are important. You deserve to be heard, you matter and have always and will always make a difference to the people in this world, most especially those people you love, which includes you. So you learn to take better care of yourself. All times are times to stay above all of the small stuff and most of it is all small stuff. So beginning right now and for the rest of your life, you relax, you thrive and you bloom into your prosperity and of the fullness that is your life, focusing on the long term goals, eyes on the part of the race you wish to get to and achieve.

You let go of all old unneeded ideas and symptoms of struggle from your past, and you let them go slowly and yet forever, letting them drift away, drifting away, drifting far, far away, relaxing right now into a masterpiece of a life that you gently and boldly create, now and in very moment, you are calm and at peace. You are in a place of calm determination as all that you wish to accomplish and all that you will accomplish, all that you do and are in fact accomplishing, you accomplish with poise, ease, grace and skill, so adeptly, so powerfully. For beginning right now and for the rest of your life, you are in control of your life. You rise above like you've always really done, and you either choose to learn or to succeed, because you matter and what's best for you is best for all involved. And while you are relaxing, your powerful mind is practically coming up with, as if you were dreaming, new successful strategies and solutions to any and all challenges. And these new potent, very dynamic, very true, very powerful strategies and solutions readily activate into your life. And whether you realize it or not, into each and every moment of your life, liberating your life and liberating and lightening you, in very aspect and regard, easily allowing you to create the masterpiece of a life you've always desired, bringing it into the right now, into every aspect of your life, physically, emotionally, mentally and even spiritually, in each and every way, beginning right now and for the rest of your life, supporting you in every way, now and forever!

If in the future you would like to relax and activate this relaxing empowerment in any form, quickly and easily, simply perform a few short deep soothing breaths of relaxation, powerfully and easily activating the power, comfort, and inspiration relaxation can and will successfully bring you. And your self-confidence, self-esteem and inner strength will immediately increase. You will detach completely from all conflicts, frictions and disharmonies and you emerge a new greater person. You are empowered, successful and liberated. You feel like you've got the whole world in the palm of your hand; you handle your life so easily. You take on becoming emotionally lighter and dynamically healthier, every time and at any time. And congratulations, you win, you thrive, you succeed! You are lighting up the world.

# Stress Relief, Patience, Life Improvement

Regardless of how people are or may be, you are powerfully remaining detached, calm and peaceful, focused, and centered and dynamically above it all, forgiving and releasing the past; truly you are and you remain, calm, peaceful and relaxed, above it all, almost as if truly in fact, you are mighty, detached. Wow is this easy! As if a parent or teacher, you are calm, clear, getting your points across, explaining, guiding, getting each and every bit of it done, activating your inner teacher, guide, instiller of wisdom and truth, easily and powerfully staying safe, centered, free, calm and detached from the emotional end of the little and big things alike. The more challenged you are becoming at any given moment, the easier it is for you to stay and forever remain, calm, peaceful, centered and relaxed, building an ever-growing reservoir of patience and understanding. The more challenged you become, most especially if you are sensing old and monotonous modes of stupidity, selfishness, and ignorance, the more and more patient and understanding you are and you steadfastly remain. You are just choosing to become and remain serene, unruffled, composed, and gentle to yourself, in each and every thought you have, each and every feeling you experience, and most especially whenever challenged. You are free of delving into foods and drinks like chocolate and fattening coffee drinks; this needs to stop – and so it does, not because I say so, but because you do and it's done, as you've moved forever into a brand new and better chapter of your life. You are in a brand new and better, more fulfilling chapter of your life. Old patterns of negativity are things of the past chapter of your life; you are bound and determined to feel good, only getting better and better, moving on, in harmony and balance, feeling good. Your words and thoughts, actions and reactions are flowing from a more loving, healed, forgiven and rising-to-the-top place, whole-and-more-focused perspective in your life. Words just seem to flow. All things that once ever stood in your way, you are mightier and mightier than; your goals come down to levels of ridiculous ease. You make time for yourself, bringing exercise goals down to simple levels, so easy to accomplish, excuse-free and enjoyment- oriented. You find and create time to read more, exercise, and take, create and make the time you need to succeed and to enrich yourself.

# Tuning-Out Outside Noise, Dogs Barking

You are so comfortable now, so in your zone, so easily able to tune out any and all noise, while tuning into a better way of life. You are easily, skillfully, successfully and dynamically tuning out and flowing beyond, that which you once found unpleasant or disruptive in any way, most especially ignoring and tuning out any and all sounds you wish to tune out, turning down and just letting go of any and all past disharmonious emotional reactions, most especially any and all dog barking, which once woke you up in the morning, now so easily tuned out and turned down.

Even the sound of a dog's bark as soon as you get up in the morning, means little or just might be completely unimportant to you; you've moved on, into a newer and better chapter of your life, even if it's a dog barking while you're sitting in your yard, so trivial, so turned down, so tuned out, even if there's a dog barking while you're eating dinner. You are rising up, rising to the top, moving on, even if there's a dog barking while you're in your yard in the evening, it doesn't matter; you are letting go of past emotional reactions and moving on unstoppably, rising up, tuning into happier times, calmer and more balanced, unshakable times, so harmonized, so balanced, so healed, even if you are or might even be conscious of hearing a dog bark while you're in your bathroom, it matters little. You are tuning out any and all things that once ever stood in your way, just like adjusting a volume control, as if you were doing it in your head. You are remaining calm, peaceful, balanced and serene, centered, in your comfort zone, finding new inner harmony and inner joy, inner wisdom and balance, moving on, most especially if there are kids screaming or shrieking while playing in a pool. You are becoming fixed, yet fluidly adaptive in all of this, easily inventing clever, healthy, right and correct ways of doing this with skill and expertise, whether you realize it yet or not. I wonder if you even yet realize how easy this is going to be for you, as your clever and adaptive mind is now working in every moment of your life to effectively accomplish this.

# Endorsements

## Some Endorsements For

## Hypnotic Scripts That Work

"A Wonderful, Wonderful Work!!! Something every modern Hypnotherapist must have (for use) in their practice!"

### Ormond McGill - The Dean of American Hypnotists - Palo Alto, CA

"John Cerbone has created powerful scripts that bring your professional expertise into the 21st century."

### Elsom Eldridge, Jr. - Winter Springs, FL

"I have always enjoyed the fine hypnotic work of John Cerbone. His gift for finding a positive way to express suggestions is one I admire. You will not find a better source of ideas, wisdom and spiritually appropriate hypnotic techniques than what he has presented. His capacity to find a way to guide clients to make changes while giving positive personal reinforcement is one we should all strive to equal."

### The Rev. C. Scot Giles, D.Min., BCC, BCH – Wheaton, IL

"John's script book is an invaluable tool that any Hypnotherapist, novice or veteran, can use. There are many gemsin this publication."

### Tom Vitale – Valley Hypnosis Inc. – Methuen, MA

"John, I LOVE your new script book! It is OUTSTANDING! You have taken the boring one size fits all hypnotic script and TRANSFORMED it into an exact and precise tool. Like a Surgeon with a scalpel, you have hit right into the heart of the issues that face our clients in the office. I really like the diversity of topics and your precise wording technique to get those we help into the most resourceful state, helping fix the problems and issues that our clients face. I decided to buy the book and I now know how great it is to use!"

### Richard Rumble - Mister Hypnosis - Dana Point, CA

"John, I have used your book and I am very happy with it. Thank you!"

## Mary Frances Hernandez - Traceform Your Life Hypnosis - Albuquerque, N.M.

"This is certainly one of the top script books I've ever seen! It's one of the very best! I would be very happy to recommend it. A marvelous job!
It's wonderful! Good work!"

## Jackie Sharp - Inner Technologies Hypnosis - Salt Lake City, UT

"I had the opportunity to read a copy of your most recent hypnosis script book,

I knew right away that I had come across something of value, something that can literally transform "the quality of life." Your method of suggestion creates a way for people to give themselves permission to live a more purposeful life while letting go of some of life's useless self-imposed restrictions. As a practicing Hypnotherapist and hypnosis instructor I have examined hundreds of scripts and on a few occasions I have recommend the better ones to my students to use as a model while practicing in the beginning to write their own scripts. I have found your scripts to be some of the most effective, comprehensive and practical ones on the market to date. They offer easy, clear, comprehensive, effective, fast and powerful ways to help the client release self-imposed limitations, thereby giving themselves necessary permission to live a more purposeful life, while enjoying a richer and fuller life experience in the process. Your scripts have the potential to literally change people's lives no matter what is triggering their problem. Keep up the good work I look forward for more of the same in the future.

Good luck and thanks for helping to make this world a better place for all of us."

## E. C. Goldberg, C.I. - Serenity and Solutions - Brooklyn, NY

"I sense a great passion for your work and I believe that is a great thing to have in this world. I have really enjoyed your script book. It is well a written book and is certainly a resource worth having. Again, thank you for your contribution to the art and science of Hypnosis and to me."

## Christopher R. Gross, CCH, LMT - Bryant, Arkansas

"It is my great pleasure to recommend Hypnotic Scripts that Work by my colleague John Cerbone, PhD. The book is filled with many useful scripts which will keep the average hypnotists referring to it again and again, and I highly recommend it."

### Lawrence Galante, Ph.D., DHom, CHt.
### Director: The Center for Holistic Arts – New York City

"I bought your Hypnotic Scripts That Work at the NGH convention this weekend
and had to drop you a note. I am a Clinical Hypnotherapist in the Boston area
and take great care with every word in my sessions and until I saw your book
I always found reason to edit every script I see.
I picked up your book with skepticism telling myself I would put it back
when I saw the first edit I would make and I'm still reading, outstanding work.
This is the best script book I have ever seen!"

### Paul Gustafson, RN, BSN, CH - Boston, MA
### www.HealthyHypnosis.com (http://www.HealthyHypnosis.com)

"John I write to congratulate you on your book, HYPNOTIC SCRIPTS THAT WORK " The Breakthrough
Book. As a Clinical Hyno Analyst / Psychotherapist, I have many so called books of scripts, but what you have
produced here has a hallmark of excellence. It is not for the shelf, It is for good clinical use [which I have had great
success with so far]the other books are for the shelf. Well done on such a comprehensive, well structured and useful
book which has become my clinical Bible."

### James A. Malone, Dip.Hyp.D.Psych [Master N.L.P. Practitioner] MICHP
### Dublin, Ireland

"Hi John, I purchased your book, Hypnotic Scripts That Work last summer, and I have to tell you that I use it
constantly. There is absolutely no other book of scripts and/or suggestions that I use nearly as much as I use yours. I
have to say that I am grateful to Paul G. for letting me know about your book in the first place. I've only been practicing
hypnotherapy for a short time, and in that time, I've reached for your book over and over again. We spoke on the phone
when I ordered the book, and I was impressed with your kindness and willingness to share thoughts and information
with me. I meant to contact you before this, but time has a way of passing far too quickly. I am now actively doing
business as Sensible Hypnosis. I can't tell you how happy I am to have your book to reach for when I need inspiration
and/or good, solid suggestions. I just thought you should know that your book has been a wonderful resource for me,
and I'm truly grateful to have it. Also, please let me know when you'll be performing in the Boston area. I'd love to see
your show. Thanks again so much. Sincerely,"

### Kim Stephenson - C.Ht. - Sensible Hypnosis, Arlington, MA

"Hypnotic Scripts That Work - The Breakthrough Book is an OUTSTANDING book, with Hypnotic scripts
that can be adjusted to suit the clients needs. A book you can refer to again and again, a must have - get this book!"

### Sean P Hammond, CI - United Kingdom

"John Cerbone's script are the best available. They flow like liquid poetry and are wonderfully effective. Each collection matches or exceeds the one before. These are a must have in any Hypnotist's office."

**Norman H. Pesner, Owner/Director**
**The Reducing Key-Hypnosis Center - Baltimore, MD**

:By Divine Reason, Diving Purpose and Divine Time, I have been blessed with the priceless opportunity to learn the mind blowing, uncontested techniques that John Cerbone has taught me. I'm really hoping that John has training, or at least workshops at the next two National Guild of Hypnotists Conventions. We, Hypnotists, are very fortunate to have the incredible talent, skills and teachings that John enriches us with. I

highly recommend John Cerbone's book, Hypnotic Scripts That Work - The Breakthrough Book and workshops to anyone who wants optimal success with clients."

**Jason Hughes, CH**
**Positive Changes Hypnosis Center - Sacramento, CA**

"John, I enjoyed meeting at the NGH. Thanks for the note, and thank you very, very much for the script book. It is awesome! The scripts are on target, very thorough and cathartic. The manner in which you weave words expresses not only your talents, gifts and hard work, but also your love for the mission of improving lives and the deep caring for those blessed and healed by your words! Keep sharing your gifts."

**With warm regards, Kathleen Peters, LMFT - Owensboro, Kentucky**

"A wealth of information, on every subject, presented in caring and supportive language that clearly helps people overcome their issues. Bravo John!"

**Susan Neri-Friedwald - New Behavior Institute - New York, N.Y.**

"The material in this book is substantial. There is a lot of new and original beneficial suggestions and techniques. This is a great reference book that every hypnotist should have."

**Robert M. Fried, CH, NGH Ocean County NJ - Chapter President.**

"Hi John, Your script book is comprehensive and thorough, and it is obvious that you have many hundreds (if not thousands) of hours invested in your scripts. I especially like the one: "You're About to Have a Breakthrough." It is a masterpiece of indirect suggestion allowing the client's inner mind to decide what to change. Your scripts are far better than many I've seen over the years; and I especially like the way you include suggestions of empowerment. Best wishes,"

**Roy Hunter - www.royhunter.com**

I definitely refer to this book for ideas. I like the energy that comes through in your writing. The suggestions are written in a compelling and positive tone. It's very good work.

### Patrick Bewe, CH - Providence Hypnosis Center, Providence, Rhode Island

If you ever had the privilege of meeting John Cerbone you would soon realize that he has a personality that's unforgettable. In "Hypnotic Scripts that Work' John has managed to infuse his unique personality into his writing. John provides an imaginative source of scripts that cover the most commonly encountered issues: Overcoming a Break-up, Overcoming Panic, Managing Sadness, Overcoming Fear, Perfecting Golf, Overcoming Insomnia, Learning Enhancement, Motivation, Stop Smoking, Weight Management etc. 'Hypnotic Script that work' is an impeccably organized manual containing a vast selection of hypnosis scripts. They have been successfully used and refined during John's years of work in the field of clinical hypnosis. I particularly like the session optimizing suggestions. The publication is solely and strictly intended for use only by professional hypnotists and professionals in related fields.

John's never ceases to expand this work as he continues to update its content annually. The provision of a CD that contains the book in PDF format is a great bonus. It presents the user with the choice to use a script as printed or alter it to fit a clients particular needs or the hypnotists own unique style. When you purchase HSTW and subscribe to John's mailing list you receive the annual updates by email. This is an expression of John's gratitude for purchasing his work and his commitment to successful hypnosis sessions for the user.

I congratulate John on producing this work and highly recommend "Hypnotic Scripts that Work". It would come as no surprise if this publication rapidly becomes the most commonly used resource for hypnotists.

Wishing you continued success.

### Martin Kiely, BCH, CI - Cork City, Ireland

"Since owning John's book, it has become a well worn friend. Entire pages are cut out ... highlighter, underlines, additions and strikeouts. When I am at a loss for words, John is not and so I pull out 'old faithful'. In other words, I 'Cerbone' 'em. Thanks Trance-Master for doing so much good".

### Linda Warsh, C.H. - Hypnosis for Health Toronto, Ontario, Canada

I purchased a copy of John's book, "Hypnotic Scripts That Work" and I am so glad I did. It is chock full of new ideas and techniques, and it covers many problems and goals I've not yet seen addressed in other books of it's kind. Thank you John!

### Carol Denicker, C.H – President, Long Island Chapter, National Guild of Hypnotists

John: Thank you so very much for sending along your book, Hypnotic Scripts That Work. I stayed up way too late, way past my bed time reading your scripts enjoying what are certain to be the tools to some of my most successful and fulfilling work. I'll keep in touch.

Best,

**Laura Roby, RN, MHA, CCHT – Santa Barbara CA**

John, I must say, I felt silly for not using your scripts before, I tend to do longer sessions, content matters and your scripts are easy to customize on the fly while doing sessions. Great work, keep it going.

**Daniel Rose, Montville NJ**


☐  **Your Endorsement might be right here in the next edition of this book.**

Please E-mail your comments to:
John Cerbone, BCH, CI
Cerbone Hypnosis Institute


**HypnotistPro.com**
**John@HypnotistPro.com                    HealerCHI@aol.com**

# Index

# Order Your PDF-CD Version of this Book Now
## Please See Our Web Site for Latest Pricing and Shipping Information

**HypnotistPro.com**
**Trance-Master.com**

---

We now have this entire book on CD in PDF format, giving you the opportunity to copy the session you want to use that you can personalize in any word processing program to suit your client's needs. To order online go to:

**HypnotistPro.com**
**Trance-Master.com**

PayPal accepted.  You'll need the ISBN 13 number from the front of this book as well as the transaction number from your purchase of the book.

If you prefer, you may send your request by mail to:

**Hypnotic Scripts That Work CD**
**PO Box 90173 -- Princes Bay Station**
**Staten Island, New York 10309-0173 USA**

Include the ISBN 13 number from the front of this book, the transaction number from your purchase of this book as well as your shipping information. Enclose a check for the current amount listed including addition shipping for International Ordering (outside the USA) made out to:

**The Cerbone Hypnosis Institute**

Lightning Source UK Ltd.
Milton Keynes UK
16 March 2010

151475UK00001B/9/P

9 781933 817354